The
ROBYN
DONALD
Collection

D1496041

CAPTIVES OF THE PAST

CAPTIVES OF THE PAST

BY
ROBYN DONALD

MILLS & BOON LIMITED
Eton House, 18–24 Paradise Road
Richmond, Surrey TW9 1SR

*First published in Great Britain 1986
by Mills & Boon Limited*

© Robyn Donald 1986

*Australian copyright 1986
Philippine copyright 1986
Reprinted 1986
This edition 1990*

ISBN 0 263 76728 0

*Set in Monophoto Times 10 on 11 pt
19–9002–56346*

Made and printed in Great Britain

CHAPTER ONE

THE nausea which had been clawing at Jennet Scarth's stomach for the past week became suddenly acute. Swallowing hard she closed great, green eyes to blot out the sight of the big house as the taxi swung around the last sweeping curve of the drive. Stone walls glimmered pale against the dark hills behind, tall curtained windows were arched rectangles of golden light in the symmetrical, Italiannate façade.

'Looks as though the party's in full swing,' the taxi driver observed, her voice slightly envious. 'Pity the bus had a breakdown, but you won't have missed much. I've heard that when the Hollingworths give a party most people stay on 'til breakfast.'

Her curiosity was patent. Visitors to Te Puriri Station in the northern province of New Zealand did not normally arrive by bus. Nothing so mundane. Expensive cars were the more usual mode of transport, or the twice daily plane from Auckland. Some even flew their own light aircraft to land on the grass strip in the hills behind the homestead.

But tonight's plane had been booked up, and although she could have spent the night in a hotel in Auckland and flown up the next morning Jennet had chosen to take the bus. If she had put off coming, she might just have turned tail and fled back across the Tasman Sea to the safety of Australia.

She smiled stiffly as she paid the driver, then stood, suitcase in hand, her eyes fixed bleakly on the red glow of the tail lights, until they were swallowed behind one of the banks of shrubs, which were such a feature of the garden.

Tomorrow it would be all round the district that Jennet Scarth had finally come back to the valley. The woman who drove the taxi was a gossipy creature, she would not keep quiet about her fare, and once she had described her it wouldn't take long for someone to realise who she was. In Takapo Valley memories were long and she had left in a blaze of the kind of publicity which needed only a slight fanning to flame up again.

Jennet's pale hair gleamed like a halo around her small face as she turned, the lights by the doors colouring the shadows to a hue so close to pink that reporters always described her as a strawberry blonde. Now she shifted her suitcase to the other hand, lifted her chin in a small deliberate gesture and turned away from the big panelled doors to walk swiftly past the graceful windows of the façade. Gravel made small crunching noises beneath her feet. She shivered, for the air struck chill after that of Sydney. In Australia spring had already come; here, although the pure air was heavy with the scent of spring flowers, it was still the last month of winter.

If only the wretched bus hadn't decided to break down she would have arrived here before the party. There was no way she was going to walk in through the front door to face the avid speculative stares of Rafe's friends.

At least, she thought with a wryness which was her only defence against fear, with people around, Rafe was not so likely to use that bitter caustic tongue of his on her. Then she smiled, for she was fooling herself. If Rafe wanted to he'd tear strips off her in front of the Queen, and tonight he was going to feel just like that. He would take no more than a second to work out her reason for returning. And he would be totally, blackly, furious.

The tension in her stomach intensified into an actual physical sensation. Just as her quick steps took her around the corner of the building she heard the doors

open behind her. Instantly she froze. Melly's clear voice
floated out, puzzled and excited.

'I was sure I heard an engine . . . oh well, too much
champagne, I suppose.'

A man's voice—not Rafe's—said something indist-
inguishable and there was a mingling of laughter which
was immediately extinguished by the heavy sound of the
closing doors. Jennet's skin was suddenly clammy, the
palms of her hands wet. Her fingers trembled as she
took the last few steps to the side door.

No light illuminated it, but by now her eyes were
accustomed to the starlight and she had no difficulty
finding the handle.

When it didn't move she was astounded. In the years
she had called Te Puriri home, no door had ever been
locked. But that was five years ago. Frowning, she felt
absurdly like a burglar as she set the suitcase down on
the step. Further on, around the next corner of the
house, was the back door, but if she tried to get in that
way someone was certain to see her. It led past the
kitchen where Joy Webster, if she was still the
housekeeper, would be busy.

Apart from two glowing windows this side of the
house was dark. Mentally she counted off the rooms.
The drawing room, then the first dark window would
be the smaller room they called the boudoir because its
graceful French furniture had made it essentially a
feminine sitting-room. That left the next window, the
one by the door, to be Rafe's office.

Stepping back, Jennet eyed its blank darkness. Surely
they wouldn't have taken to locking the windows as
well as the doors? It took only a few moments for her
nervous fingers to discover its vulnerability.

Fortunately she was wearing pants cropped at the
knee. Before she swung herself in over the sill she
listened, aware that some small sound had been fretting
at the edge of her consciousness.

Nothing impinged, however. Taking a deep breath she hoisted herself into the room's quiet emptiness, dropped to the floor then stood as motionless as a figurine. More than a few seconds passed before the unnecessarily loud thumping of her heart diminished enough for her to discern the distant subliminal beat of music coming through the walls and up from the floor. She stood motionless, staring into the heavy blackness with eyes stretched to their widest extent. Darkness pressed on to her with oppressive weight, making her uneasy, almost afraid.

It took an effort of will to force herself to remember the salient features of the office. Not that she had been in it often. Rafe had declared it out of bounds, even to Melly.

Surely the desk had faced the window. Stretching out her hands she took one tentative step, then others until she was brought up by a barrier. Her fingers trailed lightly over a stack of paper.

Yes, that must be the desk. It was, she recalled, an enormous Victorian piece of furniture, more like a table. If she followed it to its end she should be in line for the door. And beside the door there was a light switch.

Halfway in her slow progress across the room she halted, frozen into stillness like a small, hunted animal.

'Who's there?' she asked sharply, sure that she had sensed some slight movement.

There was no sound, no response at all and surely, if there had been anyone else in the room that swift, unexpected question would have been enough to force some betrayal of their presence, however slight.

Calm down, she adjured herself. She was not normally easily frightened, it was a perfectly reasonable tension which made her so edgy.

Trying hard to relax, skin so tight that she was uncomfortable, she took small, careful steps across the room, the carpet muffling any sound she might make.

It was, she recalled, an old Persian rug with exquisite mellow colours, a representation of a Paradise, or garden. Once her foot moved from its surface to the polished boards beneath it she would be close to the wall and she could grope her way to the light switch.

She was smiling when her hand touched something warm. Something that moved. Jennet's lips parted on a choked sobbing gasp. Her whole body stiffened as she swung around to flee.

A strong arm caught her across her breasts, a cruel hand over her mouth, stifling the involuntary scream which tore at her throat. Shaking with a sudden, useless fear she forgot all the precepts her instructor in self-defence had taught her as she was hauled back against a hard body. Her brainzed; it was purely instinct which brought her teeth together on the edge of the hand across her mouth, the same instinct which jerked her foot upwards and back in a sharp kick at her assailant's shins.

He swore, the short, crude words barely impinging until she recognised the voice. Then she sagged, swaying on legs too limp to hold her up.

The arm about her breasts tightened. He snarled, 'Keep quiet. Nobody will hear you if you scream,' and took his hand away from her mouth.

The sudden glare of the light caught her as she was dampening lips which were suddenly dry and sore. Her lashes dropped so that she did not see his face as he turned her towards him, but she heard the swift indrawn breath and then she was free.

She opened her eyes and smiled.

'Hullo, Rafe,' she murmured sweetly.

The dark, harshly outlined features were masklike. 'Jennet?' he sai said, the deep voice shaken. And then, more strongly, 'I might have known! What the hell are you doing climbing through the window like a bloody thief?'

'Well, the side door was locked. Why, Rafe? It never used to be.'

'Too many strangers around,' he returned impatiently. The black eyes hadn't left her face; they glittered with an icy brilliance she remembered too well. 'What are you doing here?' he demanded.

She covered a multitude of emotions with the slow seductive smile which had won her fame of a sort. 'Why shouldn't I be here? Why shouldn't I come to my sister's engagement party, even if no one saw fit to invite me?'

That superb, infuriating composure of his was firmly back in place now. He was regarding her with the cold dislike which had been his usual expression whenever he saw her.

'Half-sister,' he said laconically. 'Melly is your *half*-sister. And she's all Hollingworth, thank God. There's nothing of the mother you share in her. I'd have thought that there was every reason for you to keep away, as it's your ex-husband she's engaged to.'

'Don't be so old-fashioned.' Her voice was light, almost amused. 'It's two years since the divorce.'

'Four years since you left Derek—ran away with his cousin, at that. You learned how to humiliate in your cradle, didn't you?' His voice invested the words with harsh contempt. 'What brought you back?'

She didn't move. Not a muscle flexed, there was no variation of expression in her lovely face, yet something gave her away. His angular features hardened even further.

'I thought so,' he said savagely. 'You're too much Diana's daughter to be able to resist a chance to make trouble.'

Jennet was not an actress for nothing. Her laughter was unforced, without audible tension. Outrageously she fluttered long lashes at him.

'Oh, do be sensible, Rafe,' she said, automatically assuming the light, mocking tone which was a legacy from her first television role, that of a sophisticate, amoral and shallow.

That cool, amused voice had rapidly become one of her defences against those who failed to realise she was acting.

'What trouble could I possibly cause?' she asked with sly provocation.

'Oh, there are always buyers for your sort of wares,' he said deliberately, his eyes moving with lingering insolence over her face, cataloguing the smooth, pale skin, the faintly oriental slant of her incredible eyes, her soft promising mouth.

Reporters who stressed her strawberry blonde hair and desirable figure were accustomed to use words like exotic, or alluring, to describe Jennet Scarth. She was not, she knew, strictly beautiful, but experience, a lot of it unpleasant, had revealed that there was something about the arrangement of her features which attracted men. Most men, but particularly those who thought that because she was an actress she had no morals. They were always angry to discover that the slenderly voluptuous body and the promise of sleepy green eyes and smiling lips were not matched by an amorous disposition. Her armour was very necessary.

'I've no doubt you enjoyed saying that, but it's hardly an answer,' she pointed out. 'What trouble could I possibly cause, Rafe? Unless you think Derek is still in love with me, and that's not likely, is it?'

'Considering that you ran off with his cousin after eight months of marriage, no,' he returned evenly. 'As for trouble—well, any woman who looks like a houri and has no scruples is trouble personified.'

'Of course, all of the Hollingworths are as pure as the driven snow,' she replied, stung.

The hard line of his mouth widened in a humourless

smile. 'There are only two of us left,' he said. 'Melly and I. You are not, never have been, never will be a Hollingworth.'

The old refrain. How many times had she had that flung at her? Hundreds, probably, the first occasion long before she went to school. Rafe had always hated her as much as he hated Diana, the mother who had left her husband to marry Dougal Hollingworth. The woman from whom Jennet had inherited her face and body.

Glancing swiftly up she met his cold black stare with a gritty determination. He had eyes to drown in, so dark that his emotions were swallowed in their depths. Rafe Hollingworth, owner of Te Puriri and several other agricultural and horticultural enterprises. Rich, worldly, handsome; cold, cruel, heartless; stepbrother to Jennet Scarth.

'I may be everything you think me,' she said coolly, 'but I'm not stupid. You don't have to keep taunting me with being an outsider. You've always made it more than obvious how you feel about my mother and me. Your father forced you to be polite to Diana, but he didn't care how cruel you were to me.'

'Neither did Diana,' he said, hurting her with the same casual expertise she remembered from the past.

'Neither did Diana,' she agreed woodenly.

'Poor little Jen.' The words were a taunt, almost a curse. 'Perhaps if you hadn't been such a cold, scheming little devil you might have fooled some of us. Your mother was able to assume a surface warmth.'

Those long lashes fluttered down, hiding the pain that changed her eyes to stormy jade. 'I remember when I decided never to show my feelings again very vividly. It was when I was seven. My teacher had shown us how to make Christmas cards and I'd made one each for all of you. On the last day of school I carried them home, so excited. You'd been home from boarding school for a couple of weeks and Melly had just finished her first year at school. I couldn't wait to get home and give you my cards. I'd forgotten—or perhaps I didn't want to remember that every kid in that primary school spent the last day of school making Christmas cards.' Her smile was a masterpiece of restrained irony. 'Do you remember, Rafe?'

'No.'

She smiled again. 'It was the Christmas your father gave you his old rifle,' she reminded him.

'Hell, yes, I remember that.' His voice had an oddly soft, reminiscent quality.

'I thought you might.'

He reacted swiftly to the thin vein of sarcasm in the comment. 'What are you insinuating?'

'Nothing. It was easy enough to see that the rifle meant something very important to you.'

'Whereas your card didn't?'

She smiled again. 'Why should it? You had hated me for five years, ever since I arrived at Te Puriri. I can't really remember how you behaved.' Which was a lie. The little incident was engraved on her memory with a stark precision, just as if it had happened yesterday. Even the weather. The hot dry wind had torn through Melly's curls as the school bus set them down at the gate, snatched at their little summer dresses as they ran up the long drive, eager to give out their cards.

'Well, what happened?' Rafe's voice broke curtly into her reverie.

She shrugged. 'I was two years older than Melly so I got there first and handed out my offerings. You were all very kind. Your father told me I had done well. Then Melly arrived and I realised that you had all been waiting for her. Your voices, your faces, everything was different. I suppose I'd always known, but that was the first time that I'd ever faced the fact that whatever I did, whatever I was, I had no place at Te Puriri.'

'My heart bleeds for you,' he said sardonically.

Well, what had she expected? Sympathy? Hardly, not from Rafe. Yet that small incident had eaten into her soul.

'Was that the summer you wanted to go and stay with your father?' he asked.

She nodded, turning away. It had been stupid of her to reveal so much of herself to him, stupid and painful and dangerous. Rafe had an unerring eye for weaknesses. He could afford to as he didn't appear to have any himself. And she remembered from her childhood and the growing years that he had no inhibitions about attacking those weaknesses.

'He didn't want you, I remember,' he said now, unwittingly reinforcing her reading of his character.

'No, he didn't. Neither did his second wife. Naturally enough, I suppose. They'd had their first child a few months before. He was the apple of their eye. Naturally,' she repeated.

She felt his gaze on her averted face and just managed to avoid flinching because if she did that he would know how frightened she was and he must not know. Not now, not ever. But slowly, reluctantly, impelled by a will stronger than her own, her head was dragged around. Her gaze skimmed across shoulders as wide as a navvy's, up the brown length of his throat, past the severe strength of jaw and mouth and the arrogant line of nose until it was caught, imprisoned in the dark depths of his eyes.

'So you've come back to ruin this romance,' he said softly, dangerously. 'Do you hate Melly so much for belonging, Jennet?'

'I don't hate Melly at all.'

It was the truth. Years ago she had resented her half-sister in the bitter, all-encompassing fashion of childhood, but she was no longer a child.

'Then it's Derek——'

Her voice, fractionally higher than normal, interrupted. 'I don't hate him, either,' she said quickly,
almost believing it.

'No?'

When she turned away, he caught her arm and
pulled her to him, the long fingers of his other hand
cupping her chin so that her face was open to his
fierce scrutiny.

As before, he sensed the lie hidden in her heart. A
swift hissing breath signalled his displeasure. His lips
tightened.

'Like hell you don't,' he bit out. 'Well, you're not
going to do it, Jennet. He knows you for what you are,
now. We all do.'

Her pulses raced, then steadied. Against her skin his
hand was warm and hard. She lifted her chin and his
fingers fell away, but his other hand was still fastened
on to her shoulder.

'And what is that?' she asked, half beneath her
breath.

'A beautiful slut.'

The cruel words were spoken judicially as though he
was a judge pronouncing sentence. Under their impact
Jennet whitened, the fine bones beneath their softening
layer of skin suddenly stark, her eyes desolate above a
mouth which trembled before hardening into a line.

'You don't like to hear that.' He pretended surprise,
but she read satisfaction in his eyes and knew that he
was glad, that her pain fed something in him, some
emotion she did not understand.

'I don't think any woman would enjoy hearing herself
referred to in such terms,' she said softly, 'especially
when they are unjustified.'

His handsome, cold face smiled. 'How sweetly you
lie,' he remarked calmly. 'Your voice is as soft as a
purr, low and husky and the lies sound like a man's
most erotic fantasies. You're like your mother, Jennet,

beautiful as a dream and rotten to the core. Go back to Sydney.'

'I will,' she said quietly, lifting her chin with a determination which was new to him. 'After I've seen Melly.'

'Why?'

'Because I have to.' She raised eyes suddenly clear and decisive. 'I don't want to hurt her, Rafe, but I must speak to her.'

Rafe was tall, a couple of inches over six feet. Jennet had always considered herself tall too, but his height was intimidating. He had a habit of rocking back on his heels and staring, heavy lids lowered over his eyes so that they looked like slivers of jet. He was doing it now, trying to read her mind, that narrowed, intent gaze searching the contours of her face, probing beneath the surface to test the thoughts in her brain. Always she had met that fierce regard with a wooden expression, deliberately concealing the shades of light and laughter which normally played across her features. The years had taught her that it was dangerous to let him see what she thought and felt. This time she ignored that instinctive reaction to meet the penetration of his eyes, her own clear and quite obstinate.

'Not bad,' he drawled after a tense few moments. 'Perhaps you chose the right outlet for your talents, such as they are. Or has Diana been giving you lessons?'

'Oh, you've not changed! You're just as cynical as you ever were.'

'I learned in a hard school. Remember, my mother had only been dead a few months when Dougal brought Diana home and by then she was pregnant.'

'Remember!' She flung the word at him like a weapon. 'How could I forget? A "friend" at boarding school told me, complete with juicy details, how your father met her at a party and seduced her away from her husband to live with him here.'

'It was the other way around. She seduced him.'

'Who knows?' She pulled away, still sickened by the memory of the other girl's ghoulish pleasure when she'd related the old scandal to her.

'*I* know,' he said harshly. 'I remember her when she first came to Te Puriri. She was only nineteen, just ten years older than I was, and I remember how she——' He stopped abruptly. 'Oh, forget it!' he finished, the harsh arrogantly-boned features suddenly wooden.

Jennet shrugged. 'I'd like to be able to, but according to Freud we carry the ghosts of our childhood with us wherever we go.' A little yawn was hastily covered. 'Lord, I'm tired. Is there a room I could bunk in, or have you a houseparty?'

He sent her a level, frowning look. 'Your old room is ready.'

'Is it?' She lifted her brows. 'I'm surprised it wasn't stripped and disinfected after I left.'

He surveyed her for a bleak moment, his expression impassive, the only hint of emotion the onyx glitter at the back of his eyes. 'I'll give you half an hour to get into more suitable clothes and then I'll come up and get you,' he said, daring her to object.

'No way. I'm exhausted and I'm quite prepared to let Melly have her hour of triumph.'

His eyes held hers. 'If I have to, I'll drag you out of bed,' he told her silkily.

'Walk into my bedroom, said the spider ...' Jennet smiled, aware that he was only just restraining his temper. 'Don't bother,' she said over her shoulder as she left him, big and dark and dominating, his brows drawn together.

Once inside the bedroom which had been hers she leaned against the door, cold hand pressed hard against her throbbing heart.

'Oh *God*!' she whispered, shaking with reaction, her face white.

After a few minutes she straightened, breathing deeply and evenly, then slung the suitcase on to the narrow bed and unpacked it, moving gracefully around the small room. Nothing had changed. The green satin coverlet was still on the bed, the dainty furniture her mother had chosen for her in spite of her objections, the long curtains which hid the french windows. Even her books were still on the shelves. Sudden hot tears ached behind her eyes. She had hoped that one day she would have a daughter who would enjoy the same books. It was in this bed that she had lain the night before her wedding, so emotionally charged that she had been unable to sleep. It was this room she had longed for during the painful months of her marriage, longed for and known that she could never return to because Rafe wouldn't let her.

Well, it was over now. All of it. She had fled Takapo Valley and her husband of eight months and made a new life for herself, a satisfying life free from the entanglements and shadows of the old. And if Melly hadn't decided to marry Derek she would never have come back.

Lord, but she was tired! Since she had read her mother's malicious letter over a week ago, her sleep had been irregular, broken by nightmares and fragments of dreams. Yawning, she stowed the suitcase in the top of her wardrobe, then locked the door against Rafe and washed in the handbasin before removing all of her clothes and climbing into bed. She always slept naked.

Her last thought, before sleep claimed her was that he could hammer on the door until he was black in the face and tonight she wouldn't hear him.

Which made her shock at being ruthlessly shaken awake even greater.

'Get up, Jennet,' the deep voice commanded relentlessly. 'You've had your half-hour.'

Totally bewildered, she sat up, pushing her hair back

from her face. It wasn't until she saw Rafe's dark eyes rest on her breasts that she realised where she was. Then she grabbed for the sheet, covering herself but not before she had seen that red flare in his eyes and known it for what it was.

'You must be tired,' he said softly, and without exerting much pressure he put a hand on either side of her and pulled the sheet slowly past her breasts to hold it at her waist. He didn't look at the full curves he had uncovered; his eyes were on her face.

'Get out,' she ordered, but her throat and mouth were so dry that the words were silent and she had to swallow so that she could repeat them.

He took no notice. He did not even seem to have heard her. His broad shoulders cut out most of the light, but she could see enough of his face to make her shrink back on to the pillows. He looked—he looked as though any movement would crack the icy mask of control he wore. Tanned skin was stretched taut over the stark beautiful framework of his face. A flush scorched along the high cheekbones, his dark gaze devoured her as though he had hungered for it all of the years of her exile.

'So beautiful,' he stated through clenched teeth. 'Like every man's wildest fantasies in the flesh, promising unknown, untellable gratification of every appetite. How do you do it, Jennet? That hint of forbidden delights, erotic ecstasies, makes you a spiritual descendant of Helen of Troy, Cleopatra, Delilah.'

His hand slid across her cold skin to her breast. She flinched, but the hypnotic intensity of his gaze held her captive. An icy wave of sensation prickled over her skin; the warm slide of his fingers made her shiver.

No, she thought desperately.

She could not move. Like a statue of carved ivory she watched as his dark head bent, oh, so slowly, until his mouth burned against the curve of her breast.

Jennet drew a deep sobbing breath, held in a black enchantment like those nightmares when a nameless terror threatens and not a muscle of the dreamer's body will move.

'Rafe,' she whispered. His name sounded like an incantation, a spell, and she groaned it again as his mouth wreaked its own kind of magic on her skin.

He had never seemed bigger, more dangerous. Then, as if her voice had called him back from the brink, he straightened. Jennet watched the play of muscles beneath the fine silk of his shirt, a promise of power and domination. She was suffocated by his size, every instinct screaming her danger. Panic such as she had never felt, not even in the months of her marriage, drained the colour from her eyes.

He was no longer looking at her face. She flinched as his hand cupped the high, full curve of her breast.

'*No!*' she whispered, reacting violently to the bitter rejection which flamed in his face.

Swiftly she pushed him, her hands slipping over the muscles and sinews of his chest. For a moment he tensed on a predatory hunch, before the blindness faded from his eyes and he stood up, watching as with a shudder she hauled the sheet up to hide herself.

'Bitch,' he said bitterly. 'Beautiful, trouble-making little bitch. Sorry, Jennet, but I'm not as easily seduced as my father. Both you and Diana should have learned that lesson.'

'What do you—what are you talking about?'

He smiled, a savage, mirthless movement of the lips which had so mercilessly tormented her skin.

'Have you ever heard of Phaedra and Hippolytus?'

The reference was obscure. Jennet frowned, trying to track it down, her gaze held by the way her fingers pleated the soft cotton sheet.

'She was his stepmother,' Rafe supplied, and smiled again as he saw from her appalled expression that she had remembered.

'Yes,' he said smoothly, 'you've got it. She became enamoured of her stepson and when he rejected her she encouraged his father to kill him.

'I don't believe you,' she returned, her voice hoarse and shaken.

'Oh, come now,' he said brutally, 'after his heart attack my father wasn't much use to Diana. I gather she was always highly sexed and he lingered on for two years before his next attack killed him. Naturally she looked around for—company. I was the nearest.'

'You're lying,' Jennet said thinly, nausea gripping her stomach. 'Get out of here! You're hateful—loathsome . . .'

He laughed at that, irony grim as death in his voice. 'Jennet, you hate me because I know you for what you are, an amoral little bitch. If I'd wanted what you offered me when you were sixteen, you'd have jumped into my bed without a second thought.' He bent to run a scornful finger across her slender shoulder, stopping at her chin. 'Play your cards right and I might be more amenable this time,' he taunted.

She bit her lip, jerking away from the hateful familiarity of his touch. Against her back the pillow was cold and welcoming.

'I don't believe you,' she said hopelessly, because Rafe scorned to lie.

'Tough. I could have had her. Mother and daughter both,' he said softly, mercilessly watching her reaction from beneath those heavy lids.

'That's a foul thing to say!'

'It happens to be the truth,' he said, bored now, his expression shuttered.

He was angry with himself for using this weapon. Rafe was hard, but he possessed a strange kind of chivalry and this went against his code.

Oh, Diana, Jennet thought sickly, drawing her knees

up so that she could rest her head on them. Yet she was not surprised.

From above his voice reverberated in her ears. 'Get up,' he commanded. 'You're coming downstairs.'

CHAPTER TWO

'I'm tired,' she protested.

'My heart bleeds for you.' He was implacable. 'If you want me to dress you myself . . .'

She lifted her head, her eyes duelling with his. Neither gave way.

'Why do you want me to come down?'

'Because I want you to and on Te Puriri what I want, happens.'

Because she was tired, that was the reason. He wanted her off-balance when she met Melly and Derek. Well, he would soon learn that she had reserves of strength and courage well hidden from him. Her fragile appearance was no indication of her stamina.

'Very well,' she said cheerfully. 'I'll meet you down there in half an hour.'

'I'll wait.'

'I am *not* getting up with you in here.'

'One way or another,' he threatened smoothly, 'you're going to dress with me in this room. I know you too well. You'll find some place to hide.'

He loomed over the bed. Jennet said, 'How did you get in?'

'I have a master key.'

She nodded, then arrogantly commanded, 'Turn your back.'

'No,' he said softly. 'I might as well get some pleasure out of the evening.'

'Peeping Tom,' she flung at him before she threw the sheet back and got out on the opposite side of the bed. 'Voyeur!'

His taunting chuckle was her only answer, but she

felt his eyes on her body and it took all of her courage, all of her pride not to fumble as she pulled on tiny briefs and a half slip. There was nothing she could do about the heat which suffused her skin but her movements were steady and precise. Not once did she look in his direction. Every nerve shrank in her body, she felt raw with outrage, but she refused to acknowledge his presence.

Acting had made her an expert with make-up, and fast with it. Still silent, she switched on the lights above the dressing-table mirror, sat down and tidied her hair before her hands moved swiftly among the few bottles she had set out. It took her only a short time to emphasise her best points, her slanted green eyes and the soft bow of her mouth. After a quick, critical look. she added blusher then slipped loops of pink pearls into her earlobes.

Her hands stroked down the length of a drift of pale pink crêpe after she had pulled it over her head. Adjusting the elasticised neckline so that it revealed more of her smooth, lightly-tanned shoulders she said crisply, 'Pink sandals in the bottom of the wardrobe.'

While he got them she aligned the long cowl sleeves and pulled the waist into position, then checked to see that the slit in the gathered skirt was in exactly the right place.

Rafe dropped the high-heeled sandals at the foot of the bed. After a quick mist of *Ma Griffe* perfume Jennet bent, slid the sandals on to her narrow, beautiful feet and walked across the room and out of the door, turning towards the noise and laughter below with head held high and shoulders squared, her body swaying in the eternal female gait, sensual, an involuntary promise.

Just before she reached the bottom of the carved kauri staircase, she thought sardonically, I'm going to see Derek again and I couldn't care less. She supposed she should thank Rafe for such splendid detachment.

He had caught her up at the head of the stairs. At the bottom he slid an arm around her waist. Jennet stiffened.

He said into her ear, 'From the little I've seen of you on television you're a lousy actress, but tonight you're going to convince Melly and Derek that you wish them nothing but happiness.'

When she made no acknowledgment beyond averting her face, he continued, 'Or when it's over I'll visit your bedroom and take up that invitation you gave me seven years ago.'

The light from the chandelier glittered in her hair as she tilted her head, gazing up into his harsh, beautiful face through her lashes.

'If you do,' she promised, smiling at him with slow, practised allure, 'I'll make sure that you regret it until your last day on earth.' Her smile widened, she touched a slender forefinger to his hard mouth, meeting the sardonic appreciation of his glance with equanimity.

Like all parties at Te Puriri, this one was going well. The Hollingworths had a tradition of hospitality, an instinctive recognition of how to help their guests enjoy themselves, and this occasion was no exception. As Rafe opened the door into the big drawing-room the noise swelled out to meet them, laughter and much high-pitched chatter, a faint sound of music.

The first person she saw was Derek, his blond head bent protectively as he spoke to Melly. As they came in through the door he looked up, and although he obviously knew of Jennet's return he could not prevent the sudden fixed rigidity of his features. Melly followed the direction of his gaze. Her bottom lip quivered; she made a little hesitant movement before edging her way through the group nearest the door.

Rafe's fingers tightened unbearably at Jennet's waist. Conversation died away as avid faces swung from Melly and Derek to the two in the doorway. Jennet

laughed and swooped on to her half-sister, arms
outstretched and hugged her stiff, unresponsive form,
hissing into her ear, 'Smile, dear heart. You look as if
Banquo's ghost just bled all over your dress.'

Melly made a choking noise, half laugh, half gasp but
her body relaxed and she managed to produce a smile.
Jennet grinned at her, saw the anger and fear fade and
released her with a final squeeze. Then she took a deep
breath before she turned to face Derek, holding out
both hands.

'You're looking well,' she told him in her sweet,
warm voice, smiling up at him.

He took her hands, his expression well under control
as he surveyed her face.

'So are you, Jen,' he said slowly, a glitter deep in the
blue eyes.

Then Rafe draped his arm over her shoulders and
Derek released her. There was a strained tense moment
when no one said anything. Jennet's skin crawled.
Acting had not prepared her for this sort of thing;
unlike this one, most audiences were sympathetic.

She chucked and said mischievously, 'Well, now that
everyone has seen that we aren't going to come to
blows, I'd love a drink.'

'Champagne?' Rafe suggested in a voice as bland as it
was deliberate.

'French?' She flirted with him from beneath her
lashes.

He nodded, the hard lines of his face relaxing into
that charming smile. To everyone who watched so
eagerly it must have seemed that he was captivated by
her. Jennet met the old condemnation in his eyes with
composure.

'Oh, then I'd love some,' she said gaily.

As if she had given a signal those around them were
recalled to their manners. Conversation began to hum
again. Rafe tucked her against his side and they made a

sort of royal progress across the beautiful room, greeting old friends, Rafe introducing her to those she did not know. After those first fascinating, shocked minutes everyone had grabbed at their social masks, their enjoyment given a keener edge because everyone knew that Jennet and Derek had once been married, everyone scented drama and intrigue and many were hoping furiously that it would blow up tonight.

Jennet sipped cautiously at the champagne, remembering that she had had no lunch or dinner that day, and precious little to eat for some days past. At the moment she was balanced on a knife-edge of emotion. Too much alcohol would tip her over, and that she could not afford.

It was like a nightmare, the big, beautiful room, the crowd of superbly-dressed guests, Melly with an emerald glowing on her finger, Derek watching from beneath his lashes. And Rafe, elegant for all his size, no emotions showing in the handsome face but those he wished revealed, Rafe who kept Jennet beside him as though she was something rare and precious which he had no intention of losing.

All the time eager eyes watched them, lips moved in fascinated conjecture, voices dropped as those few not in the know were regaled with details of the events of four years ago. And probably of that older scandal that had eventuated from Diana Scarth's arrival at Te Puriri as Dougal Hollingworth's mistress, too. Yet through it all the principal actors moved easily, with almost no signs of strain.

'Did I say you were a hopeless actress?' Rafe murmured as they made their way from one group to another. 'Sad that you can't produce this technique to order. You'd make a fortune.'

She ran her fingers up his arm in a parody of the flirtatious gesture. Beneath her fingers the muscles tensed.

'You too, darling,' she purred. 'A mavellous romantic lead you'd make. All that brooding passion, and you must be the best-looking man I've ever seen.'

Deliberately she raised her eyes then let them drift over him in an open assessment of his masculine attraction. He was incredibly attractive, with his arrogantly poised black head and his lean body, the grace of which belied his great strength.

Too forceful, of course. Rafe wore his character in his face, the strong bones and disturbing exciting eyes and mouth revealing both sensuality, and a strength which was based on total, bedrock self-assurance. And complete ruthlessness. He was the sexiest man she had ever met, fascinating in a dangerous way which drew every feminine eye.

His smile was a masterpiece of irony, while beneath thick dark lashes his eyes promised retribution. 'Don't mistake me for an actor,' he said softly so that only she could hear. 'I don't deal in fantasy.'

The chiselled angular features, so much more compelling than mere good looks, hardened as she laughed, the warm gaiety of it at variance with the quickly veiled apprehension in her eyes.

Much later Derek said cheerfully, 'Dance with me, Jen?' and without waiting for an answer swirled her off before Rafe could prevent it.

But Jennet's skin tightened and she knew that he was watching them. The dark impact of his gaze registered like a blow, wiping out the pain she had thought she would feel when she met the man who had been married to for so brief a time.

In fact, Derek's voice surprised her.

'What did you say?'

Anger thickened his voice. 'I asked why you'd come back?'

'Oh, come on, Derek. Whatever you are, I'd not realised that you were stupid!'

'You are,' he said softly. 'Otherwise you wouldn't have turned up. Your credibility is at an all-time low, Jen. Not that it was ever very high, was it? Rafe has always hated you and the rumours from across the Tasman of your affairs haven't exactly raised his opinion any. As for Melly—well, she's been in love with me since she was sixteen.'

Beneath the faint bluster in his voice there was unease, just as there had been when he had spoken to his cousin the night before Jennet had run away and left him. Then, as now, he was not sure how to deal with the situation.

Jennet's green eyes smiled mysteriously up at him. 'Has she?' she asked with a note of dry mockery edging the words.

'So she says,' he returned complacently, his good-looking face almost smug. 'And I believe her.'

'I wonder how long it will last.'

His hand tightened on hers; slowly he worked his fingers so that the joints above her palm were rolled painfully one against the other. It was a childish punishment, but effective.

'If you don't stop,' she said, 'I'll slap your face. Or kick your shins.'

'You wouldn't dare.'

'Keep hurting me and see,' she invited, smiling.

The inflexible note in her voice caught his attention. His grip loosened as he said warily, 'You're bluffing.'

'I wouldn't bank on it.'

There was a tense little silence and Jennet felt a surge of confidence. At last she appreciated her freedom. Derek was no longer a threat to her in any way. It should have been a moment of euphoria yet all she felt was a kind of aching emptiness, a sad pang of disillusion.

Suddenly Derek said, 'Got your eye on Rafe now, have you? Not a hope, sweetie. He likes his women willing and we both know you've never been that, don't we?'

'Do we?' she replied, with sweet malice. 'I've learnt a lot since I left you, Derek. I don't think any man would complain about my lack of willingness now. Not even Rafe, but then, we all know he's an expert lover.'

As she expected he reacted to the implied comparison with anger. 'So it was all my fault, I suppose,' he sneered. 'Well, you'll have to pull out all the stops if you want to get Rafe into your bed. He only goes for the best, and judging from the way they fling themselves at him he must be fairly jaded.'

Jennet laughed softly. 'Don't you think I could do it, Derek?' she asked, touching the tip of her tongue to her lower lip. Beneath her lashes her eyes gleamed, mocking, seductive.

Derek couldn't drag his eyes away from her, the anger in his expression fading to be replaced by a heated awareness.

'You little slut,' he said thickly. 'Is that why you came back? Are you sick of working? You must be mad if you think you can get him to marry you. He's not like his father, obsessed by a beautiful face and a ripe body. Rafe's a loner. Women are a recreation for him.'

'Perhaps,' she said airily, deliberately letting her gaze linger on the subject of their conversation.

He was smiling down at a thin, elegant woman some years older than he. Charm radiated from him, not obscuring the arrogant, bedrock dynamism of the man. Jennet felt a tug at her senses and hurried into her speech. 'But what I do is no longer any of your business,' she pointed out.

'I can see that you might need money,' he said consideringly. 'You got nothing from me, and Dougal forgot you when it came to that trust, didn't he? Certainly your greedy mother doesn't see it as her duty to help keep the wolf from the door.'

Just listening to him no one would ever realise how furious he had been when he discovered that fact.

'So it's Rafe you want,' he went on. 'Well, good luck to you, Jen, although I'll tell you again you haven't got a hope. Apart from anything else, he's always hated you. Remember, he wouldn't even give you away when we were married.'

Oh yes, she recalled only too clearly Rafe's violent refusal to have anything to do with the wedding. He had, however, paid for it, something which Jennet hadn't known until Diana let it out a year or so ago. The knowledge humiliated her, for Dougal had left his wife extremely well off. It was symptomatic of Diana's attitude that she had assumed that Rafe would cover the costs of the elaborate, expensive ceremony she had insisted on.

'So if I were you I'd just head back to the soap operas,' Derek finished smugly. 'You really are not wanted here.'

'Well, that's a pity,' she returned, smiling cheerfully at an avidly interested neighbour, 'because I've just realised that I was right to come back.'

He knew what she meant. With blue eyes glaring at her he looked like some cornered animal, dangerous, every thinking process suspended in the instinct to attack. His chest rose and fell several times as he fought for control.

After some seconds he said remotely, 'Look, we can't talk here. If—if you're finding things difficult—well, I know I refused any support, but it's possible I was a little hasty. We could perhaps come to some arrangement.'

How like Derek to try bribery! As for refusing to support her, it was she who had considerably upset her lawyer by rejecting the alimony to which she was entitled. It was typical of Derek to forget that small fact, too. But she sensed that she could not throw away any advantage she had by flatly refusing to negotiate.

She allowed more time to pass before lying coolly, 'Well, things *are* a little tight for me now. I gather that Compton Downs must be profitable again.'

'It never was unprofitable,' he said quickly.

He lied. It had not taken her long to realise that one of the reasons why he had married her was because he thought she would bring a substantial dowry. It had been an appalling shock for him to realise that contrary to popular gossip, Dougal had not seen it necessary to leave her a share in the trust he had set up for Diana and Melly.

He emphasised, 'I never was in danger of selling up, but yes, things have improved.'

'Good,' she said, allowing a note of greed to creep into her voice.

'Not that I can afford to splash money around,' he said immediately.

'Well, of course not.'

Her eyelashes flirted with him. He was keeping a tight rein on his temper, but she could feel the resentful fury in him and was surprised that she was not afraid. During their short marriage she had lived in terror of his temper. Now she was completely in control, assessing just how much he had let his anger override his common sense. She knew how his mind worked. Even in eight months you can learn a lot about the most complex character if the incentive is strong enough. And hers had been strong, she thought wearily. One of the strongest in the world. Self-preservation.

Derek knew so little about her. His facile conclusion that she had come back to the Te Puriri to try a spot of blackmail was an indication of his lack of understanding. Like all self-centred people, he projected his own traits on to others, seeing only what he wished to. He knew that when she married him, she had resented Melly's place in the family. It would not occur to him that the years had given her the maturity to overcome this emotion left over from childhood's selfishness.

'I'll have to think about it,' she said at last.

'You do that.' He relaxed, conceited, once more sure of himself and his ability to read a situation. As he smiled down at her his satisfaction was patent. 'Just don't get greedy, Jen. Melly is very much in love, and I have a few other aces.'

Jennet lifted her lashes in a long, considering stare, allowing just the right amount of hesitation and surprise to appear in her expression.

The tape stopped then and she left him, threading her way between the dancers with quick, short steps, carefully keeping her face blank.

A hand on her shoulder made her stiffen. Rafe. Strange how she had always reacted to his touch, aware of his presence even when she could not see him.

Still without moving she turned her head to meet eyes which glittered like black quartz.

'Dance with me,' he ordered as the music began again.

With a sigh she moved into his embrace.

'Put your arms around my neck.'

His hands on her hips pulled her closer, moved slowly up until they were clasped about her waist. He met the quick rebellion in her glare with a flashing, wolfish grin.

'Please,' he mocked softly, and when she brought her hands up to rest on his shoulders, 'that's better.'

The music swelled sweetly about them, some husky-voiced singer bewailing a broken heart. Through the thin fabric of her dress, Rafe's hands were warmly possessive, She felt the play of muscles in his legs, the way her skirt whirled and then clung to the dark material of his trousers as they swayed together. Her breath came in short, shallow pants into her lungs. After a long tense moment, she had to swallow to ease her dry throat. He was holding her firmly but not too tight, and she swallowed again, unbearably stimulated. Slowly, so slowly that she wasn't even aware of it, her grip on his shoulders relaxed. Her hands slid down to his chest. She edged closer, her legs barely moving as she followed his lead. They were not really dancing, this was an excuse for him to hold her, for her to melt against him in a culturally sanctioned embrace.

The word he said beneath his breath reverberated against her hands. She could just see over his shoulder, but her eyes were glazed and fever bright, incapable of focusing, the lids pressed heavily on to hot pupils. Colour heated her skin. Almost wincing, she was helpless beneath the sensations which were weakening her limbs. They corroded away the armour she had donned, eating at her self-control. Involuntarily her body relaxed against him and she felt his harden in response and knew that he, too, was in thrall to desire.

Thank heavens the room was dimly lit. What they were experiencing was so close to the act of love that it was almost indecent, she thought incoherently. She dared not look at him. Beneath her hands his heart raced, a betrayal blatant enough to fuel her own thudding pulses. She felt the groan he gave as it forced its way from his chest and his arms tightened, pulling her hard against his tense body. For a moment they clung together like lovers at a forbidden tryst desperately keeping the world at bay.

Then the song ended and slowly, reluctantly, he loosed her.

All this time her gaze had been fixed at some point over his shoulder. Now, still keeping her eyes averted, she walked beside him to the edge of the room, her hand clasped lightly in his, a smile fixed to lips which felt swollen and tender. Savaged by a vicious frustration, she had to ignore the insistent throbbing of her nerves, the heated hunger in a body too long denied fulfilment. She was terrified.

To hide it she flung herself into the role of extrovert, laughing, reminiscing, slyly flirting and all the time conscious of Rafe's dark presence beside her. For some reason of his own he met and matched her mood, the perfect host, the perfect escort—the perfect lover. Jennet discovered what it was like to be protected for it was only his presence which kept conjecture at bay.

Hours passed, and tiredness overwhelmed her like a black pall. Her high spirits became muted. Allowing the glittering persona of a minor celebrity to be replaced by restraint she spoke quietly and leaned against him, drawing on his masculine strength. Since they had danced together she had not once looked directly at him; her eyes had lifted only as far as the assured, half-sardonic line of his mouth.

Later she would have to rationalise that fierce frightening attraction, into nothingness. She had done it before, it could—*must*—be banished again. And with practise it had to become easier, she thought, irony revealing itself in her smile.

How old had she been, the first time she had been swamped by it? Thirteen, perhaps fourteen, a gawky adolescent puzzled by the rapid changes in her body and emotions, aware that her wistful craving for Rafe's affection had been replaced by another, intensely disturbing desire. She had not recognised it, of course, how could she have? She had watched him with puzzled, longing eyes all through the holidays. He had just turned twenty-one, magnificent in all the pride of his youth and virility, and he had been quite pleasant to Jennet. But it was Melly he laughed with and teased, Melly he loved.

After that she had not seen him for almost two years. Her holidays had been spent at the house in Auckland to which Diana had coaxed Dougal to move when Jennet had been only four; Rafe had been at Te Puriri, working like the devil to overcome years of neglect and the greed which had stripped the income from the station and left little to put back in.

Yet another black mark against Diana, in Rafe's book. But when Dougal had had the heart attacks which eventually killed him, it was to Te Puriri he had come to convalesce. So Jennet had arrived from boarding school to spend the summer holidays there.

She had not thought of those holidays for years, not until Rafe had so crudely recalled them to mind in her bedroom a few hours ago, and she was not going to think of them now.

Exhaustion made her stumble. Instantly Rafe's arm caught her, firmly gripping her. Across the room her eyes met Melly's angry, bitter gaze.

Very quietly Jennet said, 'I'm going to bed.'

He must have seen the weariness in her face for he nodded. 'Very well then.'

Somehow she summoned her smile. 'Sorry I've ruined your evening.'

'You couldn't ruin anything of mine.' His voice was bored.

'Nice to be so confident,' she returned, still smiling. 'Lucky Rafe.'

As well as Melly, someone else was staring. Derek. Jennet reached up, pulling Rafe's head down so that she could kiss his lean cheek. Surprisingly he didn't resist. Her lips lingered on the rough silk of his skin; he smelled very faintly of aftershave, but overriding it was the clean, masculine tang of his body scent.

'Good night,' she said, striving to control a suddenly shaking voice and turned and left the room, back straight, head held high, moving with a dancer's litheness, and only too aware that more than half of the guests watched her go from the corners of their eyes.

Although the homestead was centrally heated, the air in the hall was cool enough to bring a shiver to Jennet's skin. Set at too high a temperature, central heating would ruin the antiques with which the house was furnished, so it was kept just warm enough to hold at bay the chill dampness of the northern winter.

- As the door swung closed behind her Jennet's eyes roved the hall. The grandfather clock ticked with sonorous deliberation. Te Puriri homestead had been decorated over the years with a mixture of antiques and good, modern furniture; it was welcoming and beautiful and just a little awe-inspiring. She loved it.

Beneath her hand the kauri bannister ran smooth and warm as she climbed the stairs. Bed had never been so desirable. Weariness was an ache in her bones, a deep lassitude which beat down the restraints in her mind. Memories came surging back like a dark flood.

Could one fall in love at sixteen? Of course not, yet the emotions she had felt then had been stronger, more potent than any since. Long days of summer had been a background for an explosion of feeling which made her tense even now. Because those holidays, Melly had spent much time with friends, there had been no one to squabble with, no one to take Jennet's mind off the king-sized crush she had developed for Rafe.

The pink dress whispered over her head. After she hung it up, she stared at herself in the mirror, her eyes moving from the high, full breasts to her narrow waist and thence to the slight roundness of her stomach. That summer she had longed for smaller breasts and a perfectly flat stomach like the models in the fashion magazines which Diana read; she had not then realised that it took rigorous dieting to keep those spare, photogenic figures.

She had yearned to attract Rafe's attention, to make him see her, just once, as she had seen him look at his girlfriend, with a kind of banked glitter in his eyes as though he was thinking unimaginable thoughts.

Ever since Jennet could remember there had been girls, even before maturity had given him that

unmistakable air of virile magnetism. Rafe was used to
easy conquests. That summer the girl in possession was
his own age, a long-stemmed brunette who had
seemed ultra-sophisticated to Jennet's eyes.

It was easy to smile now as she recalled how bitterly,
agonisingly jealous she had been, but the emotions had
been real and almost impossible for her to cope with.
Unfortunately she had nowhere to go for help. She did
not have the sort of relationship with her mother which
would have made confiding in her possible. From her
normal casual indifference, Diana had swung that
summer to irritated condemnation. Nothing that Jennet
did or said found favour.

So she had spent much of her time in a little dell she
found along the valley. Each morning she packed
herself lunch, her bathing suit and books and suntan
lotion, before making her way through the paddocks to
a small gully where totara trees surrounded a patch of
lush grass, cutting her off from the working life of Te
Puriri.

Time passed quickly as she read, and swam in a pool
in the creek and sunbathed in the nude, feeling very
advanced and rather wicked. She dreamed dreams,
wove impossible fantasies for only two characters, her
untutored mind playing with the concepts of love and
passion.

So the days had drowsed by in a lazy procession
until the day before she was due to go back to
school. She had finished *War and Peace* and had
dropped off into a light doze on the rug, her eyes
covered by her arm.

A slight sound forced its way beneath the cloak of
sleep. Rolling over she sighed, and then heard it again,
fretting at the edge of consciousness. Slowly, reluctantly,
she had opened her eyes, even then not expecting
anything other than one of the numerous safe noises,
the call of a bird or the snorting of one of the Hereford

cattle just through the fence. When her eyes registered the tall figure standing in the shade of the totara trees she had gaped, frozen with shock as hinted horrors rushed swiftly to mind. Then he moved out into the sunlight and she saw that it was Rafe, his face totally impassive except for the leaping glittering shock of his eyes as they swept the length of her slender body.

The terror receded but she blushed scarlet and sat up, grabbing desperately for her clothes.

Quite calmly he asked, 'Who are you waiting for, Jennet?'

This brought her head up. 'No one!' she answered indignantly, hauling her bikini top on with infinitely more speed than skill. Tension and nerves led her to dropping the narrow piece of cloth which covered her hips so she made herself decent by snatching her damp towel around her waist.

Rafe came to a stop by the rug and stood with his hands on his hips, staring down at her. A sleepy little breeze carried the faint scent of horse; in her lowly position he loomed above like an old avenging deity from the days when the gods were cruel.

'No?' he said.

She could see his disbelief. Another painful flare of colour seared her skin. Her mouth set in a stubborn line.

'No,' she repeated stiffly, adding rather desperately, 'I come because—because it's quiet and no one yells at me.'

His dark brows drew together. 'So this is no lover's tryst.'

'Of course it's not. I think you're horrible.'

At the tremble in her voice his frown eased and he said unexpectedly, 'Yes, I suppose I am. Sorry. It's just that you're growing up.'

She stared down at her hands until the mist across her eyes blurred them. So he had noticed. She had to clear her throat before saying gruffly, 'Do you think you could tell my—Diana that?'

His withdrawal was abrupt and ominous, but even as she cursed herself for ruining the momentary accord between them he sat down on the rug beside her and observed, 'You haven't had much fun these holidays, have you?'

'I don't know what's got into—her,' she told him huskily, the words barely audible because she kept her head lowered and turned away. In spite of that defensive posture she could feel his closeness like a blast furnace heating her skin into painful awareness.

'Life can be complicated,' he agreed, 'especially at your age, but one of the reasons why your mother picks on you is because she is eighteen years older than you.'

This brought her head up. Frowning, she tried to make sense of the statement, her eyes suspicious as they scanned the dark determined face.

He showed his teeth in a not at all pleasant smile. 'You are very like her,' he said, 'just as she used to be. When Diana looks at you she sees all the years she'll never have again. It's all behind her; you have it in front of you. Diana's suffering from what is known as mid-life crisis; in other words, plain jealousy of a younger woman.'

His compliment shocked her as much as it surprised her. Accustomed to her mother's finished, polished sophistication, she had never seen much to admire in her own youthful features. The words stumbled from her tongue as she said so, and he had smiled ironically and touched her mouth with his finger, smoothing across the sensitive skin as though he liked the feel of it. A strange fluttering sensation in her stomach startled Jennet but she did not pull away.

'Of course,' he agreed gravely. 'But you are going to be every bit as lovely as Diana. Are you going to use this pretty face to capture yourself a nice rich husband?'

Her lashes flew up. 'My father is not rich——' she began in some indignation.

'No, but my father is. She's been married to him for a long time now, you know.'

Suddenly wary, Jennet turned her face away from the cold, taunting darkness of his gaze. She didn't know what to say. Until then she had accepted her mother's second marriage as a mere fact of life. She could remember no other situation. That brief, first marriage seemed not to have existed, and her own father was a distant figure. He had remarried and was not interested in her, his new family had all his love.

At school she had been teased about the scandal of Melly's birth and the marriage which had happened too late, but she had stubbornly ignored those who had tried to use it to torment her, refusing to care about events which happened so long ago. Recently however she had found herself wondering what there was about Dougal Hollingworth which had led her mother to fly in the face of convention.

Was Rafe right, telling her that it was money, greed?

'You're just being beastly,' she muttered, wishing that he would go away. Dreams were much more satisfactory than reality. In her fantasies, Rafe was tender and kind, he did not treat her with the rather contemptuous irony which was his normal attitude to her.

'Not really,' he said now, indifferently, pushing a hand on the ground to lever himself up.

Perversely, now that he was ready to go, she didn't want him to. Without preamble she blurted out a question which had been worrying at her.

'Rafe, is your father going to get better?'

'Diana doesn't think so,' he said quietly, settling back on to the rug.

He was watching her, his eyes half closed against the hard brilliance of the sunlight. The sweetish scent of

crushed grass mingled with the moist dampness of the
bush behind them. A dragonfly hung suspended, red
and green, its wings a silver blur, then flew its short
darting flight beyond the edge of vision.

Jennet sat still, unable to breathe, her eyes fixed
imploringly on her stepbrother's hard handsome face.

'Did the doctor tell her that?' she asked, barely
voicing the words.

Rafe's broad shoulders lifted in a shrug. 'God
knows,' he said cynically. 'Diana doesn't bother to talk
to me about my father. But you needn't worry. Even if
he does die you'll not starve. She was the one who
persuaded him into forcing me to buy Te Puriri.'

Jennet had not been told of this. The bitter anger in
his tone made her shrink away from him.

'But it's yours,' she said, her high brow creasing with
the effort to understand. 'At least, it's going to be yours
when—if . . . How—why do you have to buy it?'

Looking back, Jennet could only think that his
bitterness had been so great that he had to hurt
someone. Dougal's condition made it impossible for
Rafe to vent his anger on him, or on Diana, who would
have had no compunction about complaining to her
husband. In the light of his revelation that Diana had
been propositioning him, Jennet could now only
wonder at the strength of character which had kept him
silent.

Then, however, he had lain back on to the rug,
linking his hands beneath his neck as he closed his eyes.
He looked very big, very forceful, in spite of the relaxed
position.

'As you say, the station is—or was—my father's.
After his first heart attack he decided to put it into a
trust which would have given Diana a share in it for the
rest of her life. So I decided to use a legacy from my
mother's estate to buy the place outright. That way,
you see, we're all happy. Diana gets a nice big lump

sum to fritter away when my father dies and I have complete control of Te Puriri.'

'But—it's not fair that you should have to buy it,' she protested childishly. 'You belong here.'

He gave a bark of harsh laughter. 'Hell, what's fair? It was worth it, if only to keep her sticky fingers out of the till.'

'You really hate her, don't you?' she breathed, trying to overcome the ache in her throat.

He levered himself on to an elbow, looking up into her face with lazy insolence.

'Why should I love her? She's spent the last twelve years trying to cheat me of my birthright. You don't love her either.'

'I do,' she said, horrified. 'I do, she's my *mother*.'

'And I'm your brother, of a sort, but you don't love me, do you?'

A painful blush made her duck her head away from him again. 'You don't—you haven't——' she muttered, in an agony of embarrassment.

When he answered she could tell that he was smiling. 'No, I don't, and I haven't. When I look at you I see Diana, so I haven't set myself out to win your affection. Which is why you don't like me. But from the little I've seen of you with your mother, she's never tried either. To her you've been a nuisance just like me, a reminder that she chose a poor man for her first husband. Yet you think you love her.'

It hurt to have her inchoate, unexpressed thoughts put so bluntly, and she reacted blindly.

'You're just jealous,' she flashed.

He smiled into her flushed face, those impenetrable eyes scornful. 'Jealous? Hardly. Oh, perhaps at first. My mother had only been dead for three months when my father saw Diana. It wasn't long after that she was queening it here at Te Puriri. I was bitterly jealous then, especially when the first thing she did was to persuade him to send me away to boarding school. That was when I realised that she'd stop at nothing to get rid of anyone she saw as an obstacle. You'd better be careful.'

'Why?' The word was expelled on a shocked breath as she edged back away from him. He was too big, and that first electric awareness had been transformed into something which frightened and bewildered her.

'Because you're growing into a beautiful woman,' he said coolly.

Another wave of colour scorched her skin. Jennet bit her lip. She hated the way her body betrayed her, hated the sardonic amusement of Rafe's expression as those black eyes swept over her. Before she could say anything he added, 'God help the local boys when they set eyes on you.'

'Why?' she asked angrily, stiffening.

'Because any woman with a face like yours is trouble.'

He reached out and ran a long index finger up the sun-warmed skin of her arm, his eyes gleaming with an unknown emotion as she froze. Across her shoulder it went, stroking gently down the slender curve of her throat to stop for a tense second at the point where her bikini bra divided to cover her breasts.

'Beautiful trouble,' he said softly, some alien note in his deep voice sending a frisson of excitement through her veins.

CHAPTER THREE

JENNET didn't know what to do. Nothing, not her reading, nor her daydreams, had prepared her for this subtle assault. With dilated eyes and fast-throbbing pulse she waited, every sense fixed on the sensuous movement of his fingers as it delicately traced the outline of her bikini top. It was suddenly very hot. Tiny beads of sweat burst through her skin and she held her breath, wondering what she should do, and knowing that she wouldn't do anything because his touch, his presence, held her in a spell of lazy lethargy.

He wasn't looking at her, his gaze was bent on that slow exploration, but in the hollow of his throat a pulse beat erratically and she could see a soft sheen on his skin. Fascinated, Jennet watched as her breasts bloomed. They seemed to swell, to ache for a different touch; incredulously she saw the soft aureoles harden into tiny peaks which thrust against the thin material of her bikini.

Rafe froze. For a heartbeat the whole universe stilled. He made a thick sound deep in his throat, a kind of half groan. Then he sat up in one swift movement, his hands pressed into the rug, one on either side of her hips. Slowly, almost as if he was acting against his will, his head bent and his mouth touched the soft golden skin just where it swelled above the bikini top.

Lost in a black enchantment of the senses, Jennet made no protest, unless a harsh, expelled breath could be understood as one. Her dreams of lovemaking had been confined to kisses and chaste caresses. She did not understand this hot, unrestrained flood of sensation and was unable to control it. Like a woman drowning she went under, afraid, yet unable to save herself.

He said nothing, the only contact between them was the warm sweet movement of his mouth across her skin. Her dazed eyes took in the width of his shoulders, the cage his body formed with an arm each side of her, the red sparks struck by the sun in his dark hair. Heat crawled over her, slicking her body with moisture. Somewhere a cicada played his miniature zither, monotonous, persistent, so much a part of this northern summer that the sound barely impinged. The stream trickled leisurely over smooth brown rocks, the small sound cool in the heated, dazzling world he was making for her.

Every sense was stretched; sounds and smells lingered in her brain, yet she felt that they were completely separated from the rest of the universe, held prisoners in a golden sensual bubble beneath an unknown sun.

When his mouth reached its destination, the small peak at the centre of her breasts, she whimpered, assailed by an intense tightening deep within her, an aching need which jagged through her body like a shaft of lightning.

'You mustn't . . .' she whispered, not knowing what she said, impelled by an instinct of self-preservation which for a second of clarity overrode the sensual constraints of his caress.

He lifted his head so that he could see into her blind, hot face.

'Of course I can,' he said and smiled, a fierce predator's smile as he ran his hand up the tense length of her thigh beneath the towel to touch her. His fingers were not gentle and she flinched, jerking backwards, fear replacing the languour in her wide eyes.

'You're ready for me,' he taunted. 'Would I be the first, Jennet?'

Shame scalded her, shame and a bitter anger. 'Go to hell!' she snapped, trying to push him away.

Her fingers slid over the damp cotton of his shirt.

Before she could get any purchase on the hardness of his shoulders he moved, flipping her on to her back swiftly and heavily so that the impact drove the breath from her lungs and she gasped, staring up into a face set in lines of such harsh anger that she closed her eyes to shut him out.

'Yes, you'll be just like Diana,' he said, not trying to soften the contempt in his voice. Strong, implacable hands held her still as he bent his head and forced her mouth open in the sort of kiss she had only heard the other girls at school talk about.

Anger and humiliation lent strength to her struggles, but that relentless mouth held her in bondage. After a time she thought she was going to suffocate from its hot invasion. A small feral sound throbbed in her throat as tears squeezed beneath her flickering lashes. She went limp. His weight pressed her on to the rug, one arm holding her head imprisoned, the other down the length of her body, tugging the towel free before stroking the skin of her leg.

For a frantic moment she thought that he was going to hurt her, his body was so hard and heavy. His mouth lifted, and she took a deep breath, opening her eyes to tell him just what she thought of him. The words were never spoken. She caught a glimpse of a Rafe she had never seen before, the chiselled features drawn, the black gaze sightless yet aware, before his mouth came down again, kissing her eyelids closed, touching the contours of her face in a caress as gentle and seducing as that first kiss had been frightening.

His hand slid gently on to the nape of her neck. He whispered something she couldn't hear and slid his leg between hers, and in spite of her innocence she realised that he was not punishing her, that he wanted her as much as a man could.

To her astonished horror she was unable to prevent a leaping response. Her hand lifted, to touch with shy

tentative fingers the smooth, hard curves of his
shoulders, to slide beneath his arm and splay across his
back. Without conscious design, her slender body
stiffened in reply to the demand in his.

For a moment they were sealed together, mouth
against mouth, the long sweep of breast and hip and
thigh so joined that nothing could come between them.
Rafe's big body was wracked with an intense shudder
which called forth an answering movement from hers;
she ached with a painful hunger in every cell, every
nerve and her hips lifted and thrust in a spontaneous
instinctive reaction.

He seemed locked into stasis, every muscle bulging
with tension.

Then he muttered an imprecation and pushed her
away, rolling over on to his side so that all she could see
was his back, straining with the effort of his breathing
as he took great gulps of air.

'Cover yourself,' he said savagely.

With trembling fingers, Jennet grabbed the towel and
sat up, wrapping it cloak style around her shoulders so
that it made a tent around her body.

Rafe got to his feet. She could feel the heat of his
gaze on her bowed head as he stared down the length of
his body to where she crouched at his feet, a turmoil of
emotions and sensations clawing at her.

'Just like your mother,' he said flatly.

It was all Jennet could do not to cringe away from
the fury she sensed in him. Anger rose within her like a
red tide. He had humiliated her, deliberately and cold-
bloodedly mocking her innocence with the invasion of
his experience. She was torn by frustration, a new
sensation to go with the others he had brought to life,
the sweet urgency of desire and the bitter shame.

She took a deep, shivering breath. Although she was
damp with sweat, her skin felt cold. It took all of her
willpower to force her teeth to catch her bottom lip so

that its stupid trembling would be stopped. Hot tears stung her eyes and her throat ached. The vibrato trill of a skylark seemed to pierce her eardrums, blocking out all other sounds.

I wish I could die, she thought desperately. If he says anything . . .

When he walked, he moved like a panther, silently as if his life depended on the successful stalking of prey, but she knew when he left. And knew that life would never again be the same.

Hours later, when she forced herself back to the homestead he had left for a dinner date with his current girlfriend. He was not at breakfast the next morning and immediately after that she had been packed back to boarding school, not to see him again until he came home from a trip overseas just three days before her wedding. And that had been two years later.

A kind of sob breaking harshly from her throat brought Jennet back to the present day. As if waking from a bad dream, she stared blankly around the room which had been hers on the holidays she had spent at Te Puriri.

It was incredible, but she had never before allowed herself to remember that incident. Frightened, repelled by such heated sensuality she had banished it from her mind into her subconscious, refusing to accept it and its implications.

Only a few months later her stepfather had died. After that, Melly and Diana used to spend the occasional holiday at Te Puriri, but on those occasions Jennet had always been sent to stay with her real father. Although she didn't enjoy herself she had gone without protest, as unwilling to face Rafe as he had been to see her.

Perhaps she should have made herself view things as objectively as she could. But at sixteen, who is objective? Even now it took all her willpower to think

back to that time, to accept that something had
happened to her in Rafe's arms, something which
would have to be exorcised before she was able to get
on with her life. By pretending those maddened minutes
had never happened, she had failed in a necessary part
of her growing up.

Perhaps that had been one of her reasons for her
marriage. Rafe had gone to Brazil and she had been
allowed back to Te Puriri. Derek had been there.

Even now she closed her eyes against the memories,
turning her head into the pillow after she had switched
off the lamp. It had been so wonderful, such a boost to
her precarious self-confidence, to realise that Derek
wanted her, that he thought her desirable and exciting
enough to want to marry her. Inured to rejection, she
found him irresistible. Diana had been very enthusiastic, very encouraging, turning what should have been
a summer infatuation into a commitment. For almost
the first time in her life Jennet felt valued, a person of
worth. That summer she had bloomed.

It was this seductive feeling which had persuaded her
into leaving university without a second thought. Even
Rafe's icy, adamant refusal to give her away hadn't
managed to burst the bubble of make-believe she had
lived in. Because her father had been unable to come,
an uncle had acted for him.

And then it had all fallen about her head and she had
had no one to turn to, not Diana, who had followed her
daughter's marriage with her own to a wealthy
Englishman and gone with him to live in the south of
France, not Rafe, who seemed to spend most of that
year overseas. On the few occasions he was home, he
had a selection of women with him and when he saw
Jennet, which was rarely, he had made it quite obvious
that he was not interested; couldn't care less about the
girl fate had made his stepsister.

So she had relearned an old lesson, that she must rely

on herself, that for her there was no knight on a white charger to rescue her from the mess her life had become. With the courage of desperation, she had seized the first opportunity to flee, swearing never to come back, never to think of Te Puriri again.

Yet here she was, dragged back by the past, forced into a false position because she could not bear for Melly to go through the same experiences she had endured without at least a warning.

Above the ache in her head she heard the thick sound of a car door slamming. There was a burst of laughter, and other sounds that made it clear that the party was over.

It took twenty minutes for them all to go, but at last they did. Within a few moments the sound Jennet had been waiting for, a single sharp tap in the door, brought her upright in the bed. Rafe's voice said something which was lost as Melly flung the door open.

'. . . if she is asleep,' Melly finished, switching on the light with a ruthless hand. 'Go away, Rafe, I don't need you.'

Jennet watched, her mouth smiling, the expression in her eyes hidden by her lashes.

Melly bit her lip, revealing a combination of anger and pain. 'Please, Rafe,' she said again, and frowning, his gaze very hard as it rested on Jennet's lovely mocking face, he left them, closing the door behind him.

Melly stood rigidly, her hands very still by her sides.

'Oh, sit down,' Jennet said tiredly. 'It's me, remember, your sister, not Dracula.'

'Why did you come back?'

'I'm beginning to wonder.' Jennet affected a yawn. 'Believe me, had I known that I was going to cause so much trouble, I'd have stayed away. I've had Rafe threatening me with instant execution if I upset you, and Derek informing me that no matter what I tell you

you'll remain faithful because you're besotted with him.'

'Derek didn't say any such thing,' Melly flashed fiercely.

A strike home, Jennet thought with satisfaction. She patted the bed. 'Well, words to that effect. Come and sit down, let's get re-acquainted. It's been a long time.'

Melly stared at her. 'You really mean it,' she burst out, astonished. 'You know, you're really something! Tell me why you came back, please, Jennet.'

'To see you. You are, let's face it, all that I've got for a family.'

'You haven't cared much for us for the past five years and let's face something else, Jennet, you didn't have much time for any of us before that. You hated Rafe, and you used to stare right through me—you were a funny, cold creature, making sure that nobody got near enough you to touch you.' She was sallow beneath her cosmetics except for a bright spot on each cheekbone. Her eyes, so like Rafe's, glittered angrily. 'You came back to stop me marrying Derek, didn't you?'

'Why should I want to do that? *I* left Derek, not the other way around.'

Her half-sister's long hands clenched again. 'Yes, you ran away with Trent—with another man. Ask yourself if any man would want you back after that. You're so pretty, Jen, can't you——?' She stopped to banish the note of pleading in her voice before saying woodenly, 'This is a mistake. I'll see you in the morning.'

So she wasn't as confident of her power over Derek as she wanted to seem. Jennet could have wept for her, so proud, so *young*, as she swung towards the door. Perhaps she was wrong to come back, perhaps . . .

Then she remembered the psychiatrist she had consulted. Ultimately her presence here would be kinder to Melly than her absence could ever be, even if she

caused her some suffering. But it took hours before she
was able to sleep, and she woke in the morning fretted
by the helplessness which had driven her away from the
valley.

Breakfast was served, as always, in the small room
off the kitchen. Jennet was late, but not late enough to
eat alone. As she opened the door she was met by two
pairs of identical and inimical eyes.

'Good morning,' she said cheerfully, smiling as
though it was a good morning.

Neither Melly nor Rafe returned the smile.

'Oh well, I tried,' Jennet told the cat as she sat down.
She sighed and got to her feet again, to get cutlery and
a napkin for herself.

'I thought you might sleep in,' Melly said defensively.
'Do you want some toast?'

'Just coffee, thanks.'

'You'd better eat something,' Rafe ordered. 'Or do
you have to diet constantly?'

'Not yet.'

He lifted his brows, smiling unpleasantly. 'Of course,
actresses are allowed a little more leeway than models,
aren't they?'

'You should know,' Jennet said with cool composure.
'Wasn't your last lover a model? Of sorts?'

Melly gave a gasp, hastily smothered, then handed
the coffee she had just poured across the table, her
shocked eyes darting from Jennet's serene face to
Rafe's.

He said calmly, 'Yes, she did some modelling, I
believe, but as it was a favour for a friend she was no
more a model than you are an actress.' His lashes lifted.
Offensively he finished, 'She had the same decorative
impact. Possibly with a little more style.'

Jennet grinned. 'What a nasty tongue you have,' she
marvelled. 'Shall I tell you about my debut as Juliet?'

Melly stared. 'As in "Romeo and"?'

'Yes.' Jennet sipped her coffee, her mocking glance meeting Rafe's. 'I've just finished in it at Sydney.'

There was a moment's stretched silence before Melly asked stiffly, 'Good reviews?'

Jennet shrugged. 'Not too bad, although all with a distinct air of surprise.'

Rafe broke the subsequent silence. 'What are you planning to do today?' he asked, addressing the question in an indifferent voice to Jennet.

'I thought I might go across and see Derek.'

'How?'

Ignoring Melly's swift antagonism, Jennet suggested with a light lack of emphasis, 'Borrow a car?'

'I'll need to check your driving before I let you loose in one of my vehicles,' he said.

'Rafe, I've been driving for ten years.'

'Badly for the first three, at least.'

She knew that tone of voice. Implacable; Rafe was not going to take her word for anything. Firmly squelching the desire to fling the contents of her cup at his sardonic face she drank the coffee, slowly, silently, before getting to her feet.

Joy, the housekeeper, came in, They exchanged greetings and Joy refused Jennet's offer to help with her usual brusque off-handedness. When Jennet left the room Rafe followed.

'We're going into Port Arthur for lunch,' he informed her. 'Be ready in half an hour.'

'I don't——'

He halted her progress up the stairs by putting his hand over hers on the balustrade. The long fingers flexed, effectively trapping hers. Jennet bit her lip.

'Don't be a bore, Jennet.'

She met his arrogant glance defiantly. 'But——'

'Jennet.'

Her name was a warning, a threat delivered in two soft syllables.

'Oh, very well,' she retorted as the tiny hairs up her spine stiffened.

He smiled most unpleasantly and lifted his hand from hers. For a second she stood motionless, her face blank and smooth as she looked at him. He wore a checked shirt, the long sleeves rolled up above his elbows, and a pair of working trousers which hugged his slim hips, and those long. heavily-muscles legs. He could have been a farmhand, except that the clothes he wore were totally eclipsed by the man. He was dominant male, predatory, dangerous, watching her with an insolent amusement in the black depths of his eyes.

'Casting a spell, Jennet?'

The heavy pale tresses moved like a swathe of silk about her face and neck as she shook her head, slowly, just once. She was remembering how he had looked at her naked breasts the night before. All he had wanted to do was humiliate her, yet some instinct, feminine and as old as femininity, told her that his actions were based on more than the desire to punish.

'Rafe,' she said, 'Rafe, did Diana really want you?'

His first reaction was surprise but that was swiftly hidden. In a voice that was flat and cruel he answered, 'Yes she did.'

Jennet couldn't prevent a quick, shocked breath.

He smiled, taunting her. 'When I turned her down she had a discreet affair with—well, it doesn't matter who. He was too young to know better. Fortunately as soon as he found out, his father packed him off to Australia. She doesn't cope well with frustration, your mother.'

She couldn't bear the knowing note in his voice. Quickly, as if he contaminated her, she turned away.

Soft and deadly, his next statement stopped her. 'I wouldn't turn you down, Jennet, not as I did her. Last time you were a child. The same reason doesn't apply now.'

Jennet's skin crawled. It took self-control beyond anything she had ever needed to say drily, 'On short rations, Rafe? Can't you get what you crave?'

'I crave nothing.' His hand bit into her shoulder, swinging her around to face him. He was smiling again, that hard mirthless movement of his lips which meant that he was barely able to control his anger. As if she were for sale he swept her with an insolent glance.

'You're very desirable,' he said before leaning forward to whisper, 'and not in the least innocent. I'm going to see how well you decorate my bed before you leave here.'

A spear of sharp, hot desire ran through her body, but she stood her ground, resisting the sensation. It was galling to have to bite back the answer which burned on her tongue, but something in his arrogantly smiling face warned her that she had provoked him far enough. Too far, and he was quite capable of throwing her out of the house and refusing to allow her back.

'Then I hope you sleep in black satin sheets,' she said contemptuously. 'I've heard that I show up to best advantage on them.'

'Indeed? I remember how very tempting you looked on that old rug,' he returned caressingly, adding as the angry colour surged through her skin, 'but if you like satin sheets then I'll get Joy to buy some. Who am I to deny you your whims?'

'You needn't bother. If I did feel like cutting loose it wouldn't be with a man who can't distinguish between me and my mother. You make me feel sick.'

'No, I make you feel hungry,' he said mockingly.

Damn him, but he was right. For as long as she could remember he had affected her powerfully; it was as though he stripped a skin from her so that she was acutely sensitive, as open to influence as she had been when a child. He had only to look at her, even as he was now with anger and desire warring in his eyes, and she felt that tormenting ache begin to heat the pit of her stomach. Lust, pure and simple, just the primitive basic urge to mate, yet she had to clench her jaw to prevent herself from betraying it, forcibly jerk her mind from contemplating the erotic, tantalising images which formed there.

'As for your mother,' he said softly, watching her with eyes which saw everything, 'you're a fool if you think I can't tell the difference. She *is* eighteen years older than you.'

'That's not what I meant.'

'No, I suppose not.' He picked up her hand and drew it to his mouth, holding it so that when he spoke his lips just touched the soft palm. 'Very well, then, you look like her, you behave like her and as far as I can tell, you react to men in exactly the same way. Very generously.'

What would he say if she told him that he was the only man who had ever made her feel wanton? Refuse to believe her, of course. Totally cynical, it would never occur to him that even her precipitate flight from her marriage had been completely innocent. Trent Addison, Derek's cousin, was that rare person, a chivalrous man; he had made no attempt to touch her. He had just helped her to get away.

Since she had become well known, there had been gossip and rumours about her love life, but nothing was ever openly stated. Mainly because there was nothing to comment on. Her physical reactions seemed to have been frozen in some limbo.

At least they had been frozen—until she had returned to Te Puriri, and there it was, just as if she were sixteen again, palpitatingly conscious of only one man, the one man she couldn't have, because when he looked at her he saw Diana, the woman who had usurped his mother's place, banished him from Te Puriri and with her particular brand of callousness had made him an interloper, unwanted by his father, deprived of his heritage.

Rafe was clever, with a cold, logical brain, but the events of childhood can shadow the emotions of the man and he was unable to shake off his suspicion and resentment. Reason must tell him that just because she looked like Diana, Jennet was not necessarily her carbon copy.

Unfortunately there was a little more to fuel his antagonism than the uncanny resemblance and the emotions carried over from his childhood. There was that unfortunate incident when she had surrendered so completely to him, there was her marriage and her subsequent flight with another man, her appearance in the soap opera as an amoral bitch, her arrival back here and his realisation that she wanted to prevent Melly from marrying Derek.

'Generous? Perhaps,' she said indifferently, turning away to climb the stairs. 'But not to you, Rafe.'

His soft laughter was drowned by Melly's voice, low-pitched and angry as she came down the hall.

He made no reply to whatever she had said.

Jennet stopped. Over her shoulder she saw them both watching her.

'Rafe,' she said sweetly.

He lifted his brows.

'Do you think the end ever justifies the means?'

The dark brows drew together. 'No.'

'Oh, I do hope you're wrong,' Jennet replied, bestowing a warm, mischievous smile on them before she ran lightly up the rest of the stairs.

CHAPTER FOUR

HALF an hour later she came back downstairs, humming softly to herself. She had a warm, huskily sensual voice, not strong enough to be exploited, but very pleasant on the ear. Melly waited at the foot of the stairs, her face still and cold.

'*Chorus of the Hebrew Slaves*, by Verdi,' she said, and her voice softened. 'Do you remember the first time you heard that? Rafe played it one night and you demanded instant silence. We were so astonished that we all shut up. And at the end you burst into tears and ran up to your room. I remember Rafe wouldn't let me follow you. He said that you needed time to recover yourself. Do you still react so violently?'

'I manage to hide the tears,' Jennet told her drily, 'but yes, music gives me an emotional high. I read a lot, I love reading, but it's music and some poetry which really get to me.'

Her fingers smoothed lovingly over a small sculpture on a console, an Italian figurine of Cupid and Psyche, charming, sensual yet delicate. 'Somewhere I read that when Verdi died and the funeral cortege was going through the streets the passers-by began to sing that chorus, spontaneously, everyone just joining in. I hope it's true.'

Melly smiled, her eyes puzzled. 'You're a funny mixture. Sentimental yet tough.'

She lifted her hand in a little cut-off gesture to express her failure to understand. The emerald on her finger caught in the sunlight which spilled in through the door and the stone took fire, glittering with green flames. For a long moment both women stared at it.

Jennet's nail bit into her palms. Slowly she lifted her head to look imploringly at Melly. But Melly's black eyes were as inscrutable as any Oriental's, and the strong bones of her face were clenched. Jennet turned and walked out through the great panelled doors into the winter sunshine. Her heels tapped crisply down the marble steps and along the path, the sound ceasing as she paused to inspect a big jardiniere which held a camellia just coming into full bloom. The perfectly formal flowers were striped and flecked in two shades of pink.

'Helenore,' Jennet remembered, touching a flower with a pale fingernail. 'I wonder if I can still recall their names. I'm so glad your great-great-great, or whatever he was, grandfather decided to build himself a white villa instead of a sober Victorian homestead, even if everyone thought he was mad.'

Her gaze swept across the façade with its arched, beautifully proportioned windows.

Sheltered in its valley by the enormous old trees which gave the station its name, Te Puriri homestead was embowered by flowers, many of them in urns and pots which kept Ted, the housekeeper's husband, so busy. Now camellias were arranged along the path; sharing their urns were violets and ivy and tiny cream and white narcissi. Across the lawns in borders, beneath magnolia and jacaranda trees, were other narcissi, jonquils like small suns and above them daphne bushes, the clean spicy scent of the little rosey flowers mingling with the perfume of the jonquils. Japonica and poinsettia provided colour and form, the one spikily elegant, the other lending the garden a touch of tropical colour. Clumps of polyanthus made a Persian carpet, and at a focal point down the drive a huge Taiwan cherry tree was smothered in its tiny cerise bells, the delight of every tui from miles around. The abrupt, tearing sound of their flight almost drowned out the clucks and chirps and exquisite chimes of their song.

'You really do love the place, don't you?'

Jennet suppressed a start at Melly's soft statement. She turned a dazzled face over her shoulder and met the impact of two pairs of black eyes. Rafe had joined his half-sister and was watching, his expression guarded.

'I've always loved it,' Jennet shrugged. 'I used to believe that it was the most beautiful place in the world.'

She reacted to Rafe's cold stare with the sparkling smile she used to hide her emotions. He frowned, the sunlight highlighting strong cheekbones and the autocratic line of his jaw, his eyes sweeping her in a scrutiny as intense as it was bleak.

She knew she looked good. Her tapered, pleated pants in grey silk boucle emphasised the long feminine legs and narrow ankles. With them, she wore high suede shoes of the same grey and a striped print shirt, keeping the cool wind at bay with a grey linen blazer. Just a little too formally dressed for a shopping trip in a small country town, she was, beside Rafe and Melly's splendid, natural throwaway grace, perhaps too finished, a little artificial, but she could not compete with their tall balanced bodies and striking bone structure. She needed the armour that good clothes provided.

Port Arthur had slept away most of the years since before the end of the last century when the last kauri had been felled, until ten years ago when tourists had begun to appreciate its air of dreaming peace.

The locals woke up to find themselves living in a holiday centre; many of them disliked the change but quite a few were far-sighted enough to see the opportunities this offered. Rafe had been one. As well as an excellent landowner, he was an astute businessman and had bought into the development of the little port.

What an unfair decision Dougal had made when he had forced Rafe to buy the station. No wonder Rafe

despised the stepmother who had persuaded his father
to make it. It was just unfortunate that he wasn't
entirely rational where Diana's daughter was concerned.

Not for the first time, Jennet wondered how he
would respond if she told him the reason why she
had fled her marriage. As her eyes roamed the
familiar contours of the hills, she smiled a little sadly.
She didn't have to wonder, she knew exactly how he
would react. With a total lack of belief. So would
Melly, so would anyone she tried to convince. Only
Trent Addison, the man who had rescued her, knew
why she had gone with him. That was why she was
going to keep her silence, at least until she had
worked out some plan.

'Where do you want to go?' Rafe's deep voice
intruded into her thoughts.

Startled, she looked up and met his eyes in the rear
vision mirror. When Melly spoke her voice seemed to
shatter some potent, frightening spell.

'I just want to prowl around the boutiques,' she told
him.

'Jennet?'

'I'll have a look in the craft shops,' she said a little
huskily. 'What are you doing?'

'Seeing various people,' he said. 'I'll meet you at the
Waterfront Café at one o'clock.'

It was not exactly an order, but Jennet had no
intention of being even a minute late.

When the big Audi had been locked Melly walked
swiftly across the parking lot, leaving Jennet to Rafe's
mercies. He took her elbow to support her over the
cracked, uneven asphalt; he must have felt her
instinctive withdrawal for his fingers tightened.

'Are you buying gifts?' he asked unexpectedly.

The sun gleamed in soft fire on her hair. He was
striding beside her with that flowing vitality which was

so essential a part of him yet they were miles apart, distanced by the years and his dislike.

'No,' she said. 'I want to look at the pottery. It's a hobby of mine.'

'Is it?' He sounded surprised. His fingers slid down her arm to enclose her hand and he lifted it for inspection. 'Buying it, I presume. This delicate hand doesn't look as if it's ever done any work. Certainly not dabbling in clay on a potter's wheel.'

'You presume wrong,' she said, after clearing her throat. His touch was not in the least impersonal. Quite deliberately he was stroking her palm with his thumb and the gentle little caress made her feel as though her nerves were hot wires in her body.

With a cutting edge to her voice Jennet continued, 'I'm actually quite good. I learned to pot at school. In fact, I'm almost certain I gave you an ashtray one Cnristmas before you gave up smoking.'

'Yes, I think you did.' He sounded amused now, and arrogant and dismissive all at once. 'I was rather touched. Which is more than Diana was when you gave her a vase.'

The pain of her mother's light, almost scoffing dismissal of the little green vase had long faded, but her voice was uneven as she asked, 'Don't you ever forget anything?'

'Very little. Especially not a grudge. Or a woman I want.' His fingers tightened as she tried to pull free. 'And I have a lot of patience.'

Her lashes flicked nervously at the barely hidden warning. She had to force herself to look away from him and when she did, she could still see the cynical amusement which lay at the back of his eyes.

'You won't need patience,' she retorted, her voice thick.

'Good. Does that mean I can expect you in my bed tonight?'

Colour scorched up her throat and across her cheekbones. 'Can't you drag your mind any higher?' she asked crudely, and then flushed again.

Pleased, he grinned and said 'I'll see you at one,' and left her, walking down the street with long panther strides, the automatic focus of almost every passer-by.

Jennet turned her back, but his image was engraved on the retina of her eyes. He would photograph well. That magnificent bone structure would entrance the camera, and he had presence as well as looks which would come across too. Wondering viciously whether that unclassifiable air of sexual competence could be caught in film, she made her way to the craft shop.

Still deep in discussion with the proprietor, a lean, middle-aged woman with shrewd eyes and a tentative smile, Jennet jumped when Melly's voice broke in.

'Come on, Jen, it's time to go. Hello, Mrs Clarke.'

It was ten past one.

'Oh dear,' Jennet muttered after she'd fled from the shop. 'Oh Lord, is he frothing at the mouth?'

'I don't know. I'm late, too. He'll be very thin around the lips though. Are you still potting?'

'Yes.' Jennet blinked at the glare. At this time of the year the sun was at its lowest so the rays searched in under the verandah roofs.

'What sort of things do you make?'

'Oh, ewers and bowls, plates, that sort of thing.' Jennet was deliberately vague. She had no intention of revealing that her work sold quickly and for high prices, or that it was becoming sought after by an ever-increasing circle of connoisseurs.

The café was an old building but it had been renovated and cleverly redecorated in late Victorian style. Fronting on to the pavement it was built on piles out over the sea, in past years a not uncommon method of conserving the little available flat land. Rafe was talking to another man; when he saw them he nodded and came across to where they stood.

'We'll go out on to the balcony,' he said, and took Jennet's elbow again, not relinquishing it until they reached their table.

Beneath the wide boards of the balcony the sea washed softly in the wake of a small fishing boat which was making its way to the jetty. Seagulls flew in lazy circles above it, and on a pile a black shag crouched, one wing spread out. Even in the brilliance of the sun it looked faintly sinister.

'What would you like to drink?'

Rafe gave their order to the young waitress, smiling at her with such virile charm that she blushed and had to ask for the order again.

They were attracting attention, Jennet realised with dry amusement as two teenaged girls passed by their table, their eyes swivelling in sidelong contemplation of Rafe. She didn't have to look far to find several appreciative masculine glances slanting from her to Melly.

Well, they made an eyecatching trio, the two Hollingworths so dark, she such a contrast. Two attractive women and a man who looked rather like every woman's secretly cherished dream of romance incarnate.

Of course Rafe wasn't in the least romantic. He was tough and arrogant with a temper bad enough to frighten away any sensible person, a brain as sharp as broken glass and a personality to match.

A small smile pulled at her mouth as she watched him deal smoothly with the by now flustered waitress. She'd better clean up her act, Jennet thought wryly; Rafe didn't suffer fools glady. The blandly gracious demeanour could give way to a polite, cold ruthlessness in no time at all. Or was it only to his stepsister—and her mother—that he revealed that aggression? Perhaps no one else experienced anything beyond the cool sophistication which was the usual aspect of his many-faceted character.

The idea gave her an obscure pleasure she refused to dissect. Instead, she sipped Perrier water while she studied the menu.

'The seafood is good here,' he said.

Nodding, Jennet said, 'Well, that's what I'll have.'

'Scallops?'

She nodded again.

'And hapuka?' At her surprised look, he smiled narrowly. 'I told you I forgot nothing.'

'With a brain like that you don't need the computer I saw queening it over your office,' she retorted.

He grinned at that, tacitly calling a truce. 'I like computers. Besides, it stores an immense amount of information which I then don't have to worry about. Once it's in there it's in for good, and I can retrieve it instantly.'

'Good for you,' she said lightly. 'It must make the bookwork much easier. Is Wendy Hardy still your secretary?'

'Yes, although I'll have to look for someone else soon; unfortunately for me she is going to Hamilton to live with her daughter.'

The waitress came back with their first course, very earnest as she placed the dishes carefully in front of them.

For some reason Jennet remembered the flinty note which appeared in her mother's voice whenever she spoke of Te Puriri. Diana had hated living there, so far from Auckland. Eventually her constant complaints had driven Dougal to another life, and a job he hated in the city. No wonder Rafe despised what he saw as his father's weakness.

He was different; no woman would ever sway his

actions. Presumably he would marry one day to provide Te Puriri with an heir, but even if he loved his wife she would have to fit in with his life. There would be no compromise; it was unlikely that Rafe admitted the word to his vocabulary! His naturally dominating personality had been hardened by the efforts of the flaws in Dougal's character.

As she ate the fat, sweet scallops in a white wine sauce, Jennet dragged her attention back to the conversation.

'... I'm sorry, I know you don't like them,' Melly was saying, 'but I did promise Brigit we'd call in.'

'Then we'll go,' Rafe said. 'Don't look so distressed, I'm not going to chew your ears off. I hope I can remain polite to her for an hour or so.'

'Even when you're rude you're polite! She's not so bad, you know. And it was you who said that we'd better accept her invitation to dinner before the ball. That was before Cathy said she couldn't come, of course.'

He grinned, not in the least annoyed by the imputation, before saying smoothly, 'Jennet can take her place.'

'I beg your pardon?'

Something in his expression made her uneasy. 'You can be my partner at the Mialls' party,' he told her, those heavy-lidded eyes very sharp as they surveyed her face. 'And the Settler's Ball afterwards. You'll be staying for a couple more days, I presume.'

'Yes. Yes, of course. I haven't a ball dress, however.'

'Wear what you had on last night,' Rafe said. 'It looked stunning.'

Melly said, 'As balls go it's not madly formal. We're having dinner at the Mialls' first.'

'Sounds fun. Who are the Mialls?'

'Oh, a couple who live where Brownsons used to.' Melly exchanged a complicated look with Rafe. 'He's a property developer and they bought the station when John Brownson sold out.'

'Nice?'

'I'll let you make up your own mind.'

They were pleasant enough, if a little too conscious of their wealth and the Hollingworth's social position. Brigit Miall was a thin, small woman with the sharp eyes of the born gossip. She told an entertaining anecdote, as though she had decided to compensate for the deficiencies of her person by being the best-informed woman in her circle.

The Brownson's old homestead had been demolished and an enormous, extremely well-designed house set in its place. The old-fashioned gardens had been revamped into trendiness, with an enormous swimming pool and entertainment area so well sheltered that it was warm enough for them to be able to sit out and sip long, cool drinks.

And there, under the cynically amused gaze of Rafe, Brigit launched into the inevitable, delicately pursued inquisition. Jennet smiled and parried and answered, giving very little away.

Plainly Brigit knew of her. Equally plainly she wasn't sure of her position in the family.

Those inquisitive eyes darted from the chiselled aloofness of Rafe's handsome face to Melly's grave one and then back to Jennet, assessing, impertinent, even, Jennet decided warily, a trifle malicious. So she countered with a smooth charm acquired rather painfully in many encounters with reporters. When she cared to, Jennet could assume a certain stylish arrogance which was intimidating enough to keep the Brigit Mialls of the world in line.

After a while the older woman backed off and began to drop titbits of gossip into the conversation. There was an amusing dissection of someone's tangled love life followed by a brief, pungent and extremely intelligent rundown on another's financial affairs.

John Miall drew Rafe away to ask him something about the station and Melly sauntered across the terrace to where a small Burmese kitten played with a dead leaf.

'Nice to see Melly so—relaxed,' Brigit purred.

'Yes.'

'Yes, after last year's episode she seemed very triste. I began to wonder if she was ever going to get over it.'

Jennet's brows lifted as her eyes followed Melly's progress. 'Oh?' she said, on just the faintest note of encouragement.

'I suppose it wouldn't have worked out.' Brigit paused artistically. 'Trent is absolutely gorgeous, but he does have a bad reputation where women are concerned. He's one of our dearest friends, but I'm afraid Melly was out of her depth.'

For a moment the sunny garden wavered rather horribly in front of Jennet's eyes.

'Trent?' she managed in a level voice. 'That's an unusual name.'

'Isn't it. Very suited to its owner.' Brigit sounded slightly disappointed but she went on confidingly, 'Trent Addison is Derek's cousin. Didn't you ever meet him?'

Very coolly Jennet answered, 'Yes. Once or twice.' Ran away with him, too, but Brigit might not know of that.

She was acutely conscious of the razor sharp impact of the older woman's glance as she said, 'That's right, he and Derek don't get on too well, do they? It's a pity when families fight. I know when he was staying with us last year, he wouldn't go to see Derek. That's when he met Melly.'

Jennet said nothing. After a long moment Brigit continued, 'He became rather enamoured of her. And she of him, I thought. They saw quite a lot of each other for a couple of months and then pouff! it was over. Melly went to spend the holidays with her mother and Trent flung himself into his work.' She gave a little tinkling laugh. 'I've always suspected that Rafe had a hand in it. He wasn't very happy about the affair. Not that I believe that it was an affair, of course. Amusing, isn't it? Rafe just has to be a rake, yet he hasn't much time for others.'

'Not when his sister is concerned,' Jennet agreed lightly. 'But perhaps it just died a natural death.'

'Perhaps. Although I thought they were seriously smitten and I'm rather good at that sort of thing. Not that I asked, of course. Trent is a dear friend but not even I would have the gall to ask him about his love life. He and Rafe make a pair, don't they, magnificently macho and both are very definitely off-putting if anyone intrudes on their personal space.'

Jennet smiled, her serenely composed expression hiding the furious working of her brain. This, she thought exultantly, might be the information she needed to bulldoze a way through the tangle.

Of course Rafe had had something to do with the break-up of Melly's embryo love affair. He'd probably told her that Trent Addison was the man who had seduced Jennet away from Derek. And in a way he was right, although there had been nothing of an emotional nature between them. Trent had never even seen her as a desirable woman, only as one who needed help. A tall, lean devil with ice-grey eyes and hair the colour of mahogany, he was a rangy, piratical type who had been unexpectedly, devastatingly kind to her when kindness was the last thing she had expected. Not exactly good looking, she recalled, but the reputation Brigit gave him came as no surprise. Even in the emotionally dead state she had been in when he took her away from Derek, his intensely masculine appeal had registered.

Now she realised why Derek had chosen Melly for

his next wife, when he must have known that his engagement would bring Jennet back determined to do her best to prevent it.

Aloud, she murmured, 'Yes, I suppose there are points of resemblance between them.'

'Clever, too, both of them. Trent is a genius with electronics and computers and things like that. He's building himself an empire now, exporting.' Brigit paused. 'He's been overseas for the past six weeks, just got back three days ago. I had thought of inviting him to the ball . . .'

'Had you?' Jennet gave her the full benefit of widened eyes and a small, provocative smile. 'How nice. I like Trent.'

Yes, she had been correct in her summing up. The older woman was a mischief-maker. She smiled back, those sharp eyes bright with significance.

'Well, I'll see,' Brigit said.

But Jennet caught the swift anticipatory relish in the other's voice and knew that if Brigit Miall could swing it, Trent Addison would be there.

After that they chatted until Melly came back, inconsequential stuff that merely passed the time away. Perhaps it would be too harsh to say that Brigit gloated, but as Jennet watched the thin face, she realised that the older woman was eagerly looking to an evening which would provide her with enlivening gossip for some time to come. Of course, she would be banking on every one's good manners to prevent any dangerous emotions from getting out of hand. Brigit could well be too confident; she had obviously never encountered Rafe in a black mood.

But they would all behave in public with propriety, even Derek. They had had years to learn how to hide their feelings. Not that Rafe would hesitate to make a scene, but he had better methods of making his anger felt. Derek was definitely not the man to make a fuss in public. Other people's opinion, and his social standing, mattered very much to Derek.

But if, somehow, his equilibrium could be tilted, then perhaps . . .

A chill feathered across her skin. It would be dangerous, but it might be the only way to bring the situation to a head. If Trent really had meant something to Melly . . . if Derek hated his cousin enough . . . if Jennet could manipulate events and people . . .

Unconsciously she made a grimace of distaste. How hateful, to be plotting and planning like this. As the men came back she looked up to find Brigit watching her.

Not a comfortable woman, she thought, suddenly cold. Almost certainly, Brigit was feared as well as liked. And for all the clever flattery, the amusing, skilful dropping of names, she could not hide the envy which motivated her.

On the way home Rafe and Melly were silent. Once, looking up, Jennet caught Rafe's eyes in the rear-vision mirror. They gleamed like onyx, opaque, all thoughts hidden. She felt grubby and guilty, and glanced away quickly before he could pick up the emotions in her.

Te Puriri dreamed quietly in its hidden valley, surrounded by the steep green hills which gave it riches and security and a stake in the future. It looked like a land under an enchantment, locked in a stasis where nothing changed, nothing died.

Old emotions, the ghosts of the past; pain and anger and bitter hurt, betrayals and an obsessive love, hung heavily on the warm air as well as golden moments of joy and ecstasy and laughter.

I love it so, Jennet thought wearily. All my life it's all that I've ever wanted, and I'll never be anything more than an intruder.

Once back, she sent out through the french windows of her bedroom on to the loggia where great cymbidium

orchids in pots wove an exotic, peaceful spell. It was so
hot that she collapsed on to one of the loungers and
closed her eyes, wondering why she didn't leave, go
straight back to Australia and spend the rest of this
holiday with friends on the Gold Coast. Of course she
couldn't, but oh, it seemed like the thought of Paradise
to a dying woman.

A sudden memory from last night impelled her from
the peace of the loggia to Melly's room. It was empty so
Jennet drifted downstairs, finally catching up with her
in the boudoir where she was curled up in a chair,
reading.

'Where are you and Derek planning to live when
you're married?' Jennet asked after a small amount of
preliminary conversation.

Melly looked both suspicious and taken aback.

'Derek's bought a farm south of Te Kuiti,' she
amswered slowly. 'In the depths of the King Country.'

A quick mental survey of the map brought a frown to
Jennet's brows. 'But that's at the back of beyond,' she
objected.

'Don't you see me as a pioneer?'

Jennet sat down, smiling. 'Tell me all about it,' she
invited.

At any other time she would have been amused at the
combination of eagerness and caution which struggled
for supremacy in Melly's expression. Finally, however,
the desire to confide won.

'Well, it's miles from civilisation,' she said. 'It's right
at the end of a back road towards the coast, and it's
only partly brought in. Derek says it's beautiful, pretty
steep in places with lots of bush on it but it's going to
take us a long time to bring it all in. Derek is really
looking forward to the challenge. He finds Compton
Downs too tame,' she finished defiantly. 'And so do I.'

'Do you know anyone there?'

'Well, no, but people are bound to be friendly. They

usually are in an isolated community like that.' She paused, her dark eyes, so like her brother's searching Jennet's face. As if dissatisfied with whatever she saw there, she continued, 'The house is old, but sound. Derek says we'll live in it for a year to see what we want, and then have the basics done, plumbing, a new kitchen, and then, he says, we'll probably have to make do for some years as all the money will be going back into the place.'

Again there was that note of defiance in her voice. To Jennet it sounded as though, learning from the mistakes he had made in his first marriage, Derek was all set to make sure that this wife couldn't leave him.

Appalled, but unable to show it, she asked casually, 'How many men will he need to work for you?'

'Well, for a few years, none. It will be more economic to bring in contractors and we won't be able to afford to build housing for any workers straight off. Eventually, of course, we'll need at least two, Derek thinks.'

Jennet felt sick. Vaguely she said, 'Well, good luck to you,' as she got to her feet with far less than her usual grace.

'Jennet.'

Something in Melly's voice made her stiffen. Without looking at her half-sister she answered, 'Yes?'

'You won't be welcome there, you know. You've done enough damage. Just leave him alone.' The cool voice trembled. 'If you could have seen what he was like after you left him, well, even you would have felt guilty, I'm sure. He's happy now and so am I. There's nothing you can do to break us up so why don't you give up trying?'

A quick glance was revealing. Melly had had to steel herself to say this much, but her gaze was perfectly steady and she meant every word of it, the young face set in lines which recalled her brother at his most determined.

Jennet admired her and wished achingly that she had come back on any other mission than this. But she hardened her heart and her voice, saying mockingly, 'Nothing can come between true lovers, didn't you know that, Melly? So why are you worried?'

'I'm *not* worried!'

Jennet laughed and continued out of the room, only stopping to give her sister's rigid unresponsive shoulders a hug. 'I do love you,' she said, and she meant it.

All the years when she had resented the small sister who had taken her place in her mother's heart, were dissipated like spindrift. A bitter sense of responsibility had driven her back to Te Puriri and she had come resentfully, but now she was imbued with a rediscovered affection for her half-sister.

'Remember when I pushed you into the pool so that I could practise my life-saving on you?' she asked from the door. 'You gave me a black eye for my pains, but when I cried from sheer frustration you drowned very sweetly about ten times to make up for it.'

Melly stared at her as if she had gone mad before saying stiffly, 'Yes, I remember. I'm surprised you do, though.'

'Oh, I remember lots. You'd be astounded!'

'Nothing would surprise me about you.'

Rafe's deep voice made her jump and for a moment real fear showed in her face. Within seconds she had banished it, but Melly stared, her astonishment written large in her expression.

'Oh, compliments, compliments,' Jennet mocked in her warmest, throatiest voice as she flashed a smile at the man behind her. 'Darling, you're looking rather grim. Lost a sheep or something?'

The straight sensual mouth relaxed into a smile which came perilously close to a snarl.

'No, darling,' he said, his voice very even. 'Nothing so simple, I'm afraid.'

'Ah well, I'm going to sunbathe. Do you still heat the pool?'

'We do.'

She smiled slowly and with infinite promise into his face, meeting the cold anger of his eyes with teasing amusement. 'Then I'll go and swim,' she said lightly.

CHAPTER FIVE

THE pool was another piece of Italiannate design, an elegant pretty place copied, so rumour had it, from something the builder of the house had seen in the ruins of Pompeii. It was white and there were pillars and statues of rather winsome goddesses and impertinent fauns, even a fountain which glistened and glinted in rainbow colours in the sun. The water was warm, but not enervatingly so. Jennet swam purposefully from end to end, her graceful body belying the strength and stamina she possessed. After she climbed out, she showered in the changing room and pulled out a lounger into the sun, being careful to anoint herself with a total sunblock before she lay down.

Not for her the ease with which Melly and Rafe tanned. Her skin was the sort which is prone to skin cancer; she would have liked to spend much more time in the sun but common sense warned her of the dangers. Here, as in Australia, she sunbathed with care.

However, before she had time to relax completely in the drowsy warmth she felt a shadow fall over her face. Slowly, reluctantly, she opened her eyes.

Rafe, of course, that onyx gaze leisurely assessing her body, lingering with insufferable enjoyment on the rounded curves of breasts and waist, the slender length of her legs, the seductive body hidden only by the thin white material of her maillot.

'You look,' he said cruelly, 'like an advertisement for virginity. Even to the blush!'

'Well, you'd probably be surprised by the number of men who are turned on by it,' she retorted flippantly, hating, yet strangely excited by, his open, lustful scrutiny.

'I doubt it. I find you eminently desirable myself,' he drawled, letting his glance linger on the areas of her body which revealed only too clearly how and why she appealed to him. In the most basic of ways, merely to appease an animal lust.

The colour across Jennet's cheeks deepened into a scalding flood. She felt like slapping his face, but even as her hands straightened she regained control. Whatever happened, she was not going to blow everything by losing her temper.

He knew, too. She could read the taunting amusement in his eyes as he turned away to haul his shirt over his head.

Stripped, he was—well, superb was the only word. Skin the texture of bronze silk stretched over muscles which flexed as he moved lithely, with arrogant grace. Jennet watched him from beneath her lashes, her mouth drying. Like those statues of Greek warriors, she thought feverishly, a magnificent amalgam of strength and grace and balance. Her lashes drooped. She wiped suddenly damp palms with surreptitious care on the cushions of the lounger and turned over on to her stomach, pressing her face into her arm.

There was no sound until a soft splash revealed that he was in the pool. Grimly Jennet kept her eyes closed, fighting the sensations which wracked her body. It had been a long time since she had suffered them; the last time had been years ago when he had kissed her and caressed her and she, naïve little adolescent that she had been, had offered him the responses of her untaught innocence.

Ever since then, because his rejection had scarred, she had refused to admit that she could feel desire, had repressed the sensual side of her nature. It had been one of the reasons why her marriage failed.

And if she opened herself to him again that was exactly what would happen again. So she wanted him.

So what? It was ultimately degrading, but the body has its own law, its own immutable instincts. Which didn't mean that she had to give in to them.

Or perhaps she should. All these years she had backed away from the memories of her childish crush on him and the disillusionment that had followed his casual cruelty, his careless handling. By hiding from the implications she had, perhaps, allowed the incident to become too important. After all, he had been only twenty-three, sophisticated for his age, but still a young man. Had he been clumsy with her because he just didn't know how to handle the situation?

As the sounds of his progress up and down the pool kept her conscious of his presence she tried to recall exactly how he had behaved. And reluctantly she decided that he had known exactly what he was doing.

He had been punishing Diana because Dougal had loved her more than he had Rafe's dead mother. His rejection of Jennet had been one way of denying Diana's influence on his life, of working through his frustrated anger and resentment at the woman who had enslaved his father.

Rafe, so logical, so cool-headed, was a little bit unbalanced when it came to Diana, almost certainly because his attitude towards her had been formed in childhood, in the period of intense grief after his mother's death. Hating the woman who had taken her place with a fierce emotion based on instinct, he had included her daughter in that hatred because the daughter looked like the mother and had arrived with her.

Subsequent events had only reinforced his attitude, she thought sadly. It was impossible that they should ever know each other as ordinary people.

Her reverie was interrupted by the sounds of his leaving the pool.

As he dried himself down he asked shortly, 'Do you still want to see Derek?'

'Yes, I do.' She wanted to judge just how uneasy Derek was.

'He's here now.'

Yawning, she turned over on to her side, away from him. It was unlikely that Melly would give them time together; better, anyway, to assess him without the possibility of someone overhearing.

'It will wait,' she said lightly.

'I hope you're not expecting anyone to run you around when the fancy takes you. We work, you know.'

'I know you do.' An irritating note of laughter lilted in her tone. 'Don't worry about me, Rafe, I don't need to be entertained. I'm quite capable of amusing myself.'

There was an ominous pause and when he spoke again he was considerably closer. 'Not with Compton, I hope.'

'Oh, don't be so boring,' she shot back. 'You don't have to repeat things more than once, Rafe. I'm not thick.'

'No, just childish,' he said blightingly.

She tensed as he flung her over on to her back.

'A permanent adolescent,' he said. 'Like your mother, greedy, amoral, with a child's selfish outlook and a child's lack of foresight.'

She yawned again, pretending, half closing her eyes so that he couldn't see the pain in them.

'Think what you like,' her voice was indifferent. 'Your opinion means nothing to me.'

'Do you think I don't know that?' He leaned over her, harshly chiselled features drawn into bleak lines which didn't ease when he saw the alarm flare into her eyes. 'You hate me—and fear me—because I'm one of the few men who can see right through that intoxicating femininity you use as a cloak to hide the mean little soul inside.'

He meant every word yet there was something else behind the controlled distaste, something just as potent.

'Yes,' he said with a savage inflection as he sat down beside her on the lounger. 'There's that, too.'

'I don't——'

'You lie. It's lust, and you feel it just as I do.'

Before she could react his mouth came to rest on the swell of her breast, burning through the thin dampness of her maillot. Jennet struck out at him but his fingers fastened cruelly around her elbows, forcing her arms on to the mattress and holding her still.

'No!' she ground out while her body melted into acquiescence. 'You're a swine, Rafe, a bully. Let me go.'

He lifted his head and grinned, a feral mirthless movement of his hard mouth. 'I like having you at my mercy.'

'Brute!'

He kept her pinned with the crystalline intensity of his glare, his eyes roving her face in an insulting scrutiny. 'You know, you're not really beautiful. Your features are neither classical nor cute, your eyes are too big and your mouth too wide and yet you simmer with a sexuality which stops even happily married men in their tracks. Poor old John Miall had to get out before Brigit noticed.'

'Brigit notices everything!'

'So do I,' he said smoothly as his mouth covered hers, coaxing it to open.

Just in time Jennet clenched her teeth, saying bitterly, 'You can't do this to me. I'm not one of your women, to be toyed with and then discarded like a worn-out doll.'

'No, you're a permanent part of my life. Almost part of me.'

So astounded was she by this, delivered in his most reasonable tones, that she gaped. Half a second later

she appreciated his strategy as his mouth invaded hers
in a kiss totally without subtlety or tenderness. He
wanted her and he didn't care if he hurt her; his
desperate kiss fed a brutal sensuality which should have
repelled Jennet. For a few stark seconds it did. She went
rigid beneath him, her whole being suffused with
outrage.

Then, as if his ferocity had breached some hidden
barrier, a great wave of heat surged through her body.
She sighed and his arms slid beneath her suddenly
pliant body, lifting her so that she lay against him. Her
lashes fluttered down as she was stricken by a kind of
sensory overload. The warm male scent of him, the
rapid heating of his skin against hers made her groan.
Circles of sparks danced behind her eyelids and her
mouth was filled with the taste of him, erotic,
stimulating.

A convulsive tremor shook her. Slowly she brought
her hands up to clasp his shoulders.

He delighted her, he was perfect to her.

'I could get drunk on the look of you,' he whispered
harshly, 'on the taste of you, the perfume of your skin
and hair. I could drown in your eyes.'

His voice was thick with longing and need. Across
her back his arms tightened so that she felt as if it had
happened to her, the tremor which shook him. Slowly
she opened her eyes to focus on his face, drawn in a
mask of anguish.

'Why?' she breathed, afraid yet exultant. 'Why,
Rafe?'

'God knows.' It sounded like a curse. 'It's the same
for you, isn't it?'

It was too painful to watch him, stripped of self-
possession, naked in his hunger for her.

'Oh yes,' she said, closing her eyes as she nodded,
weak with supplication and the urgency of the need he
had aroused.

'Why did you come back?' he asked against her throat.

She froze, every process in her body suspended.

Oh, he was clever, bending even his passion to serve his will. As her eyes stared blindly over his dark hair she realised with bleak comprehension that he had baited a trap for her, using the heated sexuality of their desire for each other to strip her bare of lies and evasions.

Then from behind came Melly's voice, shocked and furious, its strident edge cutting through the warm sleepy air. 'My God!' she exclaimed, as though she had discovered a sin hitherto uncatalogued. 'What are you doing?'

For a precious, secret moment Rafe's black gaze met Jennet's and in both pairs of eyes was mirrored a kind of guilty amusement.

Then Rafe straightened up and put Jennet back on to the cushions of the lounger as he said in a voice totally devoid of expression, 'What does it look as though we're doing?'

'Oh, Rafe!' Melly said sadly before she turned and left them.

Rafe laughed, a cynical, humourless sound and raked his hand through his hair, staring down at Jennet as though he hated her. Then, without a further word, he swung on his heel and left.

No doubt telling himself that he was a fool, she thought drily. As she was. Stupid to respond to his lovemaking, stupid to let him get to her. Stupid, stupid, *stupid*!

A short while later she came quietly down the stairs, her jean-clad legs suddenly tired. She had planned to prowl around the gardens but swimming and the passionate scene afterwards had exhausted her. Now, she listened carefully for voices, deducing after a moment that Derek and Melly were in the sitting-room. Silently she walked past it to the library.

Nothing had changed here except for the replacement of a pair of Japanese vases by a magnificent pottery bowl in subtle shades of green and grey. She was still admiring it, her hands smoothing tenderly over the thin transparent glaze when the door opened behind her.

Derek, his handsome face set in an expression perilously close to smugness.

'Aha, caught you!' he said with a smile which did not extend to his eyes. 'If you're planning to abscond with some loot, I'd choose something else. Take that porcelain jardiniere. It's Chinese, so Melly says, and worth a couple of thousand dollars.'

Replacing the bowl on its stand Jennet said calmly, 'In two hundred years time this will be worth as much.'

Derek's jaw tightened. With a heady sense of power which was unpleasantly exciting, Jennet realised that he was a little afraid of her.

'What can I do for you?' she asked politely.

He grinned, coming to stand too close in front of her, his bright eyes scanning her face.

'You know why I'm here,' he said insolently and lifted his hand and traced the soft curve of her mouth.

'Do I?' Her voice was steady. She was trying to cope with a strange feeling of *déjà vu*, as though this had happened before, many times. A thin, savage anger sparkled in the green depths of her eyes as her expression hardened into lines which made her look much older, much stronger.

Derek's hand dropped and he stepped back. 'Oh, I think you do,' he said easily. 'You're having a little financial trouble, I gather.'

'Actually, no.' She enjoyed his surprise, quickly hidden though it was. 'Soap operas may not be the height of culture, but they pay well. You can't buy me off, Derek. You couldn't before, if you remember, and I'm a lot better off now than I was then.'

'I see.'

As he paused, trying to work out his next move, she said blandly. 'Why don't you sit down and tell me all about your new property?'

'Who told—oh, Melly, I suppose.'

'Yes.' She sat down gracefully on to one of the big armchairs, waited with polite enquiry while he subsided, with less than his normal grace, into one opposite her. 'You know, anyone who was the least suspicious would think that you intend carrying Melly off to the backblocks so that she can't run away from you.'

'Why should she want to?'

She smiled but there was no amusement in her eyes. 'The same reason that I ran away?' she suggested.

He frowned. 'I love Melly,' he said quickly.

Jennet eyed him from beneath her lashes. Somewhat to her surprise she was inclined to believe him and for a moment she wondered hopefully if she could trust him enough to be free of this burden she had imposed on herself.

Just for a moment until the psychiatrist's dry, dispassionate words came back to her.

'I wonder,' she said calmly, 'what Rafe would do to the man who harmed Melly—in any way?' She watched him swallow before continuing mercilessly, 'Do you think Rafe would murder, Derek?'

He said quickly, No, he's a civilised man and anyway why should I harm Melly? I love her, I tell you. She's everything you're not, warm, passionate, loving.' He smiled at her start of surprise and added triumphantly, 'That surprises you, doesn't it. You're so bloody frigid yourself you can't understand how Melly could get carried away——'

'I've always heard that it's frightfully bad form to kiss and tell,' she said with cool deliberation. 'Rafe wouldn't.'

He flushed, the blood running up under his fair skin in a wave of colour and said through gritted teeth, 'You're asking for——'

'And anyway,' she interrupted, 'I don't believe you.'
'Why not?'

He reacted with the same touchy antagonism that
had always been his response when found out in a lie.
Jennet's relief was profound, but well disguised.

'Because you don't look at each other as lovers do,'
she said calmly. 'You're still hungry and Melly is still
unaware.'

'Oh, so you can tell just by looking?'

She sent him a level, dispassionate look. 'I know
Melly and I understand you.'

For some reason this made him flush again. She
didn't speak and he sat, uncomfortable and angry, a
frown marring the handsome, weak face.

'So,' he said at last, 'where do we go from here? It's
no use you filling Mel's ears with lies, you know. She
won't believe anything you say. She's stubborn and
she's in love with me.' He met her flat, unresponsive
gaze with an anger which was stronger because he dared
not vent it. 'Look,' he said, trying very hard to stay in
control, 'you and I—well, we married for all the wrong
reasons. That's so, isn't it?'

The rose-blonde head nodded slowly.

'Then can't you believe that—that I'm in love with
Melly? I love her.'

Once more she nodded and he went on more easily
now, 'Well, if that's so, why—what do you intend to
do? Remembering that nothing you can do or say is
going to make any difference.'

'What will you do the first time she makes you
angry?' Jennet asked wearily.

He whitened. 'I'm five years older,' he said with such
earnestness that she was tempted to believe him. Until
she remembered again what the psychiatrist had said.

'I know,' she said. 'Believe me, I know, Derek. And I
believe that you do love Melly, but I'm afraid I can't
accept that you won't beat her when something

happens to make you lose control. Just as you beat me. Have you ever been to a doctor about your propensity for violence?'

'No!' he shouted, suddenly furiously angry. 'Why should I? It was you, with your coldness, your frigid high-mindedness, your——'

He stopped, for Jennet was watching his hands as they curled and crooked, flexed into fists and then relaxed. When the impassioned words died away she lifted her eyes and regarded his distorted face with sorrow and regret. No fear, not a vestige of the sickening acrid terror which used to taste in her mouth whenever they quarrelled. Towards the end of their short marriage it had sprung to life whenever she had seen him.

Then he swore, savage, bitter obscenities which took him from the chair, to the window where he stood with his back to her, ramrod straight, his big hands clenched at his side while he fought for control.

He was, Jennet realised, afraid of her. Once he would have hit her but now he didn't dare and there was no way other than cursing that he could ease himself of the demons which drove him.

'Derek,' she said when the harsh monotone of his voice had died away, 'why don't you go to a doctor? They can help——'

'Because I don't need to!' He almost screamed the words. 'Because I'm not mad, damn you! Everything you got you deserved. You were in love with bloody Rafe when you married me and you're still in love with him! Do you think that did anything for my ego?'

'If you knew that—which was more than I did—why did you marry me?'

He jerked his head back as though she had hit him but still refused to look at her. 'I didn't know, then,' he said sullenly after a long hesitation.

She sighed, realising that she was unable to reach

him. But she had to try. 'If you went to see a doctor,' she began tentatively.

He was across the room and dragging her up from the chair before she had time to defend herself.

'No,' he said from between his teeth, his eyes lit by the manic glare she remembered. 'No, curse you, you conniving, double-crossing, lying bitch, I won't——'

He began to shake her, his fingers tightening like talons on the slender bones of her shoulders.

'I won't——' he swore just as the door opened and Rafe's deep cold voice demanded, 'What the *hell's* going on here?'

Derek flung her away from him, the frantic savagery wiped from his face as if it had never existed. Again Jennet was visited by that overpowering sense of *déjà vu*. This had happened the night Derek's cousin had come to visit them, the night before she had run away. In a second Derek had changed from an uncontrolled sadist to a reasonable, if angry man.

Now he turned and said loudly, 'If you don't want me to give your stepsister what she deserves, Rafe, exercise some control over her, will you? And tell her that I will not permit her or anyone else to come between Melly and me, not an ex-wife with an axe to grind, not even you.'

Oh, but he was clever! Even as he spoke Jennet's despairing eyes saw the suspicion fade in Rafe's hard face to be replaced by the intolerant contempt. Her chance of explaining just why she had come back to Te Puriri evaporated into the charged atmosphere. Rafe would never believe her now; it would have been hard enough to convince him at any time, but Derek's consummate skill at acting had cut the ground neatly away from under her feet. She didn't need his triumphant glance to see that he had chosen exactly the right approach to convince Rafe that she was interfering for the sheer delight of making mischief.

'Melly's in the boudoir,' Rafe said now, his grim expression a frightening contrast to the crystalline glitter beneath his dark lashes.

With a final victorious smile, slightly muted in case Rafe should catch it, Derek left the room. All this time Rafe had been watching Jennet, his eyes never leaving her face.

'Now,' he invited blandly as the door closed behind Derek, 'tell me what all that was about.'

Her sore shoulders lifted in a small but defiant shrug. 'Why should I? You've already made up your mind.'

'I'd like to hear your version, nevertheless.'

Angrily, humiliated by his icy restraint, she retorted bitterly, 'So that you can call me a liar all over again? No thanks, Rafe, I know when I'm up against a closed mind.' She gave a short harsh laugh. 'You've spent almost all of my life telling me how untrustworthy I am, how the fact that you like to kiss me disgusts you and makes you hate yourself. It surprises me that you even let yourself be angry when I do some other typically vulgar thing. After all, you know me so well, I'd have thought that you—that you——'

She stopped, shocked and frightened by the sudden quaver in her voice. Derek's violence had drained her of strength and she wasn't thinking straight. Time to end it.

'Oh, what's the use,' she said, turning away so that he couldn't see her face. In a voice dulled by the effort to overcome her anguish she finished, 'I think I might just go back to Sydney after all. My coming here was another mistake in a life liberally dotted with them.'

'Are you wallowing in self-pity?' he asked, apparently incredulous. 'Do I add feeling sorry for yourself to my list of character defects?'

'Don't mock me,' she said grittily.

'Sorry. Of course you feel sorry for yourself. You've been doing that ever since you realised that Diana was

fonder of Melly than she was of you. Ah—ah . . .' as
she turned on him with eyes like green flames in a taut,
white face.

'No,' he drawled sardonically, 'you're like the rest of
your sex, you don't mind dishing it out but it's a
different story when it comes to taking it, isn't it? Now,
do you want to show me how well you can drive?'

Thrown completely off balance by the change of
subject she stared at him before shrugging. 'Oh, all
right,' she said listlessly.

It was a disaster. He wouldn't let her drive the big
Audi, but insisted she try Melly's smaller vehicle, which
was not automatic. It was some years since Jennet had
used a gear lever, but on any other occasion she would
have coped, for she was a good driver.

Today, however, she missed gear changes, concentrated too hard on the clutch pedal and almost hit a
fence, then thoroughly demoralised, drove as poorly as
a nervous schoolgirl being taught by her older brother.

And beside her, silent but ominous, Rafe said
nothing until she finally managed to stop the car inside
the garage.

Then he said 'No,' and refused curtly to listen to her
excuses or pleas, striding off into his office with a rude
lack of courtesy which ordinarily would have made her
furious.

This time, however, she merely watched his tall, lean
form pace up to the house and felt only an intense
weariness.

It lasted, aided by a headache, until she went to bed
an hour later, but when she woke the next morning it
had gone and she felt a little revived.

Breakfast with a silent, mistrustful Melly was not
pleasant. Afterwards Jennet made her bed and tidied
her room, once more offered help to Joy and once more
had it more or less refused, and decided to go for a
walk. Rafe had eaten early and was, so the housekeeper

informed her, out working somewhere on the station; Joy had packed him lunch which meant that he wasn't likely to be back much before dark.

It was a relief to leave the house. Melly's attitude created a tension which roughened Jennet's nerves. No doubt the incident at the pool was half the cause of Melly's antagonism, but Jennet rather suspected that Derek had stirred coals too. She couldn't unfortunately come right out and ask. Melly would have every right to tell her to mind her own business.

Pondering on the fact that Rafe had been surprisingly easily diverted after walking in on her with Derek the day before, Jennet wondered uneasily why he hadn't tried to pry from her the background to the scene he had interrupted. In any other man it might have been forbearance, but Rafe was not forbearing.

It was a superb day, one of those rare winter days which were warmer and more promising than most that spring could produce. The air was soft and mild, the sky blue, a tender, warm colour far removed from the crystalline hue that a south wind brought with it. What a little breeze there was, came whispering in from the north-east, carrying on it a hint of the tropical isles of Polynesia.

Jennet stuck her hands in the pockets of her jeans as she sauntered along the drive. Te Puriri was a place apart, she thought dreamily, watching the antics of two courting tuis among the amber berries of an enormous melia tree. The big birds fluttered from silver branch to silver branch, glossy black wings and tails spread so that their burnished lustre of blue and green gleamed in the sunlight.

Jennet smiled as she opened the small gate beneath the tree and stood motionless, her eyes scanning the smiling fertile valley with its sheltering hills making bold statements against the sky. The drive ran down past the implement sheds and barns, all the necessary buildings of a big station, on past the houses each set in its own garden, and over a stream to pass the big woolshed at the gate. Beyond the gate was Compton Downs; by some quirk of surveying Derek's station bordered Te Puriri although the homestead was five miles away by road.

Compton Downs was in good heart, too, Jennet decided, eyeing what paddocks she could see with a critical gaze. Whatever financial troubles had prompted Derek's marriage to her had obviously been surmounted, but to buy a new block, however undeveloped, would be more than his resources allowed.

When she had lived with him she had not been allowed to know of his financial state. However she was not unintelligent and it had needed only his first outburst when he discovered that she almost literally had no money to her name, for her to realise that he needed money. Well, she thought angrily, if he married Melly he would get her income, but he had no power to break the trust as it was settled on her children. Dougal had made it watertight.

She knew then that she would have to try once more to convince Derek to see a doctor or psychiatrist. If he was adamant in his refusal then she would just have to work out some way of opening Melly's—or Rafe's—eyes to the tragic flaw in his character.

Why not now, she asked herself, her eyes narrowing as they came to rest on the station utility parked outside the implement shed. Away from Rafe's intimidating presence she could drive the wretched thing quite easily. If she missed a few gear changes, well, it was sturdily built and forgiving, and the roads in Takapo Valley were usually distinctly empty of traffic.

'Up guards and at 'em,' she said to the tuis, one of which answered with a distinct chirrup and a little song like a chime of bells.

A blackbird, resplendent in jet plumage with orange

beak and feet, took umbrage at the sound of her voice and flew shrieking away, frightening itself into a nervous breakdown.

'You, too,' she said aloud before she straightened her shoulders and strolled casually down the drive, looking around with real pleasure.

Rafe's love for his land was plain. It showed in the taut, trim fences, the new red paint on the shed and barns, the neat, well-cared for aspect of everything. There were unexpected touches too. A clump of red-hot-pokers had been fenced off so that stock couldn't eat the leaves. Against the lush green of the paddocks the pointed flowers glowed like coals of fire, each cone arrowing towards the sky. Another tui thrust its blue-black head deep into the long throat of one of the flowers then emerged to shake its head and display the white collar and bobble at its throat.

Jennet took a deep breath, forcing her mind away from the coming confrontation. A cluster of red and white Hereford cattle watched her solemnly, their heads turning as they followed her progress past them.

In the next paddock a small flock of newly shorn sheep, looking oddly long in the leg, ignored her. Any day now the first lambs were due; soon the paddocks would be full of the tiny, spring-heeled animals. A horse in a cover stood swishing its tail beneath a big old oak tree which was still tawny with old, unfallen leaves. The next blow would sweep them away and before long the tree would be radiant in its new clothes of vivid lime green.

As she came to the truck Jennet had to repress the desire to take a quick, furtive look around. Someone had obligingly parked it just where the drive began to slope quite steeply, so that she wouldn't even have to start it. She could free-wheel down the hill and when it had picked up enough speed a turn of the key and she'd be in business and at least a third of the way to the gate.

Well out of reach of anyone who might decide to see what she was up to.

Trying not to appear in the least stealthy, she climbed into the cab, closing the door with a quick sharp clunk which seemed to echo from every hill.

But no one appeared, no voice shouted, 'What do you think you're doing in that?'

'So far so good,' she told the unresponsive steering wheel.

Yes, the keys were in the ignition. Jennet took a deep breath, instantly regretting it. Although in excellent order the years had given the cab an interesting scent, a mixture of dog and fertiliser and other untraceable odours.

Nose wrinkled, Jennet eased off the handbrake. This time she held her breath as slowly, painfully slowly, the vehicle inched forward. When it began to pick up speed she grinned and patted the steering wheel.

Just in case someone lurked in the woolshed she didn't try to start it until she was over halfway down the hill, but when she did the engine struggled into life. Her grin broadened. As though she had spent her life stealing utilities she eased back into the seat.

The engine wheezed, sounding painfully asthmatic. Frowning, she listened for any further evidence of illness, but nothing eventuated. It was probably, she decided complacently just its usual noise. It certainly felt perfectly normal, although it was harder to drive than any car she had ever tried. The wheel had to be wrestled around as she took the corner at the bottom of the hill, and when she braked before heading over the bridge the vehicle jerked and almost skidded. Nervousness, she told herself, grinning.

And then there was a loud *'whoosh'* and the engine exploded into a gush of flames and smoke.

Jennet panicked. She jerked the gear lever into the neutral position and slammed her foot hard down on to the brake. Fingers slippery with sweat fought with the wheel as she aimed the utility over the bridge, bringing it to a sliding, skidding halt on the other side.

Scrabbling for the door handle, she could hear the sound of her own whimpering. Smoke billowed back into the cab, choking her, making it impossible to see where the keys were. Half-remembered photographs of burn victims made her cry out in terror.

Then the door crashed back, hurtling her out. Rafe's hands provided further impetus so that she landed on her hands and knees some distance away, her eyes dilating in horror as she saw him disappear into the smoke.

'Rafe!' she screamed after a dreadful second.

He leaped back from the cab and she realised that he'd grabbed the fire extinguisher. There was an odd hissing noise, a cloud of strange-smelling stuff and then silence as foam enveloped the engine.

Shivering, Jennet crouched on the stones, her face hidden in her hands. She could not face Rafe's demonic fury, but there was no way she could shut out the sound of his voice as he told her exactly what he thought of her, only stopping when the manager came tearing up in the Land-Rover.

Reaction, Jennet told herself, wincing. Her body shook with long, slow rigours; she noticed with a vague interest that her skin was cold and clammy. Head bent she waited meekly until Rafe ran down.

Then as she got to her feet she asked shakily, 'But what happened? It was perfectly all right until——'

'It was *not* perfectly all right. How in hell did you start it?'

'I free-wheeled it down the hill until I got down by the totara tree.' She pointed. 'That one.'

He pushed shaking fingers through his hair, closing his eyes momentarily.

'Trust you,' he said bitterly. 'The fuel line was split,

that was what was wrong with it. I noticed it when it wouldn't start this morning.' His eyes fixed hers with such shimmering rage that she took an involuntary step backwards.

Slowly he looked above her head, saying in a voice which strove for calm, 'God damn it, I only left it to walk down to the woolshed. Some great idiot, whom I'll tear limb from limb, has taken the spanners from the implement shed. It's such a lovely day that I decided to walk to the shed to get the other set. I'd barely got there when I heard it start . . .'

From behind Jennet the farm manager told him apologetically, 'I think Evan's got the spanners.'

He went into details which Jennet didn't hear, because of the humming in her ears. After a moment or two she tried shaking her head. It made her feel better but it also switched Rafe's attention back to her.

'Why?' he demanded, biting the words out. 'Why did you want the truck?'

'Well you won't let me drive anything else,' she shouted, suddenly and completely losing command. 'You said——' To her horror her voice shook so much that she couldn't continue. Sudden rainbows filled her eyes as the sun glittered through her tears.

'Oh, *hell*!' Rafe's voice was totally disgusted. 'All right, Jennet, stop it. Rick, take us back to the house, will you?'

By now Jennet was sobbing in real earnest. Rafe stalked beside her until she stumbled, then, cursing under his breath, he slid an arm about her shoulders and held her clamped to his side until they got to the Land-Rover. Boosting her into the seat, he rapped out, 'You'd better drive,' to the farm manager as he got in beside her.

CHAPTER SIX

NOBODY spoke on the way back to the homestead. Indeed, the only sound inside the Land-Rover was the stifled sound of Jennet's weeping. Rafe no longer held her but she was close enough to him to feel the rage emanating from every taut contour of his body.

At the homestead he let her get herself out of the vehicle while he said something to the farm manager, but as Jennet began to trail miserably into the house he told her angrily, 'I want a few words with you.'

She shivered, knowing what was coming. He was going to tear strips from her and enjoy doing it. The years slipped away and she was sixteen again and he was going to deliberately shred her confidence, wounding her so deeply that she would never recover from it.

'The office,' he ordered sharply, still beside the Land-Rover.

As she made her way there Jennet tried to summon up some courage. All right, so she had been a—little impetuous—but no one could have expected the blasted utility to burst into flames. Could they? And yes, she had disobeyed him. But who was he to tell her what she might and might not do?

Within a short time her tears were gone and she was, to all outward appearances, composed. A composure which fled the minute he slammed into the office and straight into the attack.

'You stupid little *bitch*!' He was so angry that the words barely made it between lips as pale as the rest of his face. 'I should have let you kill yourself out there. What the *hell* made you take the bloody truck on the one day when it could have killed you!'

She was so shaken that the truth came out. 'I wanted to see Derek.'

Instantly that white rage deepened, intensified. His eyes were like slivers of obsidian, glittering, slicing her to ribbons.

'Can't you stay away from him for one day?' he demanded in the silky voice of extreme rage.

'I wanted to see him. Alone.' It took all of her precarious self-control not to shrink back into the sofa. She had never seen him like this before.

'You're sick,' he said terribly. 'Sick, promiscuous——'

'*No!*' She launched herself at him, fists flailing. 'No, no, *no*! I am not! How dare you—how *dare* you——'

His response was automatic and painful. Her voice sobbed into silence as his long fingers clamped around her wrists, but anger fuelled the kick she landed on his shin. He swore and dragged her against him, his arms tightening across her back.

Sobbing, her face smothered in his heavy shirt she choked, 'You—I'm not sick and I'm not promiscuous. I'm not, I'm not! I'm not Diana, I'm me. What have I ever done to you to make you hate me so?'

'Shut up,' he said disdainfully and when she gulped and gasped for breath the hand pressing her face into his shoulder relaxed and he let her go.

'You look like your mother,' he said icily, 'you project the same potent sensuality. I saw my father broken by a lust he couldn't control and I vowed that it was never going to happen to me.'

'But it almost did, didn't it,' she said painfully. 'Is that why you dislike me so, Rafe? Because I almost proved that you were just as vulnerable to lust as your father?'

Incredibly he laughed, a sound totally without humour before he put her away from him. She watched as he walked over to the fireplace and stared down into the faintly glowing coals.

'Of course,' he said politely. 'You came home from school those holidays and I watched you unfurl like an exquisite flower into a frightening, but completely familiar, beauty. Diana at sixteen. And I knew how my father must have felt when he first saw her. As if he'd been translated into another world where the normal code of ethics doesn't hold.'

'You never even saw me.' Her precarious confidence cracked, was shattered into a million pieces.

He leant an arm along the mantel, resting his forehead on to his wrist. 'Of course I saw you, how could I not? You swam, you sat at the table, you rode. And I had to listen to Diana keep up a constant stream of propositions, trying to seduce me while my father was hanging on to life by the thinnest of threads. She filled me with disgust but you——' He turned his head to look at her, his expression brooding, bitter. 'Oh, I could feel myself going under. I dreamed of you. I woke aching and famished for the sight and feel of you. I told myself I wanted to get you to bed, take you as roughly and quickly as possible, use you to slake a hunger I was ashamed of. But I lied to myself. I wanted more. I wanted to crack open your skull so that I could see what your beautiful, shuttered little face was hiding.'

Appalled by his cold, dispassionate recital of his emotions she said quietly, 'So you took your frustrations out on me.'

'No, although you'll never know how close you drove me to it.'

'*I* drove you?' Anger splintered in her voice. She came swiftly across to stand in front of him, her eyes blazing. 'I didn't start it, you did. I remember——'

Then she stopped for he was smiling, a savage feral movement of his mouth, while something glittered deep in his eyes.

'So do I,' he murmured. 'I remember it very clearly.'

She should have run then, turned and fled when she

had the freedom. But she stared at him, mesmerised, and he caught her close, his arm across her hips forcing her to the realisation that he was aroused.

'No,' she cried, terrified.

'Why not? You're not a scared virgin now and God knows, there's no reason for me to hold back. I still want you.'

Ignoring the hands which pushed at his shoulders he took her mouth, forcing her head back in a kiss as brutal and unforgiving as death's. Yet in spite of the insolence of it she responded, her body wracked by an unfamiliar chill.

'No,' she moaned when his head lifted a fraction and he smiled and kissed her again, searching out the secret depths of her mouth, his own ravenous.

Her heart thudded in her chest, picking up speed until the sound of it in her pulse points deafened her. His dark face filled her vision. She closed her eyes and instantly sensation was heightened, intensified to a degree beyond pleasure. She felt the heat of his body and the tense strength of it as he swayed her backwards so that she overbalanced and had to grab him, her fingers fiercely tangling in the material of his shirt.

Then when she thought she might faint with excitement and the strange, hot sensations raging through her he released her and the contempt darkened in his eyes as he looked at her.

'Just like Diana,' he said coolly. 'Beautiful and totally without discrimination.'

How she did it she never knew but even before she thought them the words issued from her lips delivered as a taunt.

'Oh, credit me with some discrimination,' she said lightly, prudently removing herself from arm's reach. 'I'm not propositioning you, you may have noticed. Call the kisses the hero's reward for saving me from a nasty death. Next time I'll tip you. It won't be so painful.'

He had recovered as quickly as she. With a smile which blended irony and contempt he retorted, 'Or so damaging to your make-up.'

So he had the last word after all. But as Jennet walked with bent head up the stairs to her bedroom she thought over the revelations Rafe had made. Her first reaction, now that she was alone, was shock. Just sheer shock.

For long minutes she sat on the side of her bed, her eyes fixed unseeingly on the hands in her lap as she remembered, caught once more in the past's snare. The egoism of childhood had blinded her to the knowledge, but of course Rafe had always been an intruder in his own home. On Diana's arrival the tall, proud boy who would one day own Te Puriri had been relegated to a lesser status and the pain of his father's rejection must have cut deeply.

After Melly's birth Diana had been unable to have more children. If she had borne Dougal a son even Te Puriri could have been denied Rafe. Where Diana was concerned Dougal had been weak, unable to deny her anything. At her insistence he had left his heritage for a life in Auckland which was unsatisfying. He had forced Rafe to buy the station which should have been rightfully his.

When Diana had denied convention to live with Dougal as his wife Rafe had been nine, old enough to fiercely resent any woman who took his mother's place. And Diana had never attempted to win his affection or his respect. Totally secure in the power her sensuality gave her over Dougal she had treated his son with the same callous forbearance she had given to Jennet. Her casual indifference was as shattering to a child as open unkindness, although there had been occasional instances of that, too. Diana was not particularly cruel; she just didn't care.

Stupidly, uselessly, Jennet's heart ached for the Rafe she only just remembered, the grave, silent boy who had, like her, been packed off to boarding school as early as possible. Born tough, those years had hardened his basic character even further.

It's no wonder, she thought drearily, that Melly is the only one of us he can stand. Possessive, made more so by the events of his childhood and Diana's machinations, he loved Melly because she was a Hollingworth; she belonged.

Incredulously, Jennet realised that she was crying. Not noisily, just sitting on her bed with the silent tears running down her cheeks.

'You idiot,' she said in a husky, tight voice and pushed her hair back from her face before going to take the shower she had come up for.

And she tried to persuade herself that it was shock. For if she weakened towards Rafe she would never be free of him. He was an arrogant despot, and the sooner she left Te Puriri the better it would be for everyone. But first—first she had to find some way to make it impossible for Melly to marry Derek.

Beneath the sharp darts of warm water she revolved plans and plots in her brain before realising that she really only had two chances. Either she convinced Melly that Derek was still hankering after his ex-wife, or she pushed Derek until he slid over the edge into the violence that seemed an integral part of his character. Both seemed impossible.

So why didn't she just tell Rafe? His shoulders were broad enough, he would know how to handle the situation.

Oh, let's be truthful, she told herself savagely. You won't tell Rafe because you still think Derek had a good reason for hitting you. You think it was your fault, and the reason why you think it was your fault is that you were in love with Rafe when you married

Derek and you are in love with him now and you think that if you tell Rafe he will blame you too.

'You are too screwed up to be true,' she said aloud, turning the water off with a vicious twist of her wrist.

As she dragged the towel over her cringing flesh she berated herself for her convoluted thinking.

'But I can't,' she whispered at last, mopping up tears which threatened to overflow her eyes. 'I just *can't*. I love him so and he feels something pretty powerful for me, but we're both prisoners of the past. If I told him about Derek he probably wouldn't believe me, but if he did he'd despise me.'

Even as she said it she knew that she was wrong, but the taboo against revealing her experience was so strong that she could not bring herself to do it. Why? *Why* did she still cringe at the thought of anyone else knowing?

It was she who had been beaten, she who had suffered, she who should hold the whip hand. Even the clichés, she thought sombrely, dealt in images of pain and servitude. *Whip hand!* Shivering, suddenly cold, she recalled the knowing look in Derek's eyes whenever he saw her. Somehow he was still able to impress his will on her in spite of his wariness. Oh, he was afraid of her and what she might do, but whenever he saw her he felt dominant. There was a horrible, a frightening, intimacy between them, a bond based on her past terror.

What could be easier than to go to Rafe and say, 'Rafe, I came back because when we were married Derek beat me, on occasions quite severely, and a psychiatrist I saw a week ago said that he'll probably beat Melly too.'

As she climbed, shivering between the sheets she imagined the scene, saw it all in her mind's eye, but she knew that she would not do it, and calling herself a coward, despising herself for it, did not make any difference.

Her heavy lashes flicked then slid slowly down to

cover the turbulent green of her eyes. Dreamily she imagined Rafe telling her that she was not to worry, that nobody would ever hurt her again, that he would take care of her. It could never happen, but dreams were free.

How did she know that he would never use violence against her? The capacity for violence was in him; she recognised it, always had. Yet she had never feared him.

Sleepily she decided that it was because of his immense willpower. And because she recognised that for him, his capacity to hurt was allied to a fierce protectiveness for anything weaker than himself. Rafe could be tender, even gentle, with those he loved. With Melly, with a dog he had owned when he was young— on occasion, she remembered, even with the stepsister he mistrusted so. When she was hurt, and a few times when she had emerged from her shell to reveal that she was upset, he had been kind, even if it was an impersonal kindness. He was a good boss, too, demanding yet fair. The men at Te Puriri respected him but they liked him too. Hard but just, she thought wearily.

She was asleep when he came in but she reacted to his presence as she always did, as she always would. Slowly her lashes lifted; they were wet, she realised, and the sobbing which had been part of her dream was her own.

'Go away,' she commanded, only the words made no sound and when he came to stand by the bed she turned over on to her side and hid her face in the pillow, cursing whatever ill-fortune that had led him to pass her room just then.

The side of the bed sank as he sat down. He made no attempt to touch her, but after a moment he said quietly, 'I'm sorry. I had no right to abuse you the way I did.' She didn't respond and he went on, 'When I saw the engine in flames and realised that it was you in the cab I—well, I thought that I was going to have to watch you burn to death.'

Incredibly his voice faltered.

'I'd have thought you'd be glad,' she said waspishily, fighting her instinct to give in to him.

'I deserved that, I suppose.'

'No,' she sighed, turning her head on the pillow, 'I'm sorry. That was a rotten thing to say.'

'I don't blame you. How are you now? No burns?'

'No. My hands are a bit sore where I landed on them in the gravel but——'

'Let me see.'

She made no attempt to show him, so he turned her gently, smiling rather ironically as she kept them firmly under the covers.

'Show me,' he insisted. 'Or do you want me to find them for myself?'

He had only to look at her like that, eyes narrowed, mouth slightly quirked, and every nerve in her body sang into life.

Slowly she lifted her arms, keeping the sheet in place with her elbows. He examined the pink palms carefully, his expression grave if you could discount the tiny glittering points of fire in the darkness of his gaze. Jennet couldn't. Strange pins and needles were stabbing under her skin and she tried to tug her hands away. He tightened his grip, not painfully but with the determination which was such an important part of his character.

'They're all right,' she said swiftly. 'I found some stuff in the medicine cabinet to put on them.'

'Good,' he said absently. His mouth had tightened but he wasn't angry. He was watching a tiny pulse in her throat as it throbbed like a wild thing caught in a net. 'Why do we fight?' he asked.

Her shoulders lifted. 'Personality clash?'

It was a flippant little suggestion, but she was

frightened. When he was behaving like a tyrant she could hold her own against him but like this he disarmed her entirely.

'You don't believe that.'

Her tongue touched the centre of her top lip for a moment. 'No?' she said, the word hard and flat with control. 'What then?'

'This, I think,' he told her quite gently as his hands slipped from hers up her arms to slide beneath her back and pull her from the safe haven of her bed into his embrace. 'This,' he said as his mouth covered that betraying flicker in the soft length of her throat, 'and this . . . and this . . . and this . . .'

She melted like warmed wax into him, one hand clutching the thin material of his shirt, the other curving around his head as her fingers slid into his black hair. The shock of his mouth against her throat sent her spinning into some other plane, a dizzying world where the only reality was him—and her incandescent response.

She retained only enough sanity to moan helplessly, 'Oh—no . . .'

'Oh yes, I think so,' he muttered as his mouth quested across the smooth skin of her shoulder.

The sheet had slipped and she was naked to the waist, flushed and heated, the satiny contours of her body open to the fierce plundering of his eyes and his mouth and his hands.

'You are so beautiful,' he whispered as if it hurt him to speak, 'you make me ache just to think of you. When I saw you in that truck I thought—if she dies I'll spend the rest of my lfe searching for her.'

No word of love, but she knew better than to listen for one.

'Rafe,' she whispered into his throat, her longing and her hunger clogging her heart.

'I'm sick of fighting it. God knows, I've given sanity

and pride and discrimination a fair trial and they've only brought me this craving that tears at me until I can't sleep, can't think of anything but the need to lose myself in you.'

The hot tumbled words fell out as though he could not repress them, each stark syllable thick with desire's ugly brother, lust, but as they had died away his mouth was urgently searching the full curve of her breast and she stiffened in anticipation, her breath choking in her throat.

When at last his lips reached their destination she groaned harshly, swamped by desire, her body clenched. Her hands slipped beneath the material of his shirt to cling across the hard warm strength of his back.

He made a short, urgent sound in his throat and lowered her on to the pillows, following her down so that she felt his weight. Her head fell back; she said something, she never knew what, and her legs and the lower part of her body moved in convulsive involuntary invitation, rising to meet him so that for long moments they lay clamped together with only the sheet and his clothes between them.

'Yes,' he said, lifting his head from her breast to survey the glazed passion in her face. 'Yes.'

Dark colour suffused his skin. His heavy-lidded eyes were feverish, the black depths flaming with passion. She welcomed the smothering intensity of his kiss, straining to meet and match it, her body shaking with the kind of untrammelled, uncontrolled passion only he knew how to arouse. And only he could assuage the desperate need in her.

As he plumbed the depths of her mouth her hands groped down his back to his hips and held him there while she writhed beneath his fierce masculinity.

And then Melly's voice called something outside and they heard a quick question and answer from her to Joy. Rafe lifted his head and said something so explicit that Jennet's suddenly pale skin was flushed with colour.

'Will nothing go right for us?' he said savagely, frustration hardening his features as he stared down into her dazed face. Urgently, as he rolled off the edge of the bed and stood tucking his shirt back into his trousers, he said, 'Tonight, Jennet? Let me come to you tonight.'

She began to shake her head even before she had formulated the words.

'Why?' he asked softly, silkily, his expression black.

'Because——' She hesitated. Melly's feet were running quickly up the stairs. 'Because it wouldn't be wise,' she evaded while her whole body was tormented by the same frustration which sharpened his angular features.

He stared at her as though he had never seen her before and then he cursed, the obscenity ugly and jarring in the quiet room where only seconds ago there had been nothing but the wild pagan need to give—and take.

'I should have known,' he said with vicious emphasis. 'God, will I never learn?'

Diana again. Always it was Diana who came between them.

He reached the door just as Melly pushed it open from the other side. 'Out!' he said, the one biting word enough to stop her in her tracks.

For a second Melly's astounded eyes met Jennet's then she turned and walked away.

'Rafe,' Jennet said imploringly.

'Shut up.'

But she couldn't let him go like that.

'Rafe, *please*, won't you listen——'

'No. Get yourself packed. I'll put you on the plane for Auckland this afternoon.'

She drew a deep, ragged breath. 'I'm not going,' she

said, her eyes fixed on the width of his shoulders, the proudly poised head.

'You are, if I have to bind and gag you.'

'I won't go.'

He swung around and stared at her, small in the large bed, the sheet hauled high around her neck.

'What do you want?' he asked, once more in control of himself. His voice was calm, toneless, but his eyes, glinting like dark jewels, gave him away.

'I'll go after the Mialls' party,' she said desperately.

He lifted his brows. 'And will you sleep with me tonight?'

Very slowly she shook her head. He would never know how much effort it took to make the muscles move but she did it. 'Are you making that a condition?' she said, knowing that it would further anger him.

'I think you know me a little better than that. Very well then, you can stay until after the party. But I'll be watching you.'

As a threat it could not have been bettered. The cold assurance in his voice made her shiver, but although she lay with closed eyes for almost an hour, she refused to allow her brain to mull over her problems. Instead she ran through Juliet's lines, re-enacting the play in her brain until she had regained some sort of composure.

She did not expect to see Derek that day but he arrived in the afternoon, sleek, amused and arrogant. It was part of no one's plan to leave them alone together but Melly was called away to the telephone.

Derek waited until she had gone before saying insolently, 'I see you haven't managed to convince Melly to believe your lies.'

'Haven't tried,' Jennet said cheerfully.

'Why don't you give up?' He smiled, confident enough to look smug, his blond head bent in taunting commiseration. 'Melly thinks you want me back. She's always been rather jealous of you, you know. She knows that she hasn't got that certain something you and Diana have, so you can't blame her for being rather pleased that I'm in love with her now, and not you. Or for suspecting that perhaps you're regretting your dash for freedom.'

It sounded dreadfully reasonable, even if Derek simplified Melly's character. After all, Melly had basked in her parents' love; she had no cause to be jealous of Jennet.

She returned his smile, lowering her lashes in a provocative sweep.

'I think you're wrong,' she murmured and ran her tongue along her bottom lip. 'Still, I'm beginning to wonder if I didn't come back on a wild goose chase. Melly seems quite capable of looking after herself. And Rafe is here to look after her too.'

'Then you're going?'

He realised his mistake immediately. From beneath her lashes Jennet saw his quickly hidden chagrin. Derek firmly believed in the superiority of the male sex. Experience had taught him that women were stupid creatures, easily dazzled by charm and a handsome face. It would be silly for Jennet to put him on guard.

So she laughed, deep and warm in her throat, and retorted, 'Don't be silly. Rafe and I are only just getting to know each other again.'

He hated that. The shallow blue eyes became sullen as he said through gritted teeth, 'Perhaps I should tell him that you're as frigid as an iceberg.'

'I'm not,' she taunted, moving away. 'After I left you I soon discovered the reason for my lack of response to your lovemaking. No other man has ever complained. I wonder if you'll call Melly frigid?'

By now she was walking towards the door, but even with her back to him she could feel the anger she had courted.

It still came as a shock when he jerked her around to

face him. He was white, the muscles in his face working as he swore, 'You lying little whore! By God, I'll——'

Jennet did not resist when his mouth crushed hers beneath it although instant revulsion chilled her blood. He used his superior strength to hurt her, grinding her lips against her tightly clamped teeth, his fingers biting into the soft flesh of her upper arms. With a sick horror she realised that he was aroused, but before she had time to deal with the situation voices in the hall compelled him to push her away. Breathing heavily he stood glaring down into her defiant face, his hands curled at his sides, his shoulders hunched like a predatory bird.

'Smile,' she said lightly through sore lips. 'Big brother is on the way and you wouldn't want him to realise that you can't keep your hands off me, would you?'

The rigidity left his body. Colour seeped back into his skin and he jeered, 'Had you going there for a minute, didn't I, darling?'

The opening of the door stopped her from replying. As she swung to face Rafe, Jennet met his stony expression with lifted chin and hard eyes.

He said something, his eyes lingering on the swollen contours of her mouth before lifting with coldly satirical force to hold her gaze captive.

Her smile was meaningless. She made some excuse and went out into the hall, standing with her arms hanging limply by her side while she stared at the magnificent landscape on the wall opposite. Dimly she heard Melly's voice, still talking into the telephone. The ticking of the grandfather clock resounded loudly, each short deliberate sound reverberating through her head.

I'm going to be sick, she thought as beads of sweat sprang out all over her clammy skin. She couldn't move. Even the sound of the door behind couldn't free her.

'Wrapped in ecstasy?' Rafe's sneering voice enquired.

She swayed slightly as he came up behind her.

'Are you all right?'

Shivering, realising that she couldn't let him see her like this, she nodded, but he turned her, and when he saw her face he said something short and nasty beneath his breath and slung an arm like steel around her shoulders, urging her towards the small powder room along the hall.

The debilitating nausea faded. Faintly she said, 'No, it's all right, Rafe. I just need a drink of water.'

'Can you make it to the kitchen?'

At her nod he half carried her until they reached the big room. Blessedly, it was empty. Rafe deposited her on to one of the chairs at the table and ran water into a glass.

The swish of the liquid refreshed her. She sighed and rubbed her hand wearily across her brow, keeping her lashes lowered.

'Here.'

Her hand was remarkably steady as she took the glass, but because he just stood looming over her and didn't go away it shook as she tried to transfer it to her mouth, slopping a few drops on to the table.

'Oh, for heaven's sake.' Rafe sounded beyond exasperation, but his hand was remarkably gentle as it enclosed hers, guiding the glass to her mouth.

The water flowed smoothly down her throat. Until then she hadn't realised how parched her mouth was.

She shook her head and he withdrew the glass, setting it down on to the table. 'Well,' he drawled, tipping her chin, 'you look less like a cheese and more like a human being. He must have a powerful effect on you.'

The tip of one lean finger traced out the contours of her mouth. A little frisson of excitement raced up her spine. She kept her gaze adamantly fixed on the buckle of his leather belt, refusing to lift her lashes.

'I suppose I should be thankful that my kisses don't

produce the same response,' he went on, almost thoughtfully.

He was too astute not to have seen just how hateful Derek's embrace had been. If he told Melly that she had no need to worry about Jennet's effect on Derek then the only plan that Jennet had been able to formulate would be ruined. Melly's conviction that Jennet was a threat had to be strengthened, reinforced by every means possible.

So Jennet forced herself to smile languourously, a slow, feline smile and lifted her lashes so that her eyes gleamed seductively. 'How do you know?' she said sweetly. 'Actually I haven't been feeling at all well since I got up this morning. I hope I haven't given Derek a bug. He'll never forgive me.'

Silence stretched out between them, tense, unbroken by any expression of the emotions which swirled through Jennet, yet coloured by both her feelings and those Rafe was controlling. Neither gave quarter. His eyes drilled into her soul and her only protection was that foolish, sleepy smile she had perfected over the years to convince television audiences that she was a siren, a man-hunting seductress.

It became painful, a meaningless grimace, but still her lips curved and her eyes beckoned because she did not know what else to do.

At last he said relentlessly, 'If you hurt Melly I'll see to it that you never have a moment's happiness or peace again in this world.'

Such menace to be contained in a few words delivered in a voice barely above a whisper! Her mouth was parched, but she dared not give herself away by finishing the water he had brought her.

'And how,' she asked, rather proud of herself because her voice was steady, 'would you do that?'

His eyes narrowed. 'Why, marry you, of course,' he said and turned and went out of the kitchen.

CHAPTER SEVEN

A superb exit, she thought shakily, draining the water from the glass. Delivered with superb timing and intonation—everything perfect including the lean-hipped walk out of the room.

If she thought of it as a piece of magnificent theatre perhaps it wouldn't frighten her so much. He had threatened her before and she hadn't been cowed, so why was this any different? He must know that there was no way he could force her to marry him.

I'd sooner play water-polo with a shark, she thought. It would be about the same danger risk. Marriage to Derek had been hell, but marriage to Rafe would be hell with the Devil's personal supervision.

And she had better push it to the back of her mind now for it was not going to help her achieve her aim. On the other hand, the fact that Derek could still be made to want her might. The memory of his greedy mouth made her give a fastidious little shudder, but she forced herself to assess as cold-bloodedly as she could, just how, if she had to, she would use his weakness.

It would be the first time she had ever consciously and deliberately used her sexuality to manipulate a man and the thought of it made her stomach twist in a spasm, but she was a realist. In this kind of war she would have to use the few weapons she had and one of them was the disturbing collection of physical attributes which made men look at her with lust.

She got to her feet, carried the glass over to the sink and washed and dried it. When the kitchen had been remodelled, Joy, or whoever had made the decisions, had kept to the conventional concept so there was a window above the sink. It looked out over a lawn and the kitchen garden, a long border against a rock wall in which grew every herb Joy could track down as well as clusters of wallflowers and bulbs and an assortment of small shrubs, several in flower. A fantail was flitting swiftly from twig to twig, catching small unseen insects in its beak.

Behind the wall was the orchard where two almond trees robed in the palest of pinks were an intimation of fairyland. Two peach trees beyond them again held boughs of slightly deeper pink up to the sky. They must, Jennet thought, ripen well before Christmas. Tamarillo trees sheltered the exotic egg-shaped fruit, ruby-red or yellow with enormous leaves and behind them were other fruit trees, still bare and leafless.

The orchard had always been an enchanted place to Jennet. She remembered long summer days when the best shade was beneath one of the three huge avocados planted many years ago by Rafe's grandmother. In winter daffodils and jonquils bloomed in a scented carpet beneath the trees, in the autumn belladonna lilies lifted their naked pink and carmine and white trumpets. Immense hedges of Japanese cedars cut the orchard off from the station. The wall on the fourth side was pierced by a little wicket gate. The only other entrance was the farm gate used by the tractor which did the heavy work there.

Perhaps because of this she had always thought of it as a secret place, magical, not quite of this world. Before she had discovered her own little dell she had spent much of her time in the orchard.

Now she walked out across the kitchen garden to the wicket gate. One of the farm cats, a large unctuous creature with serrated ears above a smug black face, stretched its back and claws beneath a daphne bush then padded lazily after her.

Once in the shelter of the hedges the sun beat down

with unremitting force. The five sheep who kept the
pasture short lifted their heads and eyed Jennet and her
attendant with mild curiosity before resuming their
life's most important work. A single strand of electrified
wire kept them from the citrus orchard. It was sheep
height so Jennet was able to step over it. The cat knew
what it was, too. Jennet smiled as he lowered his tail
carefully before strolling under it.

Lemons and lemonades glowed like oval suns, the
mandarins were small and vivid against their glossy
green leaves.

'Now, which mandarins peel the easiest?' Jennet
asked her companion. 'Clementines or Satsumas or
Karas? I wonder.'

'Satsumas,' Rafe said, so close behind her that she
jumped and turned to face him, her expression
protesting.

'I wish you wouldn't do that,' she objected, not
trusting him an inch.

He wore that arrogant, high-handed look of his, that
'lord of all creation and answerable to none' expression
she and Melly had used to call it, and the smile on his
well-shaped mouth was neither amused nor pleasant.

'Well, help yourself,' he said. 'We don't charge for
them.'

'What are you doing here?'

He picked a mandarin, strong fingers working swiftly
as he peeled off the golden skin and threw it under the
tree.

'Here,' he said softly. 'Come and get it.'

She shook her head. It was incredible but she was
frightened. This beautiful place, in broad daylight and
yet she was afraid.

'All right then,' he said, apparently bored, and halved
the tiny fruit, offering her a portion while he ate his
share in two mouthfuls.

Reluctantly Jennet stretched out her hand and was

instantly caught and pulled to him.

'Rafe . . .' she objected.

'Open your mouth,' he said with infuriating coolness.

From beneath her lashes she saw nothing but a kind of lazy impassivity in his face yet his grip on her was too firm to make any effort to break free. Slowly she obeyed and a segment of satsuma was placed on her tongue.

When the sharp, sweet morsel was gone, he fed her another and another until he said, 'My finger is sticky,' and placed it against her lips.

Slowly, impelled by some instinct she should have ignored, Jennet's tongue curved on to his finger, working slowly around it so that the juice of the mandarin was removed.

Her lashes flickered. She could feel a familiar pressure in her throat, in her breasts, a familiar hunger in the pit of her stomach. Looking up into the ruthless face above her she was sixteen again. She remembered then the first sharp pangs of desire as if fountained through blood and sinews and nerves, igniting her, forcing her now to recognise a bitter and painful truth.

Only this man, she thought bemusedly. It had never been like this since, not with Derek, not with anyone. There had never been this conviction of absolute rightness, of—fulfilment.

What was between them was love. Passion and hatred and suspicion—and love. She should have realised much sooner. Derek had seen it. And although Rafe would never admit it, he too must know, for that was why he had to hate her. She was dangerous, a threat to that splendid self-sufficiency of his.

'You look like a wary cat,' he said softly and closed her eyes with kisses before his warm, demanding mouth moved to her temple.

Almost soothed by the persuasive touch of his lips she leaned into him, a soft sigh escaping through lips which stung with the need for his lovemaking.

They stayed locked together, his arms confining her with her cheek resting against the hard curve of his shoulder. The sun beat down on Jennet's face; in a daze of happiness she felt his mouth in her hair.

'Pretty little thing,' he said lazily.

'Don't be condescending.'

She could hear his smile. 'Beautiful, then. The kind of beauty which cuts through the civilised ethos we aspire to. Just to look at you is to want you.'

Not everyone, she wanted to tell him. Not every man, although many mistook her beauty for the woman beneath it, treating her as an object not a living, intelligent person.

But all she said, inadequately, was, 'It isn't always pleasant.'

'No, I suppose not, although men have conspired together over the years to make it seem the ultimate perfection. The mask is mistaken for the person. I know how that feels.'

Surprised into an unguarded little movement, she said nothing, but she felt his noiseless chuckle, before he continued, 'Women do it, too. They don't demand beauty but—more tangible assets. Money, security. If I came to you tomorrow and told you that it had all gone, that I had nothing but my bare hands and my brain, what would you do?'

It was heaven to stand like this, resting so confidingly against him and listening to him talking to her, for once with the tense, power-seeking cut and thrust of their usual conversation absent.

'Offer you bed and board and whatever else I could give,' she said, adding shyly, 'not that you'd ever come to me.'

'Just like that, no strings, no conditions? I find that hard to believe.' He sounded cynical beyond belief but strangely, there was no bitterness in the deep voice.

Yet the words were like small destructive blows to her body.

'Modesty sits rather oddly on your shoulders, Rafe. If you really think that your material assets are the only reason you attract women you must need your head read.'

'No, not the only reason, but certainly the main one.'

She laughed at that, the warm delightful sound tinged with some mischief, tilting her head so that she looked up into his dark, shuttered face. 'Darling, you're priceless. You're a very handsomely packaged piece of masculinity, you know, although that's not your main attraction. Derek is almost as good looking as you, but he doesn't have to swat adoring females off like flies. No, with you it's that combination of contained strength, the hint of austerity and the total and complete authority that gets us.'

He grinned, mocking her. 'Go on, you fascinate me. Have you ever thought of using that creative streak of yours? Writing plays?'

'No, I mean it.' She lifted her finger and traced the strong harsh line of his jaw, feeling the skin tighten beneath her touch. A kind of languor made her boneless, careless of consequences. The clamour in her body had eased into a brilliant awareness. Her discovery of the love she had carried in her heart for years, had liberated her from the tension she always felt in his presence. Now that she no longer had to hide from herself she could relax.

'Women can't resist self-sufficiency,' she told him solemnly, her eyes sparkling with laughter. 'We have to be needed, wanted, to make a man feel that he isn't complete without us. It's an old atavistic notion, almost an instinct, implanted in our genes. And then there's that intriguing combination of virility and austerity. Aha, we say, a sensual Puritan and our mind thrills to all sorts of delicious, forbidden thoughts.'

He was laughing openly at her now but his mouth straightened, and he asked, 'And the authority?'

'Well, we're programmed to seek security,' she returned with a limpid look. 'You see, in spite of feminism and the twentieth century and plain common sense which tells us there's no such thing as complete security, tucked away in every woman is this instinct which tells her that she should be looking around for a man to protect her and the babies from the local sabre-toothed tiger and woolly mammoth. An intelligent courageous man, preferably big.' Here she ran an exploratory hand from his elbow to his shoulder, enjoying the automatic tensing of muscle and skin before giving him a dazzling smile.

The nonsense helped her control the rising tide of hunger in her body. It also summoned that rare, wolfish smile as a response.

'As it happens,' he told her, 'woolly mammoths were vegetarians. I think they lived on buttercups and grass. But I see what you mean.'

'I thought you might.'

'Hasn't it occurred to that instinct that big men need a lot of food to keep them going? Food taken from the mouths of those babies?'

'Oh, I don't think instincts can reason,' she said, tilting her head to one side in mock thoughtfulness.

Again that slashing grin. 'So I've been right all these years in assuming that it was my bank balance which attracted women.'

'Partly,' she sighed in sympathetic tones. A mischievous glint transformed her eyes into green jewels, exotic, provocative. 'At least, the security it evokes. But you see it's not our fault, either. I mean, who can escape heredity?'

'Who indeed?' For a moment the angular features hardened. 'Why even try?' he muttered as his head lowered and his mouth took hers.

This time, freed from the fear of understanding her emotions, she allowed herself the freedom to respond fully. It seemed right that he should make a strange choked little noise in his throat before, without breaking the kiss, he stepped backwards so that he was leaning against the bole of the flowering peach. His arms tightened, pulling her against his body into intimate contact. As Derek had been earlier, he was aroused, but she wanted this, she felt no shred of distaste, willingly pressing herself against him so that her soft form was lying open to him.

His mouth was not hurtful as Derek's had been. It was gentle, but determined, seducingly sweet, summoning such intense excitement that she was overcome by it, she didn't know how to cope and she went under completely.

Only dimly was she aware of the hand that slid up to fondle the smooth skin of her back, and discover that she wasn't wearing anything underneath the prim shirt.

Beneath her fingers his skin was hot and damp, silk over steel, incredibly exciting.

Then he said something and she whispered his name, turning her face into his neck, her tongue flicking out in tiny involuntary movements to caress the salty skin.

Strange to feel a strong man flinch at such a tiny caress. Strange to feel that hard body quicken against her, his hands slide together down behind the waistband of her slacks and pull her with a swift, violent ferocity against him so that she gasped and cried out, for his need and passion sent a primitive hunger coursing through every cell in her body.

Like calling to like, she thought dazedly, holding on to his shoulders as if she was drowning. There was no tenderness, no respect in this embrace, nothing but a current of elemental fire which leapt from one to the other, ignited and fed by the abandoned response each advance met.

He was speaking, his head bent so that his mouth was by her ear, blocking out the dazzling warmth of the sun.

'What?' she said vaguely, turning her head to meet his. Her mouth searched blindly for his, found it, but he lifted his head away from her and spoke again and this time the words impinged.

'Is this how your ex-husband makes you feel?'

And while she was still trying to make sense of the pattern of words he repeated it in a voice dead and devoid of emotion.

Slowly, like a woman in the grip of a nightmare, she awoke to her actions—and his. Held in that grip, his hands cruel on her hipbones, able to feel every inch of his body and its wild response from the heavy lifting movements of his chest to the taut length of his thighs, she knew that he wanted her and that yet again he had rejected her.

And it had been so easy; he had proceeded exactly as he had that first time, lulled her into acceptance with his usually relaxed attitude, a little conversation and then the soundless cruel swoop to the kill.

And like the hawk's prey, she had been taken by something she hadn't even recognised.

She welcomed the anger which rode like a flood through her body, for it hid the shame and the persistent, wounding pain, but she forced herself to relax. The evidences of his arousal were fading. That cold, remorseless brain was once more in control.

So she said as calmly as she could above the painful slamming of her heart, 'Not quite, darling, but then Derek is not quite so experienced as you—or so well-equipped by nature.'

Her only protection was that small one afforded by her eyelids. She kept them resolutely lowered to hide the betrayed confusion in her eyes.

'Oh?' The syllable was drawled out with derisive

mockery. 'Has your instinct discarded him as not suitable material to take on a marauding cave bear?'

She couldn't manage a smile, but at least her voice had a note of lilting amusement in it when she replied, 'Experience, my sweet. Instinct can be overriden by experience. Derek does very well, but he hasn't that basic ruthlessness which you possess.'

'And that's what turns you on?'

'Either that or your money,' she said flippantly and made to pull away.

It was a mistake. His hands tightened and he chuckled softly as he lifted her, holding her so that her face was on a level with his. Startled, her lashes flew up, and her glance was caught and held by the obsidian darkness of his, opaque with warning and a cruel enjoyment of her situation.

'So keep out of his bed,' he said quietly.

Shrugging, she leaned forward and kissed the brutal, beautiful line of his mouth, reacting to his involuntary response with a knowing smile. Against his lips she said, 'I'll do what I want to, when I want to, with whom I want to, and there's nothing you can do about it, *dear, kind, noble* Rafe.' Her warm voice laughed over the adjectives, deliberately taunting.

To punish him a little further she hooked her legs around his, felt his desire surge through his body for a second and was ready, waiting, when he dropped her, the dark, autocratic lines of his face harsh and contemptuous.

He swore while she tucked her shirt back into her jeans, the imprecations heavy on the dancing air until she taunted, 'Oh, don't be so stupid, Rafe. You deserve to be punished a little. What you did was hardly Queensberry rules, was it?'

'No,' he said, and suddenly the anger was damped down, controlled as he finished, 'but it did show that I can get you into my bed any time I like to try.'

'Oh no,' she said, smiling, shaking her head so that several pink petals drifted from the soft, gleaming tresses, 'sorry, darling, you've just queered your pitch. Not now, not ever.'

'I never could resist a challenge,' he murmured reaching for her.

His mouth was just as seducingly sweet, her response as exciting, but Jennet stood in his grasp without moving. She didn't even close her eyes, noting with detached interest that when he kissed he kept his open, too. Probably, she thought knowledgeably, because it might be seen as a sign of vulnerability, a kind of symbolic placing of oneself in the partner's power. And Rafe was far too self-sufficient to do that. Far too cold, far too arrogant. Far too cruel.

And she loved him, had always loved him in spite of the instinct of self-preservation which had tried to hide the truth from her for so many years. Loving Rafe could only mean more pain, more humiliation, a constant aching rent in the fabric of her personality.

At last he released her, saying with merciless precision, 'You can turn it off and on like a——'

'Oh, why hesitate? Like a whore, I feel sure you were going to say.' It hurt, every breath, every beat of her heart, every movement of her body hurt, as if she had been tortured for weeks, years, but she had come a long way from the shy adolescent who had been so lacking in confidence. She stood straight as a wand, her eyes meeting his in cool challenge.

'Very well, then, like a whore.' He was watching her, perhaps wondering what was going on behind the beautiful empty mask of her face. Cruelly, deliberately, he continued, 'But you're little better than that, are you? You sell your body. The only difference is that instead of honestly giving it in return for the money, you make men pay for the shadow, for fodder for their fantasies. Except when you play Juliet, of course.'

'Oh, of course,' she murmured. 'Shakespeare is sacred, we all know that.'

She could bear no more. A little clumsily she turned away, but stopped the moment his hand touched her shoulder.

'Yes?' she asked, the word dipped in ice.

'Just remember, Jennet. If I see you near Derek again I'll take what you so blantantly offered me a few minutes ago. Even if you manage to keep up the masquerade of resistance.'

'But that would be rape,' she said silkily.

She could hear the cynical smile in his voice. 'No, my darling. I wouldn't rape you. Ever.' The voice lowered, became husky, promising, tormenting. 'By the time I've finished with you you'll be begging me to take you. If you think—well, there are forms of degradation even you have probably never heard of.'

As she walked away through the smiling day Jennet found herself insisting wearily that he had made an empty threat, while the hair on the back of her neck refused to lie down and she knew she was trying to fool herself. There had been a note of implacable decision in those last sentences which terrified her.

She thought once more of telling him about her marriage. Up in her bedroom, surrounded by the paraphernalia of her childhood, she sat on the bed, hands clasped between her knees and stared at her feet.

How would she do it? Rafe, I don't think Melly should marry Derek because ... and then launch into her shaming little story, for in spite of the best efforts of the psychiatrist she still felt shamed by it.

Only now she knew why. Because for all her righteous indignation, Derek had been quite correct when he blamed her complete lack of response to him on her unacknowledged, repressed desire for Rafe.

So far she had accomplished nothing. Nothing at all. Melly was still determined to marry Derek, still convinced that her sister had come back to cause trouble, and for no other reason. Derek had been too clever for her. Every time their eyes met she saw his triumph and had to stem her own despairing helplessness. The only plan her mind had come up with was acutely dangerous, now that Rafe had taken a hand in the affair.

Shivering, her skin taut, she stood up. She would have to persuade Melly that she spoke the truth and if she failed then she would stake everything on her decision to force Derek's hand.

And if that failed, she thought desperately, she would have no choice but to tell Rafe everything. He would not believe her but the revelation might make him keep a close watch on Melly. He would see to it that she was not left alone and helpless, caught in the same trap that Jennet had been caught in.

That done, Rafe warned, she would go back and pick up the threads of her life.

For there was no future for her at Te Puriri. Oh, she could become Rafe's mistress. He wanted her. If she surrendered, made it obvious that she would take him on his terms, he'd enjoy her. For a few weeks, perhaps a few months. And she would be happy for those weeks or months. Her love, that obsessional ardour which had lasted for so many years, would pave the way for another, more final, rejection.

But even as she thought of it, she knew she would not do it. If she let him, Rafe could cripple her.

We are all scarred, she thought, sombrely, our souls marked by ghosts.

Dinner was eaten rather hurriedly. Rafe had a meeting and Melly was going to see a friend who had just come home from a holiday in South America. Left to her own devices Jennet tried to read a book subtitled *Civilisation and Capitalism, 15th–18th Centuries*, before exchanging it for an amusing romp by Georgette Heyer.

Neither made any impression on her. When she looked down at her hand she was alarmed to see it trembling.

Wearily, she decided to see if she could sleep. The house was very quiet, its welcoming ambience never more soothing.

Halfway to the stairs she leaned against the wall, staring with blank eyes through the carved wooden arch with its classically capped pillars to a niche painted in *trompe l'oeil*. She had read somewhere that the Hollingworth who had built the homestead had imported Italian workmen. Perhaps one of them had painted the exquisite little scene, a marble balustrade overhung with vines and beyond that a garden, classical with cypresses and a fountain. Even after all these years the colours were soft and fresh, the little landscape as deceptive to the vision as it had been meant to be.

'Oh, *God*,' Jennet whispered, swamped by an aching sense of loss and desolation. With one last look she fled, racing up the stairs to the refuge of her room.

But she could not settle, Her thoughts, her attempts to deal with her emotions, had her pacing restlessly back and forth, until finally she pulled a jacket from the wardrobe and ran quietly down the stairs and out on to the terrace in front of the house.

Although chilly, the night was one of those magnificent spectacles turned on by winter. No wind, the moon not yet up, just the black sky of infinity and the blaze of the stars, incredibly close and clear, the Milky Way, a ragged swathe of diamond dust from one horizon to the other, the closer stars glittering in their magnificent chaste remoteness.

Walking slowly, quietly except for the soft sound of her shoes on the stones, she found the winter constellations with their euphonious names, Scorpio, Aquila, Saggitarius. And although bright Canopus and Sirius, the most dazzling of all the stars, had dipped below the horizon, there was the little Southern Crown and the two brilliant pointers to the Southern Cross to take their place, as well as blazing red Antares, sinister in the Scorpion.

Dougal had taught her the names and constellations, letting her tag along on nights when he had gone out with his binoculars to watch the skies. She shivered as she remembered him, a tired man, weary before his time, telling her to look at the stars and her own troubles would seem very small.

Perhaps they did, but at the moment even the stars couldn't make her relax. As she paced the length of the terrace, hands stuffed in the pockets of her jacket, her breath a small smoke in front of her, she tried to bring some sort of order into the events of the past weeks, to formulate some sort of plan.

Nothing happened, of course, nothing so miraculous as a new way of dealing with the situation. Yet still she paced, stopping now and then to stare for long moments up into the sky.

CHAPTER EIGHT

WHEN the lights of the car stabbed through the darkness she was standing by one of the borders, breathing in the fabulous scent of a bush of Japanese honeysuckle. Without checking pace, the big vehicle moved quietly on past the house. She heard the soft sound of its door, the faint rustle of the garage door as Rafe closed it.

She had not moved when he appeared beside her. No sound had betrayed his approach yet she knew where he was, knew that he was coming for her.

'How was the meeting?' she asked, meaningless words.

'All talk and no action. Typical.'

'No action?'

In the bright starshine she saw his swift, flashing grin. 'Well, a little. Enough to make it worthwhile, I suppose. What are you doing out here? Communing with ghosts?'

She was shaken again at this further evidence of his perspicacity.

'How did you know?'

'Oh, something in the way you looked. Haunted, I suppose.'

'We are, aren't we?' she said sadly.

He didn't pretend to misunderstand her. 'You're doing some haunting yourself.'

'Rafe . . .'

'Yes?'

She sought for words, her face turned away from him. Slowly, stumbling a little, the beautiful warm voice tentative, she said, 'If I told you—if I said that I had a good reason for coming back—would you believe me?'

'Of course I would.' He waited while she looked sharply up at him, her face a pale blur in the darkness, before continuing blandly, 'I've always known what it is. You don't want Compton to be happy.'

'No, it's not that,' she said hopelessly, pulling back.

His hands around her face were warm, almost gentle, but they held her captive. 'Revenge is not a particularly worthwhile motive, is it?' he mused as his thumb stroked across the senstitive skin of her lips. 'It is, however, one I can understand. I'm not a forgiving person myself.'

'No,' she said wearily.

He smiled, using his thumb to push aside her lips, to test the outline of her teeth in a caress which made her heart beat unevenly, crazily. Her tongue touched his skin, delicately savouring his taste and then his thumb was replaced by his mouth and she sighed and relaxed against him, searching for comfort in the most basic way.

A long time later he spoke against her throat, the words muffled but distinguishable. 'Why are we out here in the cold? My bedroom is much warmer, much more comfortable than this.'

The thread of cynical amusement in the deep tones only emphasised the raw passion there. Jennet was tempted, sorely so, for her body ached with a frustration which had become like an old friend, but she said in a remote little voice, 'Sorry, darling.'

'Jennet.'

'Mmm?'

'It's those ghosts again, isn't it?'

'You summoned them, Rafe, not me.' Her sigh tailed off into a bitter little laugh. 'It's strange, isn't it? She's not even dead.'

'No. But my father is.'

Something in the way he said it made her shiver. 'Would you—do you really wish she was dead?'

'Oh, God knows.' His arms tightened about her, crushing her, hurting her. 'If I wanted her dead then you'd have to die too, wouldn't you, and I don't think I'd like that. I have other plans for you.' And bending his dark head in the cool sweet-smelling darkness with the ageless stars wheeling above them he told her what those plans were, his voice slurring as the hot words burned across her mind and she felt the hunger and the tension in him. Felt it and responded to it, her brain at the mercy of her questing flesh while he spoke words she had never heard from a man's lips, words that were harsh with a passion too long suppressed.

'Rafe,' she muttered, shaking with the determination not to give in. 'Please listen to me.'

'I don't want to hear you talk.' He laughed soundlessly and went on, 'Deeds, not words, Jennet.'

'Please Rafe. I must tell you . . .'

He sighed, and took her hand and slid it under his jacket so that she was pressed against him, trapped by his warmth and the sensual weakness of her own desires.

'Very well, then, tell me, and after that we'll make love and the only sounds I want to hear from you will be the strange choked little noises you make when I touch you.'

She flinched but the blood was running hot through her veins and she said without hope, 'Don't you want to know why I have to stop this marriage?'

'I already know.'

'No you don't.' She was shivering but she persisted, 'Please listen to me.'

'I'll listen.'

But he wasn't going to believe her; she could tell by the bored note in his voice.

Stumbling, her voice barely audible, she said wretchedly, 'Rafe, I left Derek because he beat me.'

Silence. After a dreadful, tense few moments he

responded politely, 'I've often felt like it myself, Jennet.
I know, he told me.'

'He—*told* you?'

The broad shoulders lifted in a slight shrug. 'Last
night.'

'I see.' But she didn't.

As if she hadn't spoken, he said calmly, 'I must admit
I'd have felt murderous if I caught my wife of a few
months in bed with my cousin.'

For a few seconds she literally couldn't think. His
words went round and round her head, echoing, until at
last she managed to make sense of them. Then,
surprisingly enough, she thought with almost detached
interest that Derek had indeed been clever. To a fiercely
possessive, territorial male like Rafe, unfaithfulness
would be the unforgiveable sin.

'Is it any use telling you that I was not—that I didn't
go to bed with Trent?' she asked.

He laughed again. 'No, I'm afraid not, darling. Your
subsequent actions rather give the lie to that, don't
they? You ran away with the guy.'

It was hopeless, useless, yet still she persisted. 'Or
that Derek systematically beat me from the first?'

'Sorry,' he said, and she could tell that he was
smiling; his voice revealed a savage, contemptuous
amusement. 'Good try, though. The poor swine can't
really prove that he didn't, can he? If you'd seen him
after you left you'd know why I don't believe you. He
was, quite literally, distraught. I could have told him
you weren't worth it but you had him so tied up he
couldn't see straight.'

She couldn't bear his closeness. How could he think
so vilely of her yet hold her in his arms as if he wanted
her? But when she made to step back, his hold
tightened. He let her feel his strength as she struggled
against him, his breathing not altering until she gave up
and stood, stiff and taut in his arms.

Then he lowered his dark, proud head to rest his cheek against her forehead and said, 'But the clincher, Jennet, is the fact that you didn't complain. If Derek had made a habit of beating you you'd have done something about it, wouldn't you?'

'Come to you?' she suggested bitterly and then, before he could answer, 'you don't understand.'

'I understand too well. You married Derek because you liked having him panting with desire at your heels and because you thought he had money. He told me all about it last night. When you tired of being his wife, when you realised that Compton Downs was mortgaged up to the hilt, you did exactly what your mother did. You wanted him to sell up and get out. But he was tougher than my father and he refused. So you hopped into bed with his cousin and when Derek lost his temper with you, you ran away. Now you're intent on revenging yourself and you're not in the least choosey about the weapons you use. Only it won't work, sweetheart. We all know you for what you are, and that draws your poison before you've had a chance to strike.'

Oh, Derek had been brilliant. So skilfully playing on Rafe's prejudices, using facts to cobble together a tissue of lies which could not be disproved.

Jennet stood very still, her brain working coldly and with clear precision. Derek had always been cunning, quick to seize an advantage to manipulate people. His downfall was his conceit, that arrogance which had refused to believe that she would leave him, the same self-confidence which had made him pursue Melly when he knew that Jennet would do all in her power to prevent the wedding.

That quick confidence in his own cleverness, so at variance with Rafe's cool competence, was the only weapon she had against him. That and the fact that he still wanted her. It angered him that she was no longer in his power. Her refusal to be afraid of him, her self-assurance, hit at the basic insecurity which the whole false edifice of his personality had been erected to hide. Fundamentally Derek was weak, a bully, and he knew it, and he had given his life over to hiding it.

Jennet knew it too. She was the only other person, apart from Trent Addison, his cousin, who understood him, and although he was confident that he had made it impossible for her to harm him he was wary of her.

And that was why she was not going back to Sydney until she had seen this thing through. Somehow she must find a way of undermining that charming front he presented to the world until he stood revealed as the shoddy, unhappy person he was and Melly would be safe.

'What are you thinking?' Rafe said, shifting slightly.

Jennet tried to pull away but his hands settled her between his legs, holding her hips until she made no further resistance. She sighed again and undid his jacket, leaning into him, her cheek resting on his shirt, warm with the blood beating through his body. His hands slid in a leisurely fashion up her back; he smiled, totally confident of her capitulation.

'Tell me,' he coaxed, knowing that her body was open to his touch, that her heart was picking up speed.

'Secrets,' she said sadly.

'Always secrets in those shadowy eyes.' His breath was warm across her skin. 'Keep your secrets, darling, until you're in my bed. Then I'll have every one of them from you.'

'You don't think much of women, do you?' she said slowly, lost in a mysterious sensual world where the strength and warmth of his body and the soft, lazy movement of his mouth over her face were the only reality.

He laughed. 'I'm not a misogynist, if that's what you're thinking. But I learnt early that women aren't to be trusted.'

'Your mother died, and left you alone.'

There was a moment's silence before he said in an arrested voice, 'How astute of you, Jennet.'

His mouth had moved from the line of her cheekbone to rest on the soft hollow beneath her ear. She shivered again, common sense warned her that now was the time to stop this slow relentless seduction before it got out of hand.

'More ghosts,' she said, hardening her voice. 'There are too many of them, Rafe. And I'm slowly freezing to death.'

'Inside then.'

He didn't touch her as they walked across the wet lawn, made no effort to help her up the steps on to the terrace. She left him while he was unlocking the door, moving with no more than her usual speed up the stairs. The hall was always lit by a subdued lamp, another burned over the stairwell but the house was silent with that peculiar quietness which comes when everyone else is asleep. Jennet slipped into her room, rubbing her hands together more to convince herself that she was cold than because they were. She wasn't afraid that Rafe would follow her in. He wanted her willingly in his bed, not forced there.

Because that would give him much more satisfaction, she thought wearily. He was like the hunter who stalks his prey for the thrill of the chase. The actual kill was merely the inevitable ending to a set piece. He enjoyed this false courtship, was amused by her efforts to keep him at a distance because he was convinced that her surrender was only a matter of time.

She showered, pulled on her dressing gown and walked through the door into her room to sit down at the dressing table and brush her hair.

And for the first time in years her reflection wavered and was distorted by a film of tears.

'Oh—God,' she whispered, dropping the hairbrush to

hide her face behind her spread fingers. As the unbidden sobs forced their way into her throat she began to rock to and fro, trying to ease the pain in the physical action.

When her shoulders were caught in a grip like iron she flinched, pulling away like a stricken bird from the man behind her.

'Hush,' he said and slid his arms about her, holding her against the lean warmth of his body. 'Jennet, you'll make yourself sick. Hush, now.'

Her closed fist smeared the tears across her face but she couldn't regain control so he picked her up and sat down on the bed with her, leaning back against the headboard. Choking, gasping she burrowed into the protective strength of his body, her hands clenched on to the front of his shirt.

He said nothing more but after a few seconds his finger began to smooth the fine, soft tendrils of hair back from her wet cheeks. It moved rhythmically, sweetly, so that she felt enclosed in a cocoon of safety.

Slowly her sobs dwindled. A handkerchief appeared; she blew her nose and wiped the worst of the tears away keeping her head down so that those black eyes couldn't see the wreckage of her face. Phantom sobs made her hiccough occasionally, but she stayed where she was, afraid to move or say anything, curled up on his lap like a child. Fatigue washed over her.

After a long time he covered them both with blankets and began to slide down the bed. Jennet was almost asleep. She sighed and turned her face into his shoulder, muttering, 'Don't go.'

'No,' he said quietly.

Some time during the night she came partly awake to find herself pressed down into the mattress, lapped in warmth and peace. She smiled and slid back into sleep curving against the man who shared her bed.

He was gone when morning came, but she lay back

against the pillows and smiled again, remembering his tenderness and how secure she had felt in his arms. Surely he could not have been so gentle with her unless he felt something like affection?

Although last night's weariness had fled with last night she still suffered from the oppression of the spirits which had brought on the bout of tears. It wasn't helped by a change in the weather. Yesterday's sun had given way to a chill easterly, which whined and fretted at her windows.

Still, during the night her subconscious had come up with one suggestion. It required nerve, but she was going to ring Trent Addison. Even if he no longer felt anything for Melly it was most unlikely that he would want to see her married to Derek.

The telephone directories lived on their own shelf in the library. She would have to ring now before he went to work, because she had no idea of the name of his firm; even if she did, she might not be able to speak to him on a personal matter. Secretaries were usually very protective. A quick glance at her watch decided her. Rafe would probably be out working and with any luck Melly was still in bed. And unless Trent was a workaholic he would be at home.

At this time of the morning there was no delay; within a few minutes she was listening to the sound of the telephone ringing in Trent's house.

Almost immediately he answered, listening without comment while she explained who she was.

'I was going to ring you,' he told her crisply when she had finished. 'Brigit Miall 'phoned me last night. She told me about the engagement.'

'Are you coming?'

'Wild horses wouldn't keep me away. Have you told Melissa why you left Derek?'

She explained the situation concluding with a quick disclosure of the tale Derek had given Rafe.

'Clever bastard,' he said tightly. 'He's cut the ground out nicely from under your feet. You've not spoken to Melissa?'

'No. It didn't seem worth it. She'll believe him.'

'Hm.' Silence, then he said, 'It's a pity you didn't cite him for cruelty when you divorced him.'

'I—I couldn't,' she said weakly. 'The lawyer said it was too difficult——'

'Yes, I know. It's all right.'

'If I'd known that this was going to happen I would have.'

He said sardonically, 'If either of us had had any idea of what was going to happen I'm sure we would have acted quite differently.'

'I'm sorry,' she said tonelessly.

'My dear girl, don't be silly. I'm not blaming you for anything.' After a pause he said calmly, 'Well, I'll come up with something. If necessary I'll kidnap her.'

He meant it too. Jennet said, 'I wish I could be more helpful.'

'So do I. Still, it can't be helped. I'll see you at the party.'

'Yes. Goodbye, Trent.'

As she replaced the receiver some instinct of danger lifted the hairs on the back of her neck. Slowly her head turned to meet the peculiar glittering opacity of Rafe's gaze.

'Oh, God,' she whispered, her hand flying to her mouth.

'You lying, treacherous little slut,' he said, quite calmly, bloodless lips barely moving.

Then, as if he could not bear the sight of her he swung on his heel, leaving her to sink shakily on to a chair, her heart torn from her body.

He left Te Puriri that morning for Wellington. Something to do with the government, Melly told her. He would be back the day of the Mialls' party. So

Jennet spent the intervening days memorising her part in her next production to take her mind off the treadmill of trying to decide just how much he had heard. Her moods swung from optimistic to intensely depressed then back to optimism again.

It wasn't until the night before the party that she realised that she had given up all hope of convincing Rafe that they had some sort of future. Her hopes were pinned solely on freeing Melly.

He arrived back at Te Puriri on the afternoon plane, grim faced and with eyes which still promised retribution. Tiredness accentuated his stark bone structure but did nothing to dimish his intense, tough masculinity.

All day Jennet had been oppressed by a sense of doom, her spirits subdued by a burden which was fast becoming intolerable. Tomorrow Rafe would throw her off Te Puriri; she had accomplished nothing.

Nothing, that is, beyond falling quite desperately in love with a man who hated even the sound of her name. Every one of Rafe's prejudices had been reinforced, strengthened by her behaviour and what she couldn't help feeling were some particularly nasty tricks played by Fate. Or perhaps she was just too stupid to be able to effectively make use of the few cards she had to play.

Alone in her silent room she went listlessly across to the wardrobe. The full-length mirrors showed her a weary woman, every line of whose body proclaimed her apathy.

I am *not* going down without a fight, she told herself, forcing herself to straighten. Tonight was a night for the last throw, the determining roll of the dice in the face of fortune.

Her hands drew out a taffeta dress, black and sleek with ruffles ornamenting the camisole top and curving diagonally down the wrap-fronted skirt. Thin straps clung to her shoulders. With it she wore a wide belt of satin ribbon fastened with two silk camellias the colour of carmine. Quickly she pulled on black stockings spotted with black hailstones, thin high-heeled black shoes then sat down to brush her hair until it gleamed like blonde silk.

Her make-up was as dramatic and sensual as the dress, heavy but subtle about the eyes so that they looked like enormous sleepy green jewels and lips the exact colour of the camellias.

When all was ready she sprayed herself with *Bal à Versailles* and stood viewing her reflection in the mirror while the oriental perfume teased her nostrils. Without vanity she knew that she looked good. The tension of the past days had shadowed her eyes giving her a faintly triste appeal which was interestingly at variance with the sensual ambience she had created with clothes and cosmetics.

Absently her mind searched back over the years, recalling many of the men who had been attracted by her face and body. There had been brash men, sophisticated men, some old enough to be her father, others her own age; pleasant, unpleasant, some frightening, quite a few charming. None of them had managed to break through her defences. For years she had thought that the desperate disillusionment of her marriage had frozen her emotions. She knew better now.

When had she fallen in love with Rafe? Perhaps at the change-over from child to woman, the new-born impulses of her untutored heart and body had become fixated on him so that she could not progress beyond him. Like a colossus he had towered over her life, the only distinct figure in her memories because some time before she was sixteen she had given herself into his keeping.

The joke—bitter though it was—was that she had not even realised it. His love-making and rejection had driven her into herself and to hide the intolerable wound she had rationalised it into nothingness, striving to minimise the impact.

Her marriage had been another way of doing this. With his quick, intuitive understanding of the weaknesses of others Derek had known this and used her repressed love for another man to keep her in bondage. That was why she had stayed meekly accepting the hell he made of her life until Trent's stronger will had freed her.

But she had still been a prisoner. Now that she had accepted her emotional dependence on Rafe, and faced up to it, perhaps she would be able to escape it.

Unrequited love was not love at all. How often had she read that? Of course poets and artists and musicians refused to accept the validity of such a statement, but she must. Otherwise there was nothing ahead for her but a life as sterile as a laboratory.

Then her eye caught the tiny horse she had modelled in clay as a child and her spirits lifted. Courage flowed back through her veins. No, that was not what her life was going to be. There was her love affair with the potter's wheel and there was friendship and if she had no children of her own there were other children very much in need of love and attention. Life need never be empty; she would not be like Miss Havisham in Dicken's novel who waited in her wedding dress for the lover who jilted her, wasting her life for a phantom love and a phantom lover.

The sultry curves of Jennet's mouth tightened. Eyeing her reflection she said with a defiant lift of the chin, 'Lady, you get down there and show them you've got guts!'

They were waiting in the hall, talking in low voices. When she reached the top of the stairs Rafe and Melly both turned and looked upwards. A shiver jarred the length of her spine as she met the impact of two pairs of imperious black eyes, but imperceptibly she lifted her chin and floated down the stairs with all of the grace and arrogant confidence of a professional model, her lips pulling into a small, tantalising smile.

She felt a sudden surge of strength, her foreboding transformed into the conviction that she was going to accomplish one thing, free Melly from Derek's spell.

No, *two* things, she promised herself as Rafe's gaze moved slowly and far from subtly over her. He was never going to forget how she looked tonight. She was going to imprint her picture on to his brain so that when he was eighty he would only need to close his eyes and her image would leap into prominence, clear and sharp as she was now.

She would never know his love, never satisfy his desire, but that she would have.

'You look—lovely,' he said.

The banal little compliment gave her a pleasure that no more flowery tribute could have, because, quite literally, he could think of nothing else to say. The pinpoints of light deep in his eyes were dilated; she could sense the effort it cost him to retain control of himself.

'You look gorgeous too,' she told him generously, her eyes clinging to his. It took willpower to turn them towards Melly and drawl, 'Stunning, Mel.'

And indeed, the younger woman did look superb, the soft gold crêpe of her dress enhancing her skin so that she was a golden goddess, almost stately.

'Oh, we all look stunning,' Melly said with a snap. 'Let's go, shall we?'

CHAPTER NINE

ALTHOUGH it was quite warm the night was whipped by a brisk northerly wind which could be the harbinger of a storm. Clouds hid the moon, but its light was eerily present so that the features of the countryside could be discerned.

The journey to the Mialls' was conducted mainly in silence, but just before lifting the knocker on their door Rafe took Jennet's hand in his, enclosing it in a warm, firm, unbreakable grip. His expression defied her to object. Jennet smiled and something flickered in the depths of his eyes as his mouth hardened.

Then the door was flung open and they were welcomed inside by Brigit, very trendy in scarlet and grey. 'Come in, come in,' she urged effusively, her expression avid as her glance flashed from Melly to Rafe and thence, with a small knowing smile, to Jennet.

'Give me your wraps,' she said, masking a hint of nervousness. 'You know, you should be marketed, you three. Cloned and then sold all over the world. Every woman needs a Rafe Hollingworth, the men could have a marvellous time choosing between the sultry blonde and the raven-haired Juno.'

'What about those who prefer brunettes—or redheads?' Melly asked, failing to hide the sour note in her voice.

Brigit's gaze sharpened. Again there was that darting glance at Jennet as though they shared a secret. Jennet felt Rafe's eyes on her.

When their hostess laughed and patted his arm with a greedy little hand, he withdrew that fierce scrutiny from Jennet, smiling rather sardonically down at the older woman.

'Well, perhaps we'd have to provide wigs,' she said lavishly. 'We wouldn't need a wider range of men, though. You must come very close to fulfilling every woman's fantasies, Rafe.'

The fulsome compliment irritated him. Jennet could sense his withdrawal, but he was still looking acidly amused as they moved into the enormous, cathedral-ceilinged drawing-room. However when, with all of the *empressement* of a magician with a fabulous new trick, Brigit produced a tall man with dark red highlights in his hair, the amusement hardened into forbidding intolerance. His gaze, dark and deadly, transfixed Jennet.

'Look who arrived only an hour ago,' Brigit announced a little too hurriedly. 'I don't need to introduce you, do I?'

'No.' Trent Addison drawled the word with saturnine appreciation. 'I feel rather like a card from Happy Families. Or a character in *Dallas*.'

The good manners Brigit no doubt relied on, carried them through the next few minutes although tension fairly crackled in the air. To those who watched, which meant most of the twenty or so people already in the room, they must have appeared to be behaving with courtesy and restraint. After one quick glance which revealed that Derek had not yet arrived, Melly was gravely dignified, although her eyes never met those of the man beside her.

He and Rafe spoke commonplaces; Jennet was silent, conscious of Brigit's increasing nervousness.

She was, Jennet decided, realising that her love of mischief had led her into stupidity. You didn't throw the gauntlet down before Rafe Hollingworth and expect to get away with it. Not unscathed, anyway.

So, chattering in a slightly higher voice than normal Brigit swept them towards the nearest group, talking nonstop until John had poured the drinks and the doorbell summoned her away.

Some minutes later Jennet's gaze lingered on the forceful arrogant lines of Trent Addison's face as he inclined his head towards Melly, holding her attention with a hard charm which kept her captive. As if Jennet's glance was tangible he lifted his head. The heavy-lidded eyes narrowed, then he raised his glass. The silent toast was understood by them both.

A dangerous man, Jennet thought. But her ally. Any danger to her came from the man who said now, in tones as cold and implacable as the Polar snows, 'Blowing on old embers, Jennet?'

Jennet bit her lip, her eyes searching Rafe's face. He looked like a statue of an antique warrior, a fearsome barbarian who swooped down on the settled lands plundering what he desired, riches, slaves, women.

'Rafe,' she began impetuously, unable to suppress the note of pleading in her voice, 'it isn't what you think.'

'How do you know what I think? What's he like as a lover, darling?'

'Please, Rafe . . .'

He smiled and took a small mouthful of wine, waiting with what probably seemed to others to be politeness while she struggled to find the words to explain. Now was not the place, she thought, casting a swift glance around the room and the people in it, but she felt that she couldn't bear it if Rafe was going to spend the night crucifying her.

When her gaze came back to him she shivered, for his eyes glittered like black diamonds, icy, without emotion. As he lowered his wine glass, she saw a muscle pull in his jaw.

'I don't know,' she said at last, trying to convey her innocence with her voice and her face.

'Your acting ability is quite astounding,' he remarked thoughtfully, saluting her with a taunting copy of Trent's gesture with his glass. 'I feel that I should be applauding. I believe he's an excellent lover; he's certainly had enough practice.'

'He's probably very talented,' she said on a hard indrawn breath. 'He likes women, which is always a help.'

'Are you hinting that I do not?'

Her shoulders lifted in the slightest of shrugs. 'Exactly. You know, I'd never believed that our childhood affected us as strongly as Freud asserted until I thought of you. A classic case.'

He reacted to her provocation with a hard, taunting smile. 'Is that why you've spent your adult life flitting from man to man? Don't look so taken aback, I can read, you know. And your name appears frequently in the gossip columns, always with a different man. Are you trying to compensate for your mother's rejection? Or someone else's?'

Her answering smile was infinitely alluring, a teasing movement of lips as inviting as those of a siren. 'Do you really believe the sort of rubbish you read in gossip columns? You disappoint me. I'd have thought you a little more sophisticated than that.'

'God knows why one of them hasn't killed you,' he said, his smile failing to soften the menace which lurked at the back of his eyes.

'Perhaps I don't inspire such violent reactions in anyone else.'

He didn't like that. His brows twitched together and that muscle flicked again in his jaw. 'What are you insinuating?'

'I'm—nothing.' She had to back down because for a moment he had looked as though he was prepared to start a brawl, even here.

With narrowed eyes he watched as her glance slid sideways to where Melly stood with Trent at her side, his attitude stating that he had no intention of leaving her. He looked like a man who knew exactly what he wanted and was prepared to do anything to get it.

'What plot did you two hatch?' Rafe enquired silkily.

A little pale she turned her head and looked very straight at him. 'Nothing.'

'Liar.'

It hurt, but she managed to shrug. 'Believe that if you like. If you're so worried why don't you go over there and break it up?'

'It's because I'm not worried that I'm here with you,' he said caustically. 'Of the two I find you the more dangerous. Trent knows that if he hurts Melly he'll have me to deal with.'

'And don't you feel that you can deal with me?'

'Oh yes,' he said evenly, his eyes gleaming as they raked her face and her bare shoulders, lingering on the white swell of her breasts. 'If you hurt her I swear that until the day you die you'll never be able to remember tonight without a shudder. There'll never be another man for you because whenever you look at one you'll see only me and you'll be so afraid you'll ask only to live like a nun for the rest of your life.'

He spoke the threat as if it was an incantation, a sorcerer's curse. Jennet quailed at the savage purpose which rang in his voice like steel, realising that there was more here than his determination to protect Melly.

A little stir at the door caught her eye. It was Derek. Watching as he kissed Brigit on both cheeks Jannet thought cynically that he was an extremely handsome man. Just like a fairy prince, blond and shining and pure.

However, when he realised who stood so possessively beside Melly, the expression which tightened his features was far from regal. Confusion warred with fury; he swallowed hard twice before he regained enough control to wipe all traces of emotion from his face.

His arrival was unnoticed by Melly. Even as he set purposefully off towards her something Trent said surprised her into a crack of laughter. As his glowing head came a little closer to hers she looked up into his face, her own suddenly alight.

Derek hesitated, then moved on, one hand touching his tie in a little preening movement. When Melly saw him her vivacity died, there came a trace of guilt into her expression. Derek's eyes paused on her face, then swept on to meet his cousin's. The two men ignored Melly. His eyes never leaving the other man's face Derek touched Melly's arm in a proprietorial challenge while Trent looked at him with cool impassivity.

Then Derek made some comment and those around them laughed. Again he made that little preening gesture.

Jennet drank a mouthful of wine. She knew what that movement meant. Someone was going to feel the effects of Derek's fury before the night was out.

Aloud she asked remotely, 'Why didn't you tell Melly that I'd been in contact with Trent?'

'I didn't want her upset. Mistakenly, I thought that not even Brigit would be meddlesome enough to invite him,' Rafe told her, before asking silkily, 'did you put her up to it?'

'How could I?'

'Oh, I'm sure you're clever enough to manipulate her into it,' he said, giving her a blazing predatory smile which should have sent her shrieking from the room. His teeth showed white against the dark skin of his face and her skin heated into fire as she went under in a surge of pagan need, limitless, unrestrained.

Her ears rang with his low, fierce laughter. One arm encircled her, holding her pinned against his lean, hard strength. Jennet made a little bracing movement of her shoulders as if to carry a weight too heavy for them, and his arm tightened. Across the room Derek looked up and for a moment an expression of such dark malevolence distorted his face that Jennet flinched. Instantly it was gone, replaced by a smile which was almost normal. Oh God, Jennet thought, oh, what have I done?

Dinner seemed to drag on for hours. Lacking Te Puriri's enormous table and dining room Brigit had sensibly opted for a buffet, serving a meal which was surprisingly free from pretension. Jennet had no appetite, but Rafe insisted on filling her plate with delectable pieces of sesame chicken, some pasta salad and fresh asparagus. He refilled her wine glass as well as his own before bearing her off to sit on a small sofa in an almost secluded alcove.

Jennet eyed her plate with disfavour. Her stomach was churning, but she nibbled small portions, limiting herself to no more than half a glass of wine. Not so Derek, she noted with a chill. He appeared to be in tearing good spirits, talking a lot, eating practically nothing, and already as she watched he had disposed of four glasses of wine.

Beside him Melly was trying hard to hide her unease. Jennet knew exactly how she felt. Although more than anything else she wanted Derek off-balance, she could not help shrinking as she watched him, his gestures a little larger than life-size, eyes unnaturally bright in his flushed face.

Not too far away Trent Addison waited, his presence a safeguard for Melly in spite of the fact that just by being there he added fuel to Derek's rage.

'Time to go,' Brigit called, carefully averting her eyes from Rafe. 'We can't be too late!'

The Takapo Valley hall was large, a relic of the days after the Second World War when every community, however small, erected some sort of War Memorial. Hollingworth money had provided the wherewithal to build large and opulently; on a big kauri shield were engraved the names of all those who had died in that conflict. Two of the golden lines were Hollingworths, Dougal's older brother and a cousin.

But there was no sadness tonight. A committee had decorated the building with great bowls of spring flowers and greenery, the walls were lined with tables, nightclub style, and the entire district was determined to enjoy themselves and had dressed up in their most elegant clothes to just that purpose.

Even the band, brought up from Auckland, had allowed themselves to be persuaded to keep the music to a reasonable sound level.

The first dance was pre-empted by Rafe. Ignoring Jennet's protest he led her on to the floor, with a twisted smile, holding her so that she was pressed against him and slowly, inevitably, she responded to the insidious spell of his virility, stimulated almost beyond bearing by the play of his muscles as he moved, the effortless strength and grace, his potent aura of sexuality.

Holding herself rigidly she tried to pull away.

'What's the matter?' he asked in apparent innocence.

'I'm not in the market for dalliance,' she retorted, her lie achieving the colour of truth.

'I don't want to dally with you,' he said smoothly, tightening his arm so that she was brought up against him again. 'I want to take you. I want to own you so completely that when any subsequent lovers get you into bed it will be my face you see behind your eyelids, my name you call them by, my body you crave.'

Appalled, Jennet's lungs whistled as she dragged breath into them. Her head moved in swift negation but nothing could blunt the searing impact of his words. She did not need to look at him to comprehend his primitive elemental lust for the essence of her which even the restraints of civilisation could not control. He had shown her the hidden depths of his soul and she was terrified.

'No,' she said in a low voice.

'Oh yes. And you feel the same way. That's why it's

no use saying the multiplication table or quoting poetry to yourself to take your mind off me. You can't hide. The only poetry that comes to mind are love poems, and the sort of multiplication that I intend is strictly between two.'

Colour rioted through her skin and she groaned and turned her hot face into his shoulder.

He ended the small silence by muttering in a savage, goaded undertone, 'I want you, Jennet. I don't care what you are or what you're doing here. Why can't you accept that as your triumph and leave poor Derek alone?'

'Because I can't,' she said sadly, lifting her face to his. 'Rafe—I——'

As her voice faltered and then died away she saw his regard change, become transformed into contempt and scorn. It had held a quality close to tenderness; now he looked like a pirate, reckless and cruel, flaunting his vital charisma with no hint of mercy.

'Very well then,' he said between his teeth. 'You've made your bed. I hope you don't find the lying in it too painful.'

The music stopped then and he took her arm, threading his way through the dancers with less than his normal courtesy.

From then on the evening began to resemble those dreams marked by a series of scenes, isolated, unconnected, yet so vivid that when the sleeper wakes each one is like a picture in the brain. She danced with Rafe again, with most of the men in their party. Jennet knew that she laughed and talked, she must have made sense, but the moment the words left her mouth she couldn't remember what she had said.

Once she danced with Derek, suffered the alcohol smell on his breath and his greedy hold on her; she kept her eyes lowered so that she didn't have to face his glazed eyes.

They spoke little, but halfway through the dance he stopped moving, standing still in the middle of the floor oblivious to the startled stares from those around them while his eyes followed Melly's progress as she was whirled around in Trent's arms.

'Bastard,' he muttered, white beneath the alcohol flush.

Somebody called something to him and he realised where he was and swore and took Jennet back into his arms. But when the music stopped he left her, plunging through the dancers with complete disregard for them.

At some stage Trent solicited the next dance. Flashing him a meaningless smile she rose and went into his arms while a little distance away Derek finished yet more wine and set his glass down with a small crash on the table.

'Enjoying yourself?' Trent murmured. He had a deep, rather gravelly voice.

'Not in the least.'

'Then allow me to congratulate you on your excellent acting.'

'Oh Lord,' she groaned, 'I wish tonight was over. Trent, I'm so frightened.'

Like most strong men he was intensely protective. 'Listen,' he said urgently, 'You must not let him catch you alone. I'll be watching——'

'*No!* You stay well out of it.'

'I don't like it.'

'Neither do I,' she shivered, 'but there's no other way. Do you think I haven't tried? He's guarded his back too well. Thank God he's drinking. He was—well, alcohol always loosened any inhibitions he might have had.'

'You'd think with all that he has at stake, he'd have kept on the wagon tonight.'

With sombre intensity she said, 'He doesn't think he has anything to worry about. He's convinced Rafe, you see, and he must know that I haven't told Melly about—about the violence. He thinks he's home and dry. The only thing that is worrying him is your presence, and that is what is going to push him over the edge.'

His hand clenched on hers, making her wince. 'Sorry,' he said abruptly. 'Correct me if I'm wrong, but it seems to me that you are trying to tell me that you expect him to—attack Melissa.'

'Yes.'

'No,' he said softly. 'I won't allow it.'

'It has to be that way,' she hesitated, then went on urgently, 'he's already angry with her. Look at them now; they're quarrelling. Melly is not a meek, milk and water miss, she won't back off if he wants a fight.'

'No,' he repeated harshly.

'Trent, I'll try to deflect him but—at least promise me that you won't interfere.'

'No.'

She bit her lip. 'Then you run the risk of ruining everything. I honestly believe that even if he hits me she'll think I deserve it.'

He gritted out an imprecation, then said with such reluctance that she didn't quite trust him, 'Very well, but I don't want her hurt.'

'That's what this is all about,' she said wearily. 'Remember?'

His eyes softened. 'Yes, of course I do. I'm sorry. This must be absolute hell for you.'

She looked very seriously into his raffish, striking face, saw there a desperation which told her far more than his words. 'No,' she said carefully, 'it's not too bad. He can no longer hurt me——'

'If he marries Melissa, won't that hurt?'

Her shoulders lifted. 'That's why we must provoke him beyond bearing tonight. There'll be no other chance.'

'Then why won't you let me——'

It was her turn to interrupt. 'I don't want him dead,' she said tonelessly.

He was silent for some minutes after that before he said in quite a different voice, 'What will you do if this doesn't come off?'

'Tell Rafe, impress it on him. He won't believe me but he'll keep an eye on them.' She smiled wryly. 'Like all strong men he's very protective and he and Melly love each other. She'll go to him.'

'What is it between you two?'

'You have obviously noticed that Rafe and I do not get on.'

There was a note of cynical amusement in his voice as he said. 'Then why does he watch you as if you are his only chance of salvation? I've seen him with quite a few women, at least one of whom he was having an affair with, and he's never wasted that kind of emotion on any of them.'

'Pull the other one,' she said pleasantly.

He grinned, but obeyed her unspoken command and dropped the subject.

And then it was the last dance and Rafe swept her on to the floor. He held her loosely but she could sense the leashed anger vibrating through his lean, elegant body. The aura of danger which had kept her alert all evening suddenly hovered ominously over her, like some elemental act of nature.

Not once did he speak. Occasionally she lifted her eyes to let them linger on the rigid line of his jaw; his eyes were narrowed slivers of jet. Beneath her hand taut muscles spoke of tension and control. And something else. He was, she thought warily, on an adrenalin high, prepared for danger, wary yet confident as a beast of prey threatened in its own jungle.

Somehow Melly came home with them. The atmosphere in the car was brittle and crackling but all three remained in control. About fifty people arrived at Te Puriri, determined to keep the party going. Although exhausted Jennet slipped into her role as co-hostess with Melly, unobtrusively watching Derek who had arrived with a noisy group of people and who was still drinking, albeit more slowly. She knew the signs, only too well. He was in a white rage, fuelled by alcohol and Melly's aloofness and Trent Addison's presence. Always such a fury had escalated into violence.

Rafe, too, was watching him. He was too astute not to recognise that something ugly was brewing in spite of Derek's ready smile and boisterous high spirits. Once Rafe's eyes met Jennet's; she thought that there was a gleam of comprehension in their cold brilliance, but as he turned away immediately she couldn't be sure.

Here, amongst his neighbours, he was an urbane host, upholding the station's traditions of hospitality. This was not one of the grand occasions when Te Puriri's guests flew in by plane or came in opulent cars and displayed the sort of jewellery which normally saw only the interior of safes and bank vaults, but it was when Te Puriri revealed its true self, a working station in a farming district. And Rafe stood out head and shoulders, the big man of the district, as he would be anywhere.

The party had by now entered a noisy phase when only singing, it seemed, would satisfy many of the guests. A shy woman, a newcomer to the district, was coaxed towards the piano. Blushing, smiling, she looked rather helplessly towards Rafe.

'I can't,' she protested. 'It's a beautiful instrument.'

He gave her a smile which visibly stopped her in her tracks. 'It's tough,' he told her, 'And I know that you are a musician. Don't worry, no one will park their glasses on it.'

'They'd better not,' she returned, emboldened, as she sat down before it.

Rafe was right. She was an excellent musician. On some less boisterous occasion Jennet would have liked to hear her play up to her level, but tonight she was asked for *Tavern in the Town*, and from there swung into other songs, both old and modern, all eminently singable.

Draining the mineral water which was all that she had been drinking for some hours now, Jennet's eyes traversed the huge room which had once been a warren of pantries and sculleries and laundries. Diana had seen the potential and had them transformed into this huge room, perfect for this kind of informal entertaining. On more formal occasions the drawing-room and the ballroom were used.

Everyone—almost everyone, she corrected—appeared to be enjoying themselves. Those who didn't want to sing were clustered at the other end of the room, talking. A high pitched laugh drew Jennet's eyes to a woman in a blue skin-tight dress who was flirting rather desperately with Trent, clearly fascinated by his saturnine smile. No one had obviously drunk too much. Not even Derek ... slowly, as inconspicuously as possible, her gaze searched the room. No sign of Derek. Or Melly. Unconsciously her teeth worried her lower lip. Rafe was talking to an elderly couple, his charm never more apparent.

Where was Melly? She couldn't have been gone long, otherwise Trent would have been gone too. Jennet didn't trust him to keep the promise she had extracted from him, not if he thought Melly was being hurt.

Moving with a little less than her usual grace, willing herself to be inconspicuous, Jennet made her way to the door. Outside in the hall the muffled noise from the singers, now cheerfully rendering the *59th Street Bridge Song*, prevented her ears from picking up any other sounds. Moving down the hall she shook her head, trying to clear her hearing.

Suddenly her head swivelled. Had that been a small, choked noise coming from—where? Silence, during which she held her breath. Yes, a kind of moan followed by a man's voice. Derek's voice, and it came from the boudoir. Treading softly as a cat Jennet headed for the closed door. There was no further sound. Nervously her fingers twisted the handle.

Even though she knew what was happening behind that door the reality made her drag in a sharp painful breath. Melly was hunched over, her mouth open, eyes glazed in the intense self-absorption that only pain brings. Her hands were clasped together below her breast and little, choking noises were forced through her lips as she gasped for breath.

Derek had hit her in the solar plexus. He was standing with his back to Jennet, his hands cupped at his sides. As Jennet began to move he grabbed Melly's black hair, dragging her head up to meet his. Her face was contorted with terror and pain.

'You little bitch,' he said lightly, almost pleasantly, and slapped her face.

Melly made a pitiful attempt to ward off the blows but he laughed and jerked her wrists away.

'Leave her alone,' Jennet ordered thinly.

He froze. Then, slowly, he dropped Melly's hands and turned, his face blazing in cruel exultation.

'Well, well, well,' he said, smiling, as he came towards her, stalking her.

He looked like a demon, almost beside himself with the rage she remembered so well. Yet there was a dreadful restraint about him, and she remembered that, too.

He was not expecting resistance. Why should he? Like Melly, Jennet had only ever tried to protect herself from his hands and those attempts, feeble though they were, had always maddened him into further violence.

So he walked confidently towards her, still smiling, even handsome if you didn't look behind the false persona he had manufactured so skilfully. Only his eyes gave him away, glittering unnaturally, and his hands, balled into fists.

Jennet waited. At exactly the right moment she kicked, aiming at his most vulnerable part. He saw her intention and twisted sideways so that her foot missed its target. His hand lunged for her ankle but she was too quick and stepped back, rocking on her heels. He kept coming and she blocked his swinging fists and brought her knee up. An obscene grunt tore at his throat; his hands covered himself and he began to collapse on to his knees, eyes glazed.

Melly burst into a torrent of tears and flung herself into Rafe's arms as he came in through the door like a dark avenging angel. Above the tangle of Melly's hair Jennet, pale now, and trembling, met the bitter anger in his eyes as she rubbed the forearm Derek had hit.

'Hush, love,' he said soothingly, pulling Melly into his arms. 'It's all right, it's all over . . .'

'Oh, God,' Melly sobbed into his shoulder. 'He—he hit me . . . he said . . . he said I was flirting . . .'

'It's over,' Rafe repeated, his voice revealing none of the savage anger which was stark in his forbidding expression, 'Don't cry, Melly, it's finished.'

On the floor Derek made a retching noise. Jennet's eyes were fixed on Rafe's long fingers as they moved rhythmically across Melly's back, but she thought light-headedly that the lessons in self-defence had paid off. Then the blood drummed deafeningly in her ears. She swayed, put out a hand to steady herself on the back of a chair and bit her lip. Her eyes cleared and she straightened. Avoiding even looking at Derek she moved across to where Melly still wept in Rafe's strong arms.

'Come on, Mel,' she said quietly, her voice flat and emptied of feeling. 'I'll take you up to your room.'

With a shaking hand, Rafe smoothed the tumbled curls back from Melly's forehead. As he put Melly away from him he looked into her wet, stricken face with such bleak savagery that Jennet shuddered.

When she came down the stairs reaction had set in, and she was cold and aching. She hesitated for a moment outside the boudoir door, looking along the hall to where sounds of singing denoted that the party was still going strong.

As she watched the door opened and Trent came out, his expression aggressive.

'No,' she mouthed, shaking her head, but although he checked when he saw her, he didn't stop. Quickly she went to meet him.

'What the hell's happening?' he demanded.

'It's over,' she said with swift certainty.

'Melissa?'

'She's asleep,' she answered his unspoken question. 'She's all right, Trent. Upset, but not shattered. I don't think she was in love with him, really.'

'Of course she wasn't. She's in love with me.'

Jennet smiled a little wistfully at his unconscious arrogance. 'Well, if she is, she'll be fine. Hasn't Rafe come back yet?'

'No.'

'Oh. Well, can you sort of act as—as host? I know it's an imposition, but—we should be back soon.'

He hesitated, then gave her a wry, self-mocking smile. 'O.K., I'll subdue my instincts.'

Jennet sighed as she turned back to the room where she had left the two men; she hoped that Trent would get his desire.

Inside the boudoir, Derek was sitting on the sofa, his head in his hands, breathing stertorously. Rafe lounged against the wall with his hands in his pockets. Those wide shoulders were slightly slumped and the spare, chiselled lines of his face hid any emotions.

Both men looked across as Jennet came in but it was Derek who spoke first.

'I should have finished you off when I had the chance,' he said thickly; the words were barely distinguishable and his face was distorted, manic.

Rafe's voice cracked across his like a whip. 'That will do,' he commanded, and when Derek subsided into silence he asked, 'How is she?'

'I just gave her a sleeping pill. It worked very quickly.'

'Was that wise?'

She nodded. 'It was a mild one, and she drank very little during the evening. I was watching her. It won't harm her.'

It hurt to look at him. She had wanted to be vindicated in his eyes, but not at such cost. A less controlled man might have shown his feelings, but Rafe's head was like a bronze bust, the cold perfection of his features successfully hiding all emotions but an incredible tension. Even his eyes were hooded, the long long lashes casting curling shadows beneath them.

'So,' the deep voice said tonelessly, 'what do we do now?'

Derek blustered, 'You have no right——'

'Shut up,' Rafe said. He could have been reading a list, but something in the even, dispassionate voice stopped the other man's protest without a second's hesitation.

'Will she testify against him?' The black eyes met hers above Derek's head.

What did he want? Derek shot to his feet, hands clenching ominously at his sides as he turned to face Rafe. Once Jennet would have trembled at this, distraught with terror. Now she watched without emotion, and thought serenely, I'm free, and wondered why she wasn't lyrical with joy.

'You can't do that,' Derek threatened, flushed now,

his head thrust pugnaciously forward. 'Who the hell do you think you are, you bloody—just because you're the high and mighty Hollingworths you think you can do anything. Well, just try it! She won't testify against me.' He swung back to stare at Jennet. 'You never did, did you, Jennet? A woman can't——'

'But Melly is not your wife,' Rafe pointed out with insulting indifference. 'What did you do to her?'

Jennet told him. Again Rafe ignored Derek's protest, his deep voice clear and flat in the sullen silence.

'Well, will she testify?'

Again that commanding stare. Slowly, feeling her way, Jennet said, 'Yes of course she will, Rafe, if you want her to. There's no way she'll marry him now.'

'Christ,' Derek said, the soft word slurring through lips which were suddenly slack as he lunged towards her. 'I'll kill you, you bitch, I'll——'

'Lay one finger on her and I'll take you apart.' Rafe's voice was so heavy with menace that the hairs on the back of Jennet's neck stood up straight.

It stopped Derek. He turned from Jennet to the man who watched them both, baring his teeth. 'Yes, you want her,' he said viciously. 'You've always wanted her, haven't you? You won't get any joy out of her, you fool. She's all come-hither, she turns your guts to water with wanting her but it's like taking an icicle to bed.'

There was a moment of quiet, humming with danger. Rafe didn't move, not a muscle, not an eyelash, yet Jennet felt a wave of emotion emanating from him.

'If you beat the hell out of her, it's no wonder,' he retorted offensively. 'I don't have the same trouble.'

Jennet's breath stopped in her throat. With dilated eyes she watched as Derek's body tensed but he too was aware of the danger Rafe represented.

'She's a cold bitch,' he said unevenly. 'A tease. My God, you've seen her in action, man. She's spent her time playing us off against each other. I'll——'

'You'll do nothing.' The words crackled across the silent room. 'Jennet is no longer your wife. And you'll not get your hands on Melly, either.'

The smooth, pale head shook from side to side as if Derek was trying to clear his thoughts.

Remorselessly Rafe continued. 'It's over. You've lost everything. After the court case you'll be branded as a wife-beater, you'll be less than nothing. People despise bullies. There'll be no chance of you marrying again without someone filling any prospective wife in on the details of your—aberration.'

Derek swayed back on his heels, his face livid. One hand tightened into a fist, but when he looked at the frightening dark figure that was Rafe, the fingers straightened again. He cursed under his breath.

Without mercy Rafe's deep voice resumed, 'Your friends will avoid you, you won't be able to show your face at any parties. No more ski trips, no more . . .'

'Rafe, no!' Jennet didn't know why she objected. With implacable accuracy Rafe had chosen to attack in a manner guaranteed to drive Derek beyond reason.

Now he made a thick noise in his throat, glaring at Rafe with murder in his eyes. He looked like a maddened bull the moment before it closes its eyes and charges.

'You won't be welcome anywhere,' Rafe taunted and at last moved, turning his back on them in a gesture as deliberate as it was insulting.

So it was only Jennet who saw the fury in Derek's expression transmute into something else, an emotion she didn't recognise. For a moment he hesitated, staring at the broad shoulders and athlete's body of the man who had so accurately pointed out his future, and then he turned his head so that he was looking at Jennet.

'If you'd loved me . . .' he said incredibly, his tone almost pleading. 'I wanted you to love me. You drove me mad . . .'

Jennet closed her eyes in pain, recognising that he spoke what he thought was the truth.

Her tacit rejection was met with a harsh indrawn breath before he swung to face Rafe once more. 'As for you,' he said with gloating emphasis, 'you'll rot in the kind of hell she put me in. And I'll laugh ... I'll laugh ...'

A moment later he was gone.

'Where are you going?'

Rafe's voice hurt. Jennet stopped in her headlong rush towards the door.

'We can't let him go like that,' she begged, her glance agonised. 'He was beside himself. Rafe?'

As he moved with swift litheness towards her she flinched away from the anger in him, afraid of him as she had never been of Derek's violence.

'Oh, *don't*!' he jerked out, trying to speak calmly. His hands enveloping her shaking ones, the thumbs rubbing over the fine skin, his mouth twisting in torment. 'I wanted him to try to take me,' he admitted harshly. 'It's just as well he's a coward. I'd have killed him and enjoyed doing it.'

The self-contempt in his voice, and that deadly, cold anger, made Jennet wince. Each stark word hit her like a blow.

'No,' she whispered, trying vainly to pull her hands free so that she could cover her face, that collection of features which had been the cause of all this. Derek's appeal had burnt into her brain.

'I wish I'd never been born. So much violence ...' Guilt closed her throat.

'What the hell are you talking about?' When she couldn't reply, wouldn't meet his eyes, he insisted, 'Answer me, Jennet. You stupid little fool, how can you blame yourself?'

'You heard him,' she said quietly, staring with empty eyes at their linked hands as he pressed hers against the hard wall of his chest. Beneath the silk of his shirt she felt the heavy beat of his life force.

'I didn't love him,' she explained hopelessly. 'I never did. When—after we were married, I couldn't—he . . .' The words dried on her tongue. How could she explain to Rafe what she had only just realised herself, that her heart had been his since she was sixteen!

'Come and sit down,' he said, sliding his arm around her waist to urge her across to the sofa. 'Poor Jennet, you're shaking. I'll go and get you some brandy.'

'No,' she said, but he returned with a half a glass of it, the savage anger subsiding as he gentled her, coaxing her to drink it.

'We should go back,' she protested.

He gave her an extremely sardonic smile, the frightening stranger gone, once more the Rafe she knew so well. 'We're not being missed. Everyone's having a marvellous time singing ribald songs from their university days, with Addison in charge.'

'Oh,' she said faintly and sipped the brandy, welcoming its biting strength.

When it was half gone he said, 'Thank you for coming back, Jennet.'

Waves of tiredness submerged her, floated away with the inhibitions which had kept her silent for so many years. 'It—I felt I had to,' she said slowly. 'I went to a psychiatrist when I got Diana's letter telling me they were engaged. He said that Derek would probably beat Melly as he did me and I couldn't bear that thought. I didn't want to come back but I had to.'

'How did it start?'

'Right at the beginning.' She sighed, lashes dropping, her mouth very vulnerable. 'You know, every magazine tells you that with all the sport girls play, the first time you make love is a breeze. It is, too, for most girls. It didn't happen that way with me. I fainted. Afterwards I realised that that was the first sign. He seemed—elated, in a queer sort of way. I thought it was because it proved that I was a virgin. How could I know?'

'How could you indeed?' His voice was very gentle, not like Rafe at all. 'Finish the rest of your drink.'

Obediently she swallowed it down, accepting, even welcoming the fact that it made her head swim. She was floating, disassociated from that quiet voice and the man whose arm held her against his shoulder.

'After that it was hell,' she said remotely, closing her eyes against the hand which stroked the nape of her neck. 'By the time we got back from the honeymoon I dreaded making love. And he liked that, too.'

Rafe muttered something ugly under his breath and shifted, taking the glass from her. His other hand covered her twisting writhing ones in her lap. He had discarded his coat; beneath the silk shirt he was very hard and warm.

Sighing, Jennet said, 'I know now that he's been conditioned to see violence as a solution, but at the time all I knew was that I was terrified of him and I was— alone. I didn't know what to do. I did realise that in some strange frightening way it excited him to hurt me.'

It was impossible to open her eyes; they were heavy, stuck together. Her skin prickled as she recalled the dread Derek had roused in her.

'Go on,' Rafe prompted evenly.

'The first time he actually beat me was after a party. He'd had a few drinks although he wasn't drunk. He said I'd spent the evening flirting with someone. I tried to defend myself but it was useless, he just got angrier. So after that I only talked to the women. You must remember—you were at several of those parties that year.'

In spite of herself, her voice shook. Rafe's arm tightened. That the comfort was impersonal didn't upset her. He had misjudged her and now he was showing his remorse and the combination of brandy and adrenalin in her bloodstream was making it impossible for her to resist such a dangerous situation. Tomorrow things would be back to normal; not even tonight's traumatic events could expunge the fact that she was Diana's daughter and so suspect forever in Rafe's eyes. But for just this once she was going to rely shamelessly on his great strength to see her through.

'I remember,' he said without expression. 'Oh, yes, I remember very clearly.'

'So then he said that I made him look a fool because I didn't mix. In the end he didn't really need an excuse.' She dragged the breath into her lungs. 'You know, looking back I think I must have been insane with fear. I didn't know what to do. Diana was overseas—but I don't know that I would have told her even if she'd been here. It's incredible but he even managed to convince me that it was my fault. I didn't love him and he told me that he loved me, that I drove him mad because I was so cold.'

'Why on earth didn't you come to me? You must have known that I'd have helped.'

The harsh question made her flinch. Half beneath her breath she said, 'You—that was the year you were abroad so much. I think it was America you went to.'

'Don't try to condone my behaviour,' he said bleakly. 'I know why you didn't feel that you could expect any help from me. I was a blind, prejudiced fool. I should have noticed that something was wrong.'

'It wasn't your fault,' she whispered. 'I couldn't bring myself to tell *anyone*, Rafe.'

'But if I hadn't been so bloody censorious and arrogant . . . So *blind*, so wilfully, deliberately blind . . .'

'No, no!' She stared up into his face, dark now with torment and self-contempt. She couldn't bear that he should be wracked by such anguish. 'Rafe, don't! He was so clever. He made sure that there weren't any of the sort of bruises which might give him away. And if you remember, he was always charming to me in company; he used that charm like a weapon.'

'Oh, I remember,' he said grimly, his fingers clenching on hers until they hurt. 'I used to watch you . . .' He broke off abruptly.

Cuddled in against his shoulder, Jennet could hear and feel his breathing, taste the scent of him, masculine and exciting. The tender, sensuous stroke of his thumb across her palm was an erotic little caress which made her acutely conscious that she had to free herself before she was betrayed by her reactions.

'Rafe, we'll have to go back to the party,' she said huskily, forcing herself to straighten up. He let her go and she stood, one hand on his shoulder to support her rubbery legs.

He stayed sitting, his expression sombre, then looked up at her and smiled with bitter irony. 'You're right, of course. Hospitality is a sacred duty.'

If it was, he rather abused it. Within fifteen minutes everyone had left, most of them convinced that the decision had been theirs alone.

Even Trent had gone although the long, considering look he gave Jennet indicated that very soon she was going to have to tell him exactly what had happened.

CHAPTER TEN

RAFE and Jennet turned away from the door just as the telephone shrilled its urgent summons. Jennet felt a faint premonition of doom as Rafe picked up the receiver.

'Yes?' he said shortly. Then his expression changed into that hardness he wore to cloak emotion. His eyes fixed on to Jennet, slim and exhausted in her black dress in the dimness of the doorway. 'Where? Are you *sure*? How—oh yes, I see. All right, I'll be right down.'

'Rafe, what is it?'

He replaced the receiver heavily. 'That was Trevor Brown. He has the dairy farm by the Takapo stream. He heard a car go over the bridge. It was Derek.'

'And . . .?' She didn't dare articulate the words, as if saying them might give them substance, make them into solid realities.

'He's dead.'

She gasped, her hands flying to her breast.

'I goaded him into it,' he said harshly.

'No, Rafe.'

'You heard me. You stood there and heard me taunt him. I did it coldly and deliberately.' The cold mask hid his emotions, but she could feel the pain in him. 'I wanted to hurt him as you had been hurt. Instead I pushed him over the edge.'

Jennet ran across to where he stood. Her hands reached up, enclosing his lean face, the fingers curving around the high, stark cheekbones. Her voice was urgent yet very tender, compelling belief. 'Rafe, you didn't want him dead, did you?'

He focused on her face with difficulty. 'Didn't I?'

She stood on tiptoes, willing him to respond, to convince him in spite of the resistance she felt in his rigid body. 'Even if you did, darling, he has always been a bad driver, careless, pushing his luck, While we were married he had two accidents, I'll bet there have been several others since then.'

Slowly he nodded, his gaze lingering on the sweet curve of her mouth, the earnest conviction in her beautiful face.

'I'm sorry,' she said. 'Sorry that he's dead, but, Rafe, he would never have got help, would he? He was too arrogant. Sooner or later there would have been another woman like Melly and me.' Her hands slid down his neck, touched the dark hair at the nape before she hugged him fiercely to her. 'That psychiatrist I went to said that violence is self-perpetuating. Derek had probably been beaten as a child, or seen his father beat his mother. If he had children they would have grown up like him.'

'All that doesn't alter the fact that I sent him over that bridge,' he said raggedly.

Jennet took heart from the fact that he didn't push her away. 'Darling, it wasn't just you. He'd been drinking heavily then he was forced to face up to what he was and accept the fact that he'd lost Melly.'

His eyes swept her face as his hands moved slowly to hold her pressed against him in a fierce embrace without passion.

Slowly his head bent; into her hair he said quietly, 'Thank you, Jennet. You are—very kind. Don't wait up for me.'

He meant it, so, after stacking the glasses into the dishwasher, she went upstairs, her feet dragging slightly. She felt strange, unreal, a sensation which persisted while she undressed and went to see how Melly was. Resting quietly, Melly's face was smoothed by a deep, dreamless sleep. As she stood for a moment watching

her Jennet remembered Trent Addison's expression
when she had whispered that the engagement was off.
He hadn't smiled, but the clever, cynical face had
relaxed. Whatever he felt for this half-sister of hers, it
wasn't just the cold desire to seduce. Only time would
tell, of course, but perhaps Melly could find happiness
with him.

Quietly Jennet set off towards her bedroom. At her
doorway she hesitated, frowning. It was a cold night,
getting colder, and when Rafe got back he would be
freezing. She decided to put his electric blanket on.

Since he had become the owner of Te Puriri she had
never set foot in the suite of rooms set aside for him.
The bedroom was austere now, a far cry from the
mannered opulence of Diana's reign. Someone very
talented had decorated it in muted browns and blacks
relieved only by touches of gold. A highly dramatic
room, she decided, looping the belt of her dressing-
gown around one hand as she pivoted slowly, her eyes
taking in the huge bed, a wall of books, a splendid
modern chest of drawers, Italian by the smooth
sophistication of line and proportion, and an antique
secretaire which was equally sophisticated and just as
superbly proportioned.

In this room, in that bed, a woman's white skin
would have all the sheen and allure of a pearl.

'I love you,' she whispered to its absent owner, her
hand switching the electric blanket on then covering her
mouth as she yawned. The bed was immensely inviting
but some sense of self-preservation steered her to one of
the armchairs by the French windows. Yawning again,
she collapsed into it. Just for a second, she promised
herself, she would stay just for a few moments until she
summoned the strength to get back to her own bed.

Twice she caught herself nodding and jerked awake,
but the third time her pale head slid sideways across the
back of the chair and she slept.

The dream began slowly, as if she had woken up from a deep sleep. Her first sensation was of warmth and the smoothness of sheets against her skin and a feeling of well-being so profound that she smiled in the darkness and made a funny little noise in her throat, half grunt, half yawn.

She was in bed but she was not alone. Nothing touched her but she could feel the heat of a man's body, feel his presence.

In the way of dreams she knew that it was Rafe who lay breathing peacefully beside her. Freed from the constraints of reality she whispered his name into the darkness and was not surprised when he turned from his back to his side so that he lay facing her. She said his name again and put out her hand and touched his face, knowing by instinct where it would be. Against her fingers his skin was warm and slightly rough as she followed the hard line of his jaw. He said nothing but his hand came up to her shoulder, smoothing the skin, caressing the outline of her shoulder-blade and spine, all heaven in his touch. She sucked in her breath and her fingers trembled against the firm shape of his mouth. Slowly his hand found its way down the sensitive inner skin of her arm until his hand reached hers, holding it still against his lips.

He rubbed his jaw against the palm, a tiny abrasive movement which set her nerves tingling with delight. Then his warm mouth moved from finger to finger, kissing, biting gently, suckling, until her breath came swiftly past her throat and the steady beat of her heart began to pick up speed.

Yet except from his hand over hers and his mouth against it they were not touching. Only in a dream could such a small contact be the most tantalising caress that she had ever experienced.

From a centre deep within, heat began to build, a slow strange combustion that spread by degrees throughout her entire body, kindling fires in pleasure points of whose existence she had never known until now.

When his mouth left her hand she whimpered softly with disappointment, but he said unevenly, 'Touch me, darling,' and guided her fingers to the place where his neck met the bare width of his shoulder.

Only in a dream could she permit herself to respond so wantonly, only in a dream could she know that to skim her hand over the expanse of smooth supple skin was to give him exquisite pleasure, almost as much as it gave her to touch him. Her hand drifted lower, tracking pathways through the tangle of hair across his chest, explored the strong cage of his ribs, spread over the exact spot where his heart slammed into her palm.

The wall of his chest lifted, then fell as if breathing had become painful to him. Drawn by his strength and her need she moved closer to him, but still they were not touching, only her head was close enough for her lips to meet his throat. She pressed a kiss there, and wondered how it would feel to explore him with her mouth.

His skin was taut, slightly damp yet hot. Tentatively Jennet touched it with her tongue, enjoyed the masculine taste and touched it again while her hand slid down his ribs towards his hip.

'Do you know what you're doing?'

The question made her laugh. This was a dream, who knew what was going to happen in a dream?

Her lips moved against the skin of his throat as she told him. Her wide-open hand came to rest across his flat stomach. Beneath it the strong muscles tensed.

'Jennet,' he said in a strange, thickened voice.

'Hush,' she whispered, kissing up his throat and beneath his chin. 'I love you. This is all I'll have. Don't spoil my dream.'

He lowered his head, caught her mouth with his and

kissed the tremulous width of it, tiny soft kisses which stirred her unbearably so that she moaned into his mouth.

Then he said, 'Very well, I won't spoil your dream. I love you.'

Of course he did. That was what dreams were for. To give you the momentary illusion of happiness.

'Then kiss me properly,' she begged.

So he did and it was joy and ecstasy for this time there was no anger, no contempt, no driving need to conquer. His kiss was sweet. He coaxed her lips apart to taste the soft depths revealed to him yet she was not frightened or repelled, not even when he slid an arm across her back and pulled her close to him, and she realised that, like her, he was naked, and, like her, he was very, very aroused.

'You are so beautiful,' she whispered.

He laughed, a deep soft sound in his throat. 'Men aren't beautiful. You are the beautiful one, so beautiful I ache when I see you and my bones shake in my body with wanting you.'

Then he took the initiative, his mouth assessing the contours of her face, pushing her head back so that her throat was a bow for his kisses. She shivered as his teeth bit gently down the arc of it and without knowing what she did, her body twisted fiercely against him. In this dark bed, in this dark room, she knew exactly what she wanted, had wanted for years, and because it was a dream she could ask him openly.

'I want you to love me,' she whispered.

'I do,' he vowed, his breath searing across her sensitised skin. 'I will. It's going to be like no other time for us both.'

His words made her body leap into life, excited her to boldness. Smiling into the darkness she said, 'And you will never forget. Whenever you dream, you'll wish that I was with you, like this.'

'I have, for years,' he said on a groan. His hand slid across her skin to cup her breast.

Needles of sharp desire transfixed her with pleasure so acute that it was almost pain. Gasping, she twisted on to her back, her hands clenching on to his skin.

'Rafe,' she cried, shattering as her body writhed into abandon, 'Rafe, I can't—I want——'

'I feel like the lord of all things,' he muttered. 'As if this world and everything in it is mine because you are my world and from now on you belong to me.'

His mouth fastened on to her breast, closed over the erect nub, warm and moist and fantastically exciting. The gentle tugging made Jennet groan in anticipation and frustration, her body in flames, as her hands pulled at the smooth hardness of his shoulders, urging him silently to take her with the strength and power she had craved for so long.

'Please,' she pleaded, barely able to form the word because she was shivering with fever, forlorn, empty, racked by desire.

'Yes, now!' he said triumphantly.

Then at last she felt the weight of his body and knew the fierce rapture of his possession. She was overwhelmed by sensation yet it was fulfilment, soaring ecstasy which tore his name from her lips in an agony of supplication until her body convulsed beneath and about him and she went sobbing over the edge into darkness, his muffled groan echoing in her ears as his body trembled in ecstasy.

For of course it wasn't a dream. And she had known, right from the moment she woke. This was Rafe's bed, in Rafe's bedroom. She had just seduced him and it had been like a foretaste of heaven. And now would come the reckoning.

She lay with her breath catching in her throat, eyes tightly closed against him, weighed down by his still shuddering body while her brain screamed at her to run, anywhere, away from this shame above all others. But she couldn't move. His heart was beating so loudly that she could only just hear the heavy rasp of his breathing. When at last the frantic hammering of his heart began to slow to something like normality she tried to move away.

'No.' His voice was barely audible as though he was having difficulty speaking, but the hand that pinned her to the pillows was uncompromising.

'No,' he said again, more strongly. 'You're not going to leave me, not now, not ever again. I won't let you. This is real, Jennet, my heart's love, my dearest girl. I've waited so long for you. You've always belonged to me only I was too stubborn to accept it. Can you forgive me for that?'

Dumbfounded, she could not answer.

After a silent moment he moved, lifting himself on to the mattress beside her. She flinched as his arms crushed her against the hard length of his body, holding her in a grip as strong as death, as strong as love.

'Do you want me to beg?' he muttered into her hair. 'I'll do that. I'll do anything I must to keep you here. Only tell me again that you love me, tell me that you'll never leave me.'

She could not bear it. Tears burned beneath her eyelids and she choked.

Very quietly he soothed, 'It's all over, darling. It's all right. You're safe now.'

Sobs tore through her, heavy and cleansing, washing away the brittle crust the years had formed over her emotions. Rafe was wonderfully gentle, holding her tenderly until she was gasping and empty, snuffling miserably into the handkerchief he found for her.

'Oh, hell,' she muttered drearily.

His chest lifted in a soundless chuckle. 'Feel better?'

'I feel as though I've been through the wringer.' She stretched and gave a small squeak of shock, calling on flippancy to cover the profound emotional turmoil which his shattering disclosure had produced. 'All of me, you brute. What did you do to me? You don't know your own strength!'

'Not used to the exercise, darling?' When she flinched he muttered something beneath his breath and scooped her against him, his mouth on her forehead. 'Have there been any other men for you since you ran away from Derek?'

'No,' she said simply. 'I thought I was frigid. That's why——'

She was stopped by an enormous yawn and the conviction that she was talking too much.

But he prompted, with a hint of the implacable determination she knew well, 'That's why what?'

She capitulated. 'Why I was so shocked when I came back and you—and I—well, if you must know, I took one look at you and I was sixteen again and in all the turmoil of an adolescent crush. Every time I looked at you or you looked at me I went hot and cold and prickly. It was just as though the years between had never happened. I was furious and frightened and excited.'

'And now?'

'Oh, now.' A few hours ago she would almost have gone to her death rather than have him know this. 'Now,' she said sweetly, 'I love you.'

'After only three days?'

'I always have, since before I knew what it was all about. It's just deepened over the years.'

Very quietly he said, 'I don't mind if it's only desire as yet, Jennet. God knows I've done nothing to make you love me, I've behaved like a swine to you for years. And it's no excuse that everything I've said and done was because I loved you and despised myself for it. You want me, that's enough to build on. I'll do everything I can to persuade you into loving me but I want the truth now. There must be no lies between us, not ever again.'

So he still didn't trust her, or himself. It would take years for her to prove that she loved him, but she would do it. She was strong enough for anything!

She hugged him to her, moving so that she cradled the dark weight of his head against her breast, holding his strength to the softness of her body.

'Oh, I love you,' she said, resting her cheek on the crisp hair, her tone making the statement into a vow. 'I want you, make no mistake about that, but I'd love you if you never touched me again. It's lasted for more years than I care to remember, most of them spent away from you. I might stop loving you when I die, but I doubt it.'

'Darling,' he said thickly. 'Oh, my darling, I know. I'm incomplete without you, half a man.'

'Yes.'

How long they lay entwined in an embrace without passion Jennet didn't know. Perhaps they slept. If they did it was to wake in the same position.

She asked quietly, 'Why didn't you kick me out, Rafe?'

'I wanted to know why you'd felt forced to come back. I knew it wasn't just mischief.' He reacted to her astonishment with a smile, turned it into a kiss before saying, 'Oh, I had you tarred with Diana's brush, but although I refused to admit it, I've always known that you weren't that sort. To be completely frank, neither is Diana. She's totally self-centred, completely selfish, just as amoral as a cat and with a cat's blithe disregard for anything but her own comfort, but she had the virtues of her vices as well, and she didn't ever make mischief just for the fun of it. There was always a reason. And although she's malicious, she's never been vindictive. Neither have you.'

Shaken by his cruelly dispassionate judgment she

tightened her arms around him, leaning her cheek on to
his head. The stringy thickness of his hair was a
pleasant friction against her skin, the clean, tantalising
masculine scent of him stimulated her. Dreamily she
forced herself to listen to the deep beautiful voice.

'When I caught you off-guard, you looked haunted.
And although you hid it well, I sensed your fear of
Derek and it made me wonder. You've never been
afraid of me, and God knows, I've given you enough
cause.' He paused before finishing, 'And I was never
entirely happy with Melly's engagement to him. There
was nothing I could put my finger on, but something
didn't ring true.'

'Poor Derek,' she sighed. 'To die so young.'

'Yes.'

They were silent, each thinking of him, then abruptly
Rafe said, 'All the same, he could have done something
about it. He must have known that there was help
available for him if he asked for it.'

Which, it seemed, was going to be Derek's epitaph.
Even in love, Jennet realised her man was not anything
less than uncompromising and tough.

'Darling,' he murmured, 'you've got commitments in
Australia, haven't you?'

'Yes.' She told him what they were, a television serial,
a short season of one of Ibsen's plays.

'You'll have to honour them.'

'I'm afraid so.'

He sighed as he pulled himself up on to the pillows
and turned her so that she lay with her face against his
throat.

'Very well then,' he said. 'We'll have to get Derek's
funeral over and it would be cruel to Melly to marry
immediately. How the hell am I going to wait?' His
voice roughened. His mouth found her ear and he
began to whisper his need and desire. Words she had
never hoped to hear, soft blunt words which excited her

beyond belief so that her response was immediate and incandescent.

When next they lay at peace the cold grey light of dawn was trickling past the curtains.

'It will be good for our characters,' she told him sleepily, trying to raise her spirits. Then she spoilt it all by clinging desperately to him, burying her head in his shoulder. 'Oh, darling, darling, please take care. Don't go riding any horses and watch that damned truck doesn't explode again and be careful what you eat. I think I'll die away from you. I love you so. I love you so.'

'Hush,' he soothed, incredibly gentle, his hands trembling as they shaped her. 'My sweet lady, my soul's other keeper, don't cry. You be careful too. Watch out for maniac drivers and make sure nobody drops anything on to you from a skyscraper. And don't fall off the stage into the pit.'

'I promise.'

They kissed, slow, sweet, sleepy kisses to keep time at bay until they had to part, while outside every bird in the valley serenaded them.

After a while he asked urgently, 'Am I expecting too much of you? Can you be happy here, so far from any city? I couldn't bear it if you were unhappy. If you want to go on with your acting, we'll come to some sort of arrangement.'

If she had questioned the depth of his love, this effectively would have silenced her. That her uncompromising, ruthless Rafe should be prepared to surrender his primitive desire to be the centre of his woman's life, filled her with joy.

Pressing a kiss on to his chin she said, 'No, oh no. Acting has always been a stop-gap for me. I enjoy it and I'm quite good at it, but—does Port Arthur still run a good amateur dramatic society?'

'Yes.'

'Well then, I'll offer to help there. My real desire has always been to pot seriously. I'm better than quite good at that, and I'll improve. The owner of the craft shop at the Port told me that there are deposits of the right clay not too far away, and I'll have fun experimenting with glazes.'

She lifted her head to stare into the features which had always been so austere; the tender, amused adoration she saw there led to an alarming increase in her pulse rate.

'I suppose you'll want me to build you a kiln,' he teased, catching her chin with his finger.

'Please.'

He grinned and bent his head and kissed her, tracing the line of her mouth with the tip of his tongue. 'I can see that I'm not going to be able to resist you.'

'You don't have to any longer.'

'No, thank God. Darling, you don't know how good it is to feel you here, where you belong, after all these years. I should have recognised my fate when you were sixteen. It would have saved a lot of pain and misery all round.'

She shook her head. 'No, it wouldn't have worked. Nobody is ready for marriage so young. I would have bored you when you'd become used to having me in your bed. It's better this way.'

'It's certainly worth waiting for,' he said, making her blush with the narrowed intensity of his gaze, and the whispered love words that accompanied it, until at last it was time for them to leave the bed where their love had been consummated.

They were married on a glorious spring day in the small church in the valley where Hollingworths had prayed for generations.

Jennet wore pink the exact colour of the shadows in her hair, a soft, gently draped dress which revealed the slender elegance of her form while it gave her a little extra height. The colour and cut of the dress emphasised her striking beauty, but softened the potent allure that had been her despair. Melly, tall and slender in a deeper shade of pink, attended her. Derek's betrayal and death had left her numb, but she was fast recovering her normal spirits and she had asked to be Jennet's bridesmaid. Trent Addison was overseas, but letters arrived from him frequently and were answered with despatch.

At the altar, Jennet lifted adoring eyes to her tall, grave husband, met the leaping brilliance of his regard with a happiness which neither Derek's death nor Diana's presence could diminish.

Afterwards, in the hotel in Auckland where they spent that first night, before flying out to a friend's house on a tropical island in Fiji, they came together in a fire-storm of passion, all restraints gone.

'I'm sorry,' Rafe murmured huskily, when at last they lay quietly in each other's arms. His mouth touched the still heated skin where he had hurt her. 'I'm so sorry, my heart. It won't happen again, I promise, I swear.'

'I enjoyed it.' Jennet stretched like a sleepy cat, all temptress, her green eyes gleaming with lazy promise. 'And you bear a few marks, too. I like to watch you lose control and know that it's all my doing. Perhaps there's a little of Diana in me after all.'

He laughed. 'Gives you a sensation of power, does it?'

She had made a mistake mentioning her mother, though. Rafe's lashes hid the expression in his eyes but she sensed his withdrawal. He could not have forbidden Diana to attend her daughter's wedding, but it had angered him to watch her, still beautiful, still potently glamorous, dazzle the guests as she carried out the duties of a hostess with her usual confident *élan*.

Now Jennet's heart swelled as Rafe left the bed to

walk across to where champagne waited. Even in her mood of relaxed fulfilment, she felt a singing in her blood at the sight of him, so superbly balanced, his wide, smoothly muscled shoulders set above the tapering wedge of his body, the proud black head, the glowing, dark gold skin.

He was hers, and he loved her and she would die for him. Ghosts from the past could not be allowed to shadow their life together.

'I'm sorry I mentioned her,' she began, accepting the chilled, faintly golden wine. 'I'm sorry that she spoiled the wedding for you.'

He shrugged. 'Nothing could spoil the day I finally made you mine,' he said. 'Diana means nothing, is nothing, not now.'

Watching him over the rim of the glass, Jennet accepted that he was speaking the truth. Until that moment she had not realised how tense she had been. Now she sipped the cold, exquisite wine and felt her body relax into the pillows.

'Except that she's the mother of a very dear sister,' he said teasingly, 'and of the wife I love with all my heart. I should thank her. One day perhaps I will.'

'She won't be particularly pleased,' Jennet said slowly.

There was a touch of ruthlessness in his narrowed glance. 'I don't know that I ever made it my object to please Diana,' he said, adding unexpectedly, 'cctually, things could have been much worse. It was my father's tragedy that he allowed his desire for her to dominate and control his life.'

He came over and sat down on the side of the bed, the chiselled bone structure of his face softening into tenderness as he bent and kissed the hollow between her breasts.

'It wasn't her fault that I fought so desperately against exactly the same thing happening to me,' he said. 'I despised my father for his weakness; by the time I was seventeen I'd vowed quite consciously never to put myself in any woman's power. When I got to be twenty-three I thought I had my life under control. No woman had ever come close to me, I owned Te Puriri, I was all set to lead a bachelor's life until I could find the right sort of woman to give me heirs. A woman who wouldn't expect too much.' He laughed in self-mockery. 'Then you came home and all my smug satisfaction vanished like frost in sunlight, and I could see history repeating itself. I don't suppose you'll ever have any idea of what it was like for me those holidays. It didn't help to realise that you were every bit as conscious of me.'

'You were about as approachable as a hungry lion,' she said smiling, yet tender, as she traced the autocratic line of his jaw with her forefinger.

'That's vaguely how I felt.' His hand captured hers and he held it palm against his mouth. 'With a super-human amount of control I managed to leave you alone until that last day, but when I saw you lying like a dryad in your little dell, it was more than flesh and blood could stand.'

'I wouldn't have known,' Jennet said wistfully. 'You seemed fully in control until——'

'Until I was stupid enough to touch you.' He put his champagne glass on the cabinet by the bed, lifted hers from her hand and set it down in the same place. Then he swung himself on to the bed, sliding his arm beneath her shoulders to turn her to face him. 'And you responded so sweetly, with such innocent ardour, that I almost took you. I had to get the hell out of there, run away like a schoolboy caught stealing apples.' He laughed beneath his breath, 'And I'll never know where I got the strength.'

'But you are strong,' she said with quiet gravity. 'Strong and kind and generous.'

'How you can be so blind ...' He groaned and lowered his head to rest his forehead against hers. 'I know I've been all sorts of——'

'Hush.' Her fingers pressed his lips into silence.

His mouth moved into a kiss. Very quietly he asked 'Why did you marry Derek?'

'Oh, I don't know.' She sighed, choosing her words with care. 'I suppose—he made it obvious that he wanted me. I wasn't happy at university and Diana—well she was all for it. I was a coward and I took the easy way out. I think I knew that I wasn't in love with him but I thought—I hoped that we'd be able to make something of it. I was too young and stupid.'

He nodded, staring into her eyes as if he was trying to see into her soul. In his black depths there was pain and self-contempt and anger.

'I drank myself to sleep the night of the wedding,' he said.

'What??'

He gave her a twisted caustic smile. 'Don't look so shocked. I know you think I'm perfect, but I've committed all the usual stupidities. That night, after the festivities I retired to my room with a bottle and used it to stop myself from thinking of you in his bed. I literally couldn't bear to stay sober. I wouldn't give you away because I couldn't. I wanted you so much and I hated myself and you for the effect you had on me. I was a coward, and because of it we both suffered.'

Memories raced through Jennet's mind, somehow cleansed of pain and degradation. She hugged him close, resting her cheek against the short crisp hairs of his chest; the tactile sensations swarmed her blood and made her catch her breath.

A little half smile touched her mouth as her ear picked up the rapid increase in the rate of his heart beat.

Aloud, in a voice that was a little too even he said, 'What made you run away, finally?'

'Trent, of course. He arrived unexpectedly one night, just after Derek had hit me. Derek covered up, but Trent had seen—and heard—enough to work out what was going on. He left the next morning as he'd said he was going to. Derek went off to a sale in Kaitaia and as soon as he'd gone Trent came back. He just made it impossible for me to stay. He took me to friends of his in Auckland, made me see his lawyer, just took over.' She looked up into a face suddenly carved in granite. 'I know you don't like him much, Rafe, but I think he probably saved my life.'

'I didn't like him because I was bitterly jealous. He must have wanted you.' He held her startled eyes with his own, in a menacing stare. 'Did you sleep with him, Jennet? As a token of gratitude?'

Her eyes widened at the latent violence. 'No. *No*, Rafe! And he didn't want me. He knew Derek. He said that even as a child he was given to bouts of violent behaviour, that no one could control. He was sorry for me. He didn't touch me.'

He closed his eyes before forcing her head back on to the pillows with a kiss of savage intensity. Her surrender was complete and slowly the kiss was transmuted into tenderness and love. When it was over he lifted his head and made a small sound, his eyes fixed on the softly swollen contours of her mouth.

'How the hell am I going to prevent this bloody jealousy? It's barbaric, humiliating, yet I have no way to control it. I disliked Trent because I thought he'd had you. That's why I broke up his romance with Melly, such as it was.'

'When you learn to trust me you won't be jealous,' she promised.

He laughed at that, a soft, breathy sound which barely made it audible and brought his hands up to frame her face with a curious, gentle fierceness.

'I love you so,' he whispered, and it was all there in

his expression. His love was a fierce emotion, a strong, compelling force, predatory, even hard, yet in the tremor of the hands that cupped her face there was a rare tenderness and a vulnerability only she would ever see.

'I love you,' she said quietly. 'I wish I could tell you in a hundred different ways, but words can't do it, can they?'

'I can think of another way,' He smiled as his mouth touched hers. 'It doesn't involve much talking, but it gets the message across.'

Jennet felt his body harden, quicken against her, and the swift fire of her own response. Her mind visualised his face as it would be twenty years, forty years from then, and she knew with a great leap of the heart that whenever he looked at her it would always be with love, stronger than passion for all its strength, sweeter than tenderness for all its sweetness, rooted in both yet transcending them.

This, her heart told her, this is our world, and it is ours forever.

A WILLING SURRENDER

A WILLING SURRENDER

BY

ROBYN DONALD

MILLS & BOON LIMITED
Eton House, 18–24 Paradise Road
Richmond, Surrey TW9 1SR

*First published in Great Britain 1986
by Mills & Boon Limited*

© Robyn Donald 1986

*Australian copyright 1986
Philippine copyright 1986
Reprinted 1986
This edition 1990*

ISBN 0 263 76728 0

*Set in Monophoto Plantin 10 on 10.5 pt
19–9002–57387*

Made and printed in Great Britain

CHAPTER ONE

IT was his height which first caught Clary's eyes.
That, and the way the cool English sun summoned
flames from the tawny head held so confidently.

A sudden scatter of applause from the crowd
dragged her attention away from the tall stranger. Her
slim capable hands added to the polite clapping as a
flushed little girl tried to persuade her pony to leave
the ring with some dignity. Amanda was a perfectionist, so her failure to clear two of the jumps would
set her fretting for days. She would not, however, be
grateful for any open commiseration.

Clary's dark-blue gaze shifted from her oldest
charge to scan the crowd. Mostly mothers, except for a
few au pairs like herself holding the fort for those
parents unable to be there, they all looked similar to
Clary's antipodean eyes. Well-cut skirts and Husky
jackets, headscarves tied against the nasty little wind
amounted almost to a uniform. Even Mrs Crowe,
Amanda's mother and Clary's employer, a supremely
elegant woman, blended into the crowd.

Clary's roaming eyes found the older woman. With
every appearance of pleasure she was greeting the
stranger, smiling up into his dark, striking face with
open appreciation.

The tawny head inclined; there was a flash of white
as the man smiled in response and said something
which made Ginny Crowe and the two women with
her break into laughter. Leona Sedbury—*Lady*
Sedbury—smoothed a possessive hand over his
forearm, mutely stressing her position as his escort.

The soft lines of Clary's mouth hardened as she
took in the physical attributes which had sent every

woman within reach into a pleasurable little flutter.
His lean body, perfectly poised, was a sensual lure in
itself, but the face above it radiated a magnetism
which was frightening. The features were almost
classically perfect except for an arrogant beak of a nose
and an uncompromising mouth. Until he smiled, and
then ruthlessness was transmuted into a potent,
blazing charm.

Clary swallowed, recognising the odd tightening of
her nerves. One did not reach the age of twenty-five
without experiencing attraction, that primitive call of
one sex to the other which signalled virility and the
ability to impregnate. It was stupid to be so shaken by
a blind natural force based only on the need to
reproduce the species, but when the man smiled cool
sensuality had crackled into vivid life.

Clary had good reason to distrust that sudden flare
of excitement. In instinctive, involuntary defiance she
straightened her shoulders, her expression altering
into controlled indifference.

Perhaps it was the sudden movement, perhaps the
smooth sheen of sunlight on the soft bronze waves of her
hair which caught his attention. Eyes which were a
strange mixture of gold and green lanced across the
intervening space, assessed her coolly and com-
prehensively. Clary suffered the scrutiny of those eyes,
almost wincing as they took in the measure of her face
from the winged brows to the cleft chin which she and
her brother had inherited from their father. The
stranger's gaze probed the soft contours of her mouth,
the wavy cap of hair and the scatter of freckles across her
straight nose, the long lovely line of throat and neck.

No emotion disturbed the strong beauty of his face;
it could have been a bronze mask turned towards her,
yet Clary shivered, suddenly afraid. She sensed a
response to the wildfire which ate through her body.
For long moments they stared at each other across air
which was as charged with energy as an electrical field.

A quick flame of colour scorched across her cheekbones, the pale skin revealing too blatantly the swift rise of blood beneath it. Astounded, she watched as an answering wash of colour smouldered beneath his bone-deep tan. It was as though that sudden attraction was some incandescent element, dangerous and beautiful as fire.

Across the heated, shimmering distance between them his eyes sent a message with all the impact of a laser.

Clary stiffened. The brutal, honest admission of desire produced such brazen arousal in her body that it was revealed only too plainly in her resentful eyes as they were held pinned by his. He was intent on staking some claim, imprinting her with the glamour of his lean face and the swift feral grace of a body perfectly proportioned, perfectly balanced.

Yet even while she exerted the willpower to turn away it was with the knowledge that when she remembered him it would be the stark power of the man she would recall, not his physical beauty.

Fortunately her bewildered glance fell upon a disconsolate little figure in jodhpurs wending its way towards her through the crowd. Almost dizzy with relief Clary scooped up the younger Crowe, who had been bouncing impetuously in her pushchair.

'Come on, darling,' Clary said, 'let's go and meet Amanda.'

Holding Beth like a shield she took the few steps necessary to reach Amanda, who, like all true horse-lovers, immediately began telling her how badly she had let down her pony.

She was still in full spate when her mother joined them a few minutes later.

'Well, it's over now,' Ginny intervened briskly. 'Everyone has trouble at first, don't they, Clary?'

Fixed by her minatory eye Clary smiled. 'Never having jumped I wouldn't know, but the first time you tackle anything you make mistakes. That's how you learn.'

Mrs Crowe nodded as Amanda's upturned face lost its woebegone look. 'Clary's right, of course, even if she doesn't ride. Somehow one always assumes that every New Zealander grows up in the saddle, but you're a city girl, aren't you?'

'I am. New Zealand's biggest city, at that. A tiddler by the rest of the world's standards, but it's the nearest thing to a metropolis we've got.'

'It doesn't appear to be big enough to keep Morgan Caird occupied.' Mrs Crowe nodded towards the bold stranger who now stood on the opposite side of the ring with Lady Sedbury and her husband, the owner of the local manor house. 'Mind you, he's more like a force of nature than a man, which probably explains why he has interests all over the world.'

'He's from Auckland?'

'Yes. His grandfather and Sedbury's were brothers.' Which, her tone revealed, made him *one of us*, acceptable.

Clary hid her astonishment with a smile, fascinated as always by the ramifications of a social system she barely understood even after three years spent mainly in the United Kingdom.

Ginny caught her amusement and laughed, saying: 'Oh, you colonials! You always manage to look smug as well as puzzled when you catch us being snobs. I refuse to believe that you don't have some sort of class system in your antipodean paradise.'

'Of course we do.' Clary's response was equally light. 'It's not nearly so rigid, though.'

Mrs Crowe's slender shoulders lifted in a little shrug. 'Oh well, it's all good clean fun. I should have thought that Morgan Caird would be known to you, he's quite famous even here—and not just for his looks.'

'An actor?'

'Hardly.' Mrs Crowe reacted to the waspish little suggestion with faint surprise. Her eyes were perceptive as they rested on Clary's disciplined features. 'I believe he's what is known as an entrepreneur.'

Clary's gaze skimmed the baby's hair to arrive at the tawny head poised so arrogantly above broad shoulders. 'Really?'

'Really. Don't you approve of entrepreneurs? Have I discovered a chink in that egalitarian armour you New Zealanders wear so righteously?'

'Never met one,' Clary told her cheerfully. 'Don't they go around buying up businesses and sacking old retainers? Asset-stripping, or some such thing?' Clary was deliberately vague, deliberately flippant, hoping that her employer would take her words to mean that she disliked the man instead of being unbearably attracted to him.

'I think it's a lot more technical than that,' Ginny said drily. 'Something like bringing together money and ideas and expertise. Whatever, Morgan Caird is a very clever man who has done exceptionally well for himself.'

'I believe you.' He certainly possessed that glittering air of success, that total assurance which came perilously close to arrogance.

'A fascinating creature. Leona Sedbury wanted him to stay longer than just one night but he put her off. She made a teasing comment about the woman he has left in London; apparently she's a stunning creature but she doesn't like the country. Anyway, Leona stupidly said something about it being a pity, and got a polite but very definite snub for her pains. Leona is a silly woman but she got the message.'

It was unlike Ginny Crowe to gossip and she didn't wait for any response, turning away immediately to ask Amanda about the rider then in the ring. Altogether too percipient, Clary decided wryly as she

shifted little Beth from one hip to the other, smiling
tenderly at the tired, rosy baby face. Somehow Ginny
had divined that wild reaction in her au pair and had
delivered her warning. Morgan Caird was not free.

Well, in the pleasant routine of her life with the
Crowes Clary would soon forget that he had looked at
her with naked desire and that her own sexuality had
flamed up to meet it. It had happened before, it would
happen again, that strange fever in the blood which
some called chemistry and some desire. Clary called it
lust, and despised it. At too early an age she had seen
the havoc it made of people's lives, the ruin that the
careless satisfaction of that most primal of urges
brought in its wake, and she had no intention of
allowing her pleasant life to be turned upside down by
it.

I'll never see him again, she told herself very
firmly.

Still, she was not altogether surprised later in the
afternoon when Ginny appeared, her face totally
without expression as she said, 'Leona Sedbury has
just rung to ask if you would like to come with us to
her party tonight. It's all very impromptu, very
casual.'

It was nursery tea-time. Beth opened her mouth and
after a moment Clary popped the spoon into it, coldly
angry because her hand was shaking.

'I hope that you told her I was needed as a baby-
sitter,' she said shortly.

'No, I said that I was sure you would like to come.
Mrs Withers is quite happy to look after the children
and it will be nice for you to meet someone from
home, even if you don't like him much.'

Looking up sharply Clary met her employer's
amused glance with a wry expression. 'You're very
kind,' she said slowly, 'and probably right.'

'I often am. I shouldn't worry about Leona's
manners, either. She's quite impartial about those she

offends. Just put on a pretty dress—that coppery one would be very suitable—and enjoy yourself. You'll know most of the people there.'

Well, yes, but not socially. However Clary was curious as well as cautious and a party at Chase would give her something to write about in her next letter home. So she nodded and agreed, her mind going to the letter which had been delivered that morning. It was a strangely unsatisfying communication in spite of the breezy chattiness which was her mother's epistolary style. If she hadn't known her better Clary would have assumed that life at home was going on its usual pleasant way, but she could remember other letters disturbingly similar to this one, too cheerful to be true. Letters written to hide a broken heart; letters from a woman whose husband had left her for a much younger lover. Helen Grey had developed that particular style to hide the truth so that Clary could sit her University Entrance examinations without added stress.

As always whenever she thought of her father Clary's expression hardened into a frightening severity, until little Beth's whimper forced a smile and a remorseful cuddle.

'It was a long time ago,' she said gently, almost as if to reassure herself, 'and it's all over now. But oh, I wish I knew what's bothering my mama.'

Not that there was anything she could do about it. The twelve thousand miles which lay between them might just as well be infinity for all that she could do to bridge them. Suddenly angry with herself for having promised to stay with the Crowes another five months, she was consoled by the fact that whatever worried her mother she had Angus and Susan to support her through it.

Angus was so utterly dependable, bless him. He had been the perfect older brother, a little reserved perhaps, but completely reliable, as strong as a rock.

His wife was pleasant, although she too was reserved; Clary had met her a year ago when they had flown across to London for their honeymoon. She would have chosen someone warmer, more spontaneous and outgoing for Angus, but he had obviously been completely bowled over by his wife's fragile beauty, and Clary knew that the paths of the heart are not always easily understood. As always when she thought of Susan, Clary crossed her fingers in foreboding. Then she laughed and gave Beth another hug, saying cheerfully, 'All gone, my little bird. No more.'

Beth gave her an enchanting gummy smile and clapped her hands before holding out imperious arms.

'OK.' Clary released the highchair catch. 'Come on, honeybun, time for your bath, and then cuddles with Mummy, and then, chickadee, bed!'

The copper dress did suit her, Clary decided as she finished her toilet by spraying some of her precious 'First' perfume on her throat and wrists. The glowing copper lent warmth to her pale skin and the silky material swathed her body with loving precision, but it was subdued in design so she wouldn't stand out; with any luck she could spend a pleasant evening inconspicuously watching the county enjoy itself. If she did get to meet the guest of honour—well, they could discuss such peculiarly New Zealand things as sheep, and Rugby, and mountain-climbing . . .

Unfortunately for her decision to blend with the wallpaper Lady Sedbury greeted her as if she were a long-lost bosom friend and introduced her to Morgan Caird with the sly little declaration, 'Morgan is *very* anxious to meet you, Clary. He described you so graphically that I knew immediately who you were.' Her glance lingered on Clary's high full breasts, and the long line from hip to ankle with enough meaning to bring the angry colour to her victim's cheeks.

Clary lifted goaded eyes to Morgan's handsome face

but saw nothing there except an aloof appreciation. However bold his appraisal that afternoon, he was giving nothing away now, parrying his hostess's poisonous little dart with an impersonal courtesy which cooled Clary's anger.

Like well-trained actors the Crowes and he defused the situation with the kind of effortless good manners which should have made Leona Sedbury ashamed. It didn't. When the Crowes moved on, taking a thankful Clary with them, it was with the memory of malice in Lady Sedbury's smile and sleepy blue eyes.

However the first part of the evening was enjoyable enough. That same relentless courtesy ensured that no one evinced any surprise at the sudden social elevation of the Crowes' au pair, and after a while she found herself in cheerful conversation with a young married couple. They had relations in New Zealand and were thinking of going there for a holiday, so they were eager for information.

Clary obliged, trying hard not to allow her homesickness too free a rein, and thought she was doing rather well until she noticed that she had lost the woman's attention entirely. Sudden awareness widened the eyes which had been fixed on Clary's face; they looked past her now and one hand moved automatically to touch an errant lock, lingering there in a gesture as unconscious as it was provocative.

The deep crisp voice with its faint New Zealand accent fell painfully on Clary's ear as Morgan Caird greeted them by name. Good memory, she decided and stood without looking his way while he charmed both husband and wife. No doubt an entrepreneur would need an excellent memory. The charm would come in handy, too.

He had other skills as well, probably equally useful. She wasn't in the least surprised when after a short time she found herself alone with him, separated from everyone else by an exquisite screen; in fact, she almost admired the adroitness with which he disentangled them from the English couple.

'Superbly done,' she said. 'I'll bet you have no trouble in your boardrooms.'

He grinned down at her, appreciating the sarcasm. 'Very little I can't handle. Now, what part of New Zealand do you come from?'

The usual question, asked by all expatriates, however temporary. 'Auckland,' she told him remotely, concentrating very hard on the beautiful colours and textures of the silk screen. 'However, I haven't been there for some years.'

'Getting your overseas experience?'

Her shoulders lifted slightly, dismissively. 'Yes.'

Half of one of those years had been spent nursing in a refugee camp in the Far East, but he wouldn't be interested in that. Refugees, with their almost insurmountable problems, tended to embarrass most people. They felt guilty because there was so little they could do; they didn't want to hear about children who starved or died of unpronounceable diseases.

'When do you go back home?'

Another small shrug. Still without looking at him she said, 'In the autumn. I promised my employers I'd stay until the baby is a year old.'

'When you picked her up today I thought she was yours.'

Something in the deep tones impelled Clary's glance towards him. She fell an immediate captive to the strange glittering depths of his eyes. He looked tense, those perfect features too prominently emphasised as though the skin had tightened over them.

Hastily she renewed her scrutiny of the screen. A peculiar shortness of breath made her unusually hesitant. 'I'm surprised that you were so explicit in your description of me to Lady Sedbury. Or do you not care whether a woman is married or not?'

'Oh, I care,' he returned, quiet voice at variance

with the hard authority of his features. 'But nowadays
a child doesn't necessarily mean a marriage. Then
there was always the possibility that you were no
longer interested in its father.'

'Do you do this often?' she asked with totally
spurious interest. 'I mean, I believe you're only going
to be here one night. I've also been told that you have
a girlfriend waiting for you in London. Can't you
spend even one night alone?'

The directness of her attack astounded her but she
refused to back down; instead her chin lifted a fraction
as she met his hard, bright glare.

His anger was clear. The wide sensual mouth had
tightened into a thin line, the handsome face suddenly
invested with an implacable authority which probably
had sent whole boards of directors cowering. Well, not
me, Clary thought with defiance.

And then the harshness dissolved into amusement
accompanied by an open, bold appraisal which made
her conscious of heat building in the pit of her
stomach.

'All that because I was crass enough to describe you
to Leona as well-endowed,' he said with smooth
mockery. 'I'm sorry. I also told her that you had hair
the colour of new gum leaves, and a curly, very
kissable mouth, that you were just the right height for
a man as tall as I am, and that the cleft in your chin
gives you an air of enchanting wilfulness.' A long sun-
browned finger detailed the cleft with a lover's touch
before moving to outline the sweep of jaw and the coil
of her ear.

Bewildered by the sudden rush of sensations which
held her in thrall, Clary blinked. Her throat was too
tight to allow any sound to escape; that warmth which
had begun in her stomach washed through the rest of
her body. Her last ounce of common sense told her
that she must look a perfect fool, staring mesmerised
into his face while he smiled down at her with the

masterful assurance of a man who knew he could break
hearts.

Hoarsely she muttered, 'I'll bet you didn't tell her
all that, either.'

'I may have missed out a few adjectives.' He moved
closer, broad shoulders shutting out the room and the
people behind him. 'I didn't tell her that your eyes are
the colour of the sheen on a tui's wing, or that there
are eight freckles on that arrogant little nose, either.
But I knew. And that your legs are long and slim and
shapely, or that your waist is excitingly curved
beneath those lovely breasts. I also didn't tell her that
I've discovered in myself a quite startling ability to
fantasise, and that, in the short time between the
moment I first saw you and now, I've already
overworked it! I daresay Leona would have understood, but she has this unfortunate habit of blurting
out the truth at the most awkward moments. Besides,
I wanted to tell you myself.'

Oh God, Clary thought desperately as his finger
stroked across her full bottom lip then moved up her
cheek to trace the high winging flare of a brow. This
had never happened before, this overwhelming
abandonment to sensation. Secure behind the walls of
her contempt for those who couldn't control their
sexuality, she had always been able to subdue the
inconvenient manifestations of desire.

Was this glowing flood of heat and fire what had
dragged her father from his wife's arms? Clary's scorn,
and the contempt she had felt for her father since his
love affair with a woman twenty years younger than
he, were replaced by a bitter comprehension. At that
moment Morgan Caird dominated her completely.
The cool logic which usually characterised her thought
processes was gone, swept away by a primitive,
animal need. All that was feminine—all that was
female—in her called to be taken by his male strength,
possessed and used and impregnated.

And then cast aside, she thought savagely, noting the glitter of triumph in the narrowed eyes, the hint of satisfaction in the curve of that disciplined mouth.

Stepping back she said harshly, 'Very pretty, Mr Caird. Unfortunately I'm not in the mood for ravishment by poetic phrases tonight.'

She expected him to be angry. At the very least he should have been irritated by her rejection.

But the infuriating man smiled almost sympathetically, as though he understood her panic, and took her hand and said, 'Then let's see if I can seduce you with the perfection of my dancing!'

She tried to jerk free but he was ready for such an obvious manoeuvre. As his fingers tightened she exclaimed, 'Ouch.'

'Sorry, did I hurt?'

He wasn't sorry, and he knew that he hadn't hurt her. That grip was his far-from-subtle way of asserting control as he guided her towards the room where music was projecting an insistent, potent lure. She was too tense to notice the covert glances they were getting from many of the guests. And when, in the dimly lit room, he turned her into his arms, she admitted to herself that she was really frightened.

Of course he danced well. That perfectly balanced athlete's body probably did everything well. Including making love. A hot shiver quickened her shallow breathing as a sudden image of him bending over her, of her flung wantonly across a great bed, was followed by even more explicit imagery, the contrast between her pale fine skin and the dark shading of his, his strength and her comparative weakness——

Oh God! she thought, pornography! In my own brain! Stiffly she pulled away from the body her own craved.

It was a tactical mistake. Until then he had been holding her fairly loosely but now his arm tightened and she was pulled into such close proximity that his

jaw brushed her forehead, the texture of his skin allied
to the strength of the frame beneath it making her
angrily aware of her capacity for eroticism. With
savage enjoyment she heard the sudden harsh breath
he gave, felt the moment when every muscle in his
lithe frame locked into rigidity.

'When are you going back home?' Yes, that was her
voice, so heavily regimented that it was expressionless.

'A fortnight from now.' He bent his head so that the
answer was almost whispered into her ear. His breath
was warm, sensuously activating nerves she had never
before known she possessed.

Taunted by his faint male fragrance she rested her
forehead against his neck.

'Come up to London with me,' he said thickly, the
words seemingly jerked from him without volition.

So this was temptation! Intuition told her that his
proposition was totally out of character. It would be
just as uncharacteristic of her to agree.

But oh, how to refuse when every nerve and cell in
her body begged for fulfilment?

'What about the girlfriend?' she asked at last in an
icily remote little voice.

'Oh God, she's not important. Nothing matters any
longer—but this.' He had guided them into another
secluded corner—later, when she recovered her sanity
Clary would realise that such expertise in discovering
these corners bespoke considerable experience—and as
he spoke his hand swooped down past her waist and
for a long moment her hips were forced against his and
she was left in no doubt as to his arousal.

Although she could not have prevented him he did
not attempt to kiss her, but his gaze burned across her
throbbing mouth. The clamour of her senses silenced
her. It was the most erotic experience of her life, yet to
onlookers it must have seemed as though they did
nothing more than dance, for they were still swaying
in time to the music.

'Stay with me,' he said between his teeth. 'Come back to New Zealand with me.'

She shuddered with longing, but shook her head.

'Please,' he whispered. 'Please, Clary, I need you.'

'You know I can't.' But her hand stole up to curve into the side of his face, her sensitive fingers feeling the life impulse at the austere temple, her palm over the sharply defined cheekbone, the heel of her hand sensitised to the muscles clenched along the strong jaw. Gold-green eyes blazed into hers, willing her, compelling her to surrender.

'I only know that this has never happened to me before.' The warm strength of his hand held hers in place as he turned his face into her palm, kissing it with a driving passion which had no place for subtlety. 'I looked at you and it was like being spun out of this time, this dimension, into one where the old romantic values hold true. Love at first sight, the princess in the tower, the enchantress who can snare a man's heart from his body. . . My God, if you'd been married I was going to seduce you away from your husband, and I have never had anything but contempt for men who sleep with married women! I must have you, but you terrify me . . .'

The thick, impeded declaration faded, as though he dared not face the implications of what he was saying. Shaken by the ferocious intensity she glimpsed in his face Clary fought fiercely to contain the whirlwind of response which raged within her.

'Then leave me alone,' she managed to whisper after a false start. 'I don't want this. I can't go with you, I have responsibilities here. And you have a responsibility to the woman who's waiting for you in London.'

He muttered something short and explicit beneath his breath then pushed her away. 'I won't let you escape so easily,' he said tonelessly, reasserting control over his emotions with an effort which showed. 'I can't dance any more with you, but there are other things we can do to fill in time. I want to know you, and not only in the Biblical sense.'

Heat scorched up her cheeks, ached through her body. On legs which felt as though someone had removed the bones, she walked with him into the room where those who didn't want to dance were occupying themselves with talk and flirtation.

I must be mad, she thought bitterly. Frustrated and ready for a fling with the first personable male who has shown an interest in me for a time.

'Relax,' he said, all the passion of a few minutes ago hidden by a sardonic smile. 'You look as though someone had punched you in the stomach.'

She managed to produce an answering smile, taking comfort that in this crowd it should be easy enough to lose him. So she greeted their host with equanimity, gracefully accepted his heavy-handed compliments and waited for an opportunity to get away.

Plenty came her way, but she got nowhere. From beneath hooded eyes Morgan watched and kept her right beside him, either physically with an arm across her shoulders or by making her such an integral part of the conversation that she could not slip away without being rude. By nature an observer rather than a participator she found it a strain, almost as much as an evening spent fighting off his advances would have been. When at last the Crowes came over she greeted them with a smile which beseeched help.

'We're on our way,' Ginny said, her shrewd eyes amused yet oddly sympathetic.

'I'm ready to go.' Clary mixed just the right blend of tiredness and regret into the words as she moved to separate herself from Morgan.

But no one outmanoeuvred Morgan Caird. He came to the car with them, and before putting Clary into the back seat he claimed both her hands, kissing one then the other, the backs first followed by a slow sensuous caress of both palms, folding her fingers over to keep the kisses intact.

'Until we see each other again,' he said, mockery almost hiding an undertone of raw emotion.

Very inadequately Clary said, 'Goodbye,' and almost fell into the car, scrubbing her hands against her thighs to rid herself of his touch.

From the front Ginny's laughter grated on her nerves. 'What style,' she exclaimed. 'My God, the man has everything!'

Except integrity. Bitterness stung Clary's throat and eyes. Freed at last from the spell of that overwhelming masculinity she was able to appreciate clearly just what sort of swine he was. *I must have you*, he had said, so intent on his own selfish desire that he didn't consider hers at all!

Thank heavens he was going back to London the next day.

She spent the night trying extremely hard to sleep, and failing. It was with enormous gratitude that she watched the sky lighten and heard Beth's early-morning whimper.

Routine was soothing, inducing in her enough composure to banish both her memories of the night before and the shameful fantasies which she had not been able to control in the sleepless hours in her bed. Unfortunately her calmness was shattered when the daily came in, looking interested and speculative.

'It's a man on the phone for you, dear,' she said, smiling. 'Sounds ever so like you.'

Clary set down her coffee-cup. Subconsciously she had known that he would contact her before he left Chase; with a stern expression she picked up the receiver.

'Clary? How did you sleep?'

'Like the dead,' she said.

His laughter was soft and knowing. 'Liar! I couldn't either. That over-active imagination of mine kept me awake. When can I see you?'

'You can't,' she said baldly. 'I mean it, Morgan. I don't want anything to do with you.'

'Well, that's a pity,' he observed, all humour banished from the deep voice so that it sounded flatly relentless. 'Why?'

'Because you frighten me,' she blurted.

That made him laugh, although there was no amusement in the sound. 'I frighten myself,' he told her. 'And you scare the hell out of me, but the only way to cure fear is to face it. So when am I going to see you next? I know you have this coming weekend——'

'No. Not then, not ever. *Never*. I don't want to have anything to do with you—with the sort of man you are.'

'And what sort of man is that?' he asked with silky clarity.

Clary shivered but went ahead just the same, venting her fear and frustration into the cutting words. 'The sort of man who propositions one woman while still entangled with another. And trying to convince me that she isn't important is not going to advance your cause any, either.'

'Clary.'

Just her name, spoken without emotion, yet she couldn't hang up. Her fingers ached with tension but the receiver stayed pressed to her ear.

'Clary,' he said again and this time she bit her lip at the implacable purpose in his voice. 'I won't let it end like this. Whatever there is between us is something I have never known before and I want to experience it fully. If I have to I'll hunt you down. Don't make me.'

Her teeth bit into her lip until the pain made her wince. 'Don't think you can threaten me into your bed,' she said thinly.

'Threaten, force, bribe, blackmail—I don't care how I do it. I want you,' he said tonelessly. 'I'd prefer to persuade, though. Clary——'

'No!'

This time she managed to cut the connection, slamming the receiver down viciously.

Back in the kitchen she said to Mrs Withers, 'If anyone else rings please tell them I'm not at home. I'm taking the baby for her vaccination now.'

'And if he calls in, dear?'

'Tell him you don't know where I am. Please.'

'Well, you know your business best, I suppose. All right, I'll tell him.'

Mrs Crowe had gone up to London for the day leaving Clary with the small car. Expecting any minute to see Morgan appear she popped Beth and a bag of necessities into it and left in a hurry. Just as if he were an ogre, she thought, trying for her normal sense of humour. Not that he looked like an ogre; she frowned fiercely, trying to banish his image from her mind. But it stayed all the time she waited patiently for Beth's vaccination and even as she comforted the indignant baby she could still see the lithe graceful body, the slashing beauty of his features and that worldly mouth.

'Darling, darling, do hush,' she whispered into the soft, baby-smelling hair. 'Come on, poppet, time to get you home. Do stop crying!'

By the time they arrived back the daily had gone but she had left an envelope propped up against the kettle. Clary didn't need to read the little note written on the back of it to know who had left it. *He came!!! You're mad!!* Mrs Withers had written.

After Beth had had her lunch and gone grumpily to bed Clary made herself a cup of tea. Only when it was poured did she slit the envelope and unfold the paper inside.

Clary, he wrote, *I meant what I said. I'd much rather you came willingly to me, but if I have to I will find you if it means tearing the world apart. Last night I begged. Next time I might just take.* It finished with an address—at the Connaught Hotel—and a telephone number.

'Charming,' Clary said contemptuously, crumpling the paper before throwing it into the rubbish.

He was nothing but a conceited, big-headed flirt, making threats he must know he couldn't carry out. Her rejection had hurt his pride and he didn't know how to cope with it. But she couldn't help remembering the desperation with which he had pleaded with her to go with him. Until then he had appeared vastly self-possessed, with a pride and disciplined arrogance that was intimidating. It seemed incredible that such a man should have surrendered to the wild urgings of a physical attraction, however intense.

CHAPTER TWO

THE Crowes said nothing to her about Morgan Caird, for which Clary was thankful. She was having enough difficulty prising him out of her brain without any reinforcement from outside.

So it was with a sinking heart that she met Lady Sedbury outside the village shop a few days later. She had to stiffen her sinews to meet the narrow smile with which she was greeted, and the faint flash of malice which seemed ever-present in the older woman's expression.

'And what you been buying, Amanda?'

'It's Clary's birthday present,' Amanda told her importantly. 'She's going to be twenty-five next Saturday.'

'Ah, what it is to be twenty-five! How is this momentous occasion to be celebrated?'

'Clary is going to London. She is going out to dinner with friends, but they haven't chosen the restaurant yet. Clary doesn't know very many restaurants in London.'

Lady Sedbury's rather feline smile was reflected in her long blue eyes. 'Adrian's is an excellent place to dine,' she observed. 'It's not madly expensive and the food is divine.'

'Adrian's,' Ginny observed when Amanda reported the little exchange. 'Yes, you'd almost certainly enjoy it, Clary. It has an English menu—good regional dishes and superb salmon and venison. You could do a lot worse.'

So Clary rang Donna Evans, who was organising the London end of things. 'Oh, yes!' said Donna enthusiastically. 'I read a review which raved about their steak and kidney pudding. I'll make reservations today.' Donna adored steak and kidney pudding.

On Saturday morning Clary was driven to the station by her employer who waved her off with strict injunctions to enjoy herself. Until the train was out of sight Clary waved the handkerchief decorated with horseshoes which was Amanda's present, then settled back into the seat, pleasantly cheered by the anticipation of two whole days of freedom.

There had been a parcel from New Zealand, from her mother, and a card from Angus with a cheque in it; before settling down with the biography which her employers had given her Clary wondered at that card. The message in it was affectionate enough but there was no indication that Susan had had anything to do with it; she had not signed it and Angus had not included her, and that was unusual.

'Oh, don't go looking for trouble,' she adjured herself sternly as she opened the biography, hoping rather fervently that it would keep her mind off the fact that Morgan Caird was in London. She was becoming quite good at banishing him from her mind although the prickling unease his name sent through her was a little harder to dismiss. Still, by blocking out that evening, by refusing to recall any of it, she was overcoming the weakness of a brain and body which were too easily traitors.

Donna was waiting, her brilliant curls lighting up the drab, busy station. 'You've lost weight, you louse!' she exclaimed, hugging Clary with her usual enthusiasm. 'Don't you dare think of dieting for the next forty-eight hours. We are going to enjoy ourselves!'

Which they did, with the help of Donna's vibrant personality and the Victoria and Albert museum and Clary's determination to put away the unease which niggled at her, at least for this weekend.

Back at the flat which Donna shared with three other girls, two away for the weekend and one incommunicado in a bedroom, they drank coffee, caught up on news from home, and got ready.

'I thought I saw Angus's wife the other day,' Donna called from the bathroom as she applied her mascara. 'In Harrod's, but I couldn't get a close look at her. It was as crowded as usual. Same gorgeous fall of red hair, though. Whoever it was was in the designer room.'

'Not Susan. Angus hasn't made his fortune yet.'

Clary smoothed her dress down over her hips. It looked good, the rich blue fabric clinging caressingly. Another timeless design, the long full sleeves and shirt collar suited her height and the narrow belt emphasised her slim waist. She used a smoky violet to shadow her eyes and a slight smoothing of blusher because the blue tended to make her pale skin look even paler.

'Ravishing,' Donna pronounced, vivid as a firecracker in yellow and gold which she wore with the panache and flair that was an integral part of her character. 'Ah, this sounds like the boys.'

The boys were both English, brothers, the older of whom, James Preston, was Donna's boyfriend. His brother John was, like him, tall and thin and pleasant. Clary had met them before and liked them.

The restaurant was warm and gracious, with a head waiter who combined authority with an air of benevolence which caused Donna to compare him to Mr Pickwick. The service was good, too. The first drinks came quickly, and they were left to peruse the menu in peace; apparently Adrian's did not believe in hovering unnecessarily. All in all, Clary decided as she sipped her sherry, it had the makings of a very enjoyable dinner.

It continued to be a good evening until just before it finished. Donna was slowly absorbing a superb summer pudding when she looked over John's shoulder and exclaimed, 'Clary, isn't that your— Clary!'

For Clary had seen too, and her face was as white as the cloth beneath her plate.

'No, don't go, you can't make a scene . . .'

But Clary was already on her feet, her eyes enormous in her face as she watched Morgan Caird and his companion being ushered to their table.

'Oh my God! Oh, *stop* her!' Donna moaned, but it was too late.

Moving stiffly like an automaton Clary made her way across the room. She was terrified, her whole body clenched in a bitter amalgam of pain and anger, yet nothing could have stopped her as she walked between the tables, oblivious to the low murmur of interest which followed her. A pace away from the table the two occupants saw her. Morgan got to his feet, his face carved from stone, but Clary ignored him completely.

'Hello, Susan,' she said to the beautiful red-headed woman who was staring at her as if she had appeared from hell. 'Where is Angus?'

And watched with cold cruel eyes as her sister-in-law's lashes fell in shamed confusion.

'Sit down.' Morgan's voice was soft but uncompromising, as were the fingers which fastened on to her arm and urged her down into a chair.

'Where is Angus?' she repeated mercilessly.

Susan's tongue touched her lips. She sent a desperate glance to Morgan and he said, 'Susan has left him. Clary——'

'To be your mistress? The one you told me twice was of no importance?' Her voice cracked on a laugh. 'That was when he was trying to talk me into taking your place, Susan. Or joining you, I'm not sure which.'

'You'd better have something to drink,' Morgan said, his expression impassive. A waiter appeared, and a moment later, two brandies.

Susan drank hers quickly, shivering, her eyes avoiding Clary, but Clary shook her head.

'I've already had enough,' she said coldly. 'If I have any more I might get maudlin. You'd have a worse scene on your hands then.' She stared at Morgan with open contempt. 'I'm not sure that even your practised sophistication could deal with that.'

'Try me and see,' he invited grimly.

She considered this for some moments. Perhaps it was the wine she had drunk with her meal which gave her such an odd disconnected feeling. Beneath the outward calm there was a freezing, savagely vindictive rage which could not be unleashed, or she just might kill them both.

'When did you leave Angus?' she asked politely, turning her blank eyes to her sister-in-law.

Again Susan shot a terrified glance towards Morgan but Clary intervened, 'Answer me yourself, please.'

'A—a month ago.'

Clary nodded almost judicially. 'About the time my mother's letters became evasive. Have you left him for good, or do you plan to go back after this little fling?'

'Clary, for God's sake——'

'But I want to know, Susan.'

Susan gave a long shuddering sigh. 'I've left him for good.'

'Then I hope that you have extracted quite a lot of money from your lover,' Clary said without compunction, 'because I don't think your tenure is exactly secure.'

'That will do!' Morgan did not raise his voice but it cracked like a whip. As Susan's lips trembled he reached over to cover her shaking hands in a protective gesture which cut through Clary like the bitterest of betrayals. 'If you want to hurt anyone,' he said, staring at Clary, 'try me. It won't be quite as much fun because I'm a lot tougher than Susan, but you are welcome to use me as a whipping-post. If you are prepared to take the consequences.'

She smiled with fierce irony. 'Could anything hurt

you? Monumental conceit like yours is armour against anything the world can throw your way, isn't it? Why shouldn't Susan suffer a little? I don't suppose Angus is feeling overly cheerful at the moment, and I can guarantee he isn't eating in a place like this with a woman as accommodating as she is.'

She rose, meeting Morgan's compelling, controlled anger with a faint cold smile. Both ignored Susan's imploring repetition of her name. Darkest-blue eyes flamed into green-gold ones. 'I hope you enjoy yourselves as much as I have,' she finished, turning to nod at the couple who arrived beside them. 'Lady Sedbury, Lord Sedbury,' she said tonelessly before walking back across the room.

'We're ready to go,' Donna told her quietly. Clearly she had filled in some of the details to the men, who looked both shifty and protective, as men anticipating a scene do. 'Hold your head high and smile. John, take her arm without beng too obvious.'

They were kind, and they shielded her from the too-interested eyes of the rest of the diners, and Clary was more grateful than she could ever express. Once in the car long shudders racked her body; she had to clench her teeth and her hands to prevent the tears from coming.

At the flat Donna dismissed the men, forced a large brandy down her throat then dealt kindly and competently with the bout of weeping which followed, holding Clary in maternal arms until she had cried herself to a standstill.

'You'll feel better if you wash your face,' she advised. 'Get into your nightdress and I'll make some tea. Do you have a headache?'

'Yes, but it will go. I don't need a pain-killer.'

The tea was fragrant and faintly lemon-flavoured, exactly as Clary liked it. Together they drank it in silence, until Donna said, 'I suppose you had to find out some time, but what filthy luck that they had to choose that restaurant!'

By now the pounding in Clary's head had receded. She looked across at Donna's sympathetic face and gave an odd little grimace. 'That wasn't luck.' Briefly she explained Lady Sedbury's part in the choosing of Adrian's.

'But she didn't know Susan. I don't understand . . .'

'She knew that Morgan Caird would be there. With Susan. With his mistress.'

'But—oh. *Oh*, I see! Oh, for heaven's sake. Where did you meet him? Down there? I see, I wondered why you were so intense. Honestly, you scared the living daylights out of me. Susan, too. She really did seem to shrink. You looked like everybody's image of an avenging angel, I kept looking for the fiery sword. Shut me up, I'm gabbling.'

Clary's eyes filled with tears. She drained the rest of her tea then blew her nose. Looping her hands around her knees she said quietly, 'It was just an unhappy coincidence that Morgan Caird's lover happened to be my sister-in-law.'

'Morgan Caird!' Donna set her cup down. 'He's well named.'

Clary looked her surprise and Donna elaborated, 'Henry Morgan was a pirate on the Spanish Main. If I remember correctly he turned respectable after a lifetime of wickedness. Morgan Caird looks as if he'd have enjoyed being a pirate and I shouldn't think there's a respectable bone in that superb body. How hard did you fall, Clary?'

'Well, I didn't go to bed with him.' She told Donna as much as she felt necessary for her to know, downplaying that searing attraction in a monotonous recital of facts.

'Why on earth should her ladyship want to upset you? Or embarrass you? She sounds a right bitch.'

'I think—from things I've heard—that she likes little flirtations. Nothing serious, just fun. I suppose she thought that Morgan might join her in her games. Perhaps she was piqued when he didn't. I don't know, perhaps she saw a chance to punish us a little. If I hadn't taken her suggestion about Adrian's, well, she'd have lost nothing. She wouldn't have known that Susan was my brother's wife. That was the filthy luck. I'm so sorry I spoiled the evening.'

Donna said something brief and explicit which brought a smile to Clary's pale lips. Suddenly immensely weary, she was purged now of all emotion but her anguish for her brother. Angling her head against the back of the rather uncomfortable chair which was the best the flat had to offer, she said, 'Lord, but I made a fool of myself!'

'Hardly anyone noticed. You know Londoners, they wouldn't have bothered if you'd stripped naked in front of them! That's what I like about them.'

Silence, broken only by the swish of a late car heading home through the rain.

'Clary?'

'Mm?'

'What happened between you and Morgan Caird? It's not like you to lose your cool so completely over a man.'

The controlled curves of Clary's mouth twisted caustically. 'I believe it's known as lust at first sight,' she said. 'It was as if—as if my body took over. It was horrible—I felt so helpless.'

'And did he feel the same way?'

'He said so. I think—yes, he did.'

Another period of silence while Clary fought the acrid sense of betrayal which ate corrosively into her, fuelling a resurgence of the vitriolic anger she had suffered when she had seen Morgan's tawny head inclined towards Susan's, her long, beautifully manicured fingers so possessively resting on his arm. Then as now, Clary's whole being had cried out in bitter protest.

Without asking Donna poured them both another cup of tea. To take her mind off the torment which racked her Clary said dully, 'I'd better ring my mother. She'll tell me how Angus is.'

'Shattered, I suppose.'

'I'm afraid so. He worshipped Susan. The *bitch*!'

'He's better off without her,' Donna said with brisk common sense. 'It's a cliché, but it's true.'

Clary pushed a hand through her tumbled hair. 'My father died of a broken heart,' she said without emotion. 'When his lover left him he crawled back home like a beaten dog and withered away. He loved her to the point of obsession.'

'And you think Angus—oh, Clary, I'm sure you're wrong.' Donna was appalled. 'I've only met him a couple of times, but your brother struck me as being a very strong character with far too much personality to give up like your father, whatever the temptation.'

Clary closed her eyes. 'Oh, God, I hope so,' she whispered. 'If anything happens I swear I'll kill Susan. And Morgan Caird.'

'You're so tired you don't know what you're saying,' Donna told her, secretly more than worried at the pitiless determination which hardened Clary's face into an ancient, primitive mask. 'Come on, let's go to bed. Things always seem better in the morning.'

They did, but not much, and it was an exhausted Clary who spoke to her mother across twelve thousand miles, telling her nothing of Morgan Caird, only that she had seen Susan.

'I won't tell Angus that you met her,' Mrs Grey said after her first shocked exclamations. 'I honestly think that the less said of her the better.'

'How is he?'

There was a slight silence intensified by her mother's sigh. 'He's taking it very hard. He's working like a maniac at his job, and as far as I can tell he spends most of the night in his workshop. He hasn't said much, you know Angus. He's confident that this latest thing he's working on will come to something. It's something to do with navigation in aeroplanes.'

'At least he's got something to do,' Clary said softly, remembering the grey-faced man who had been her father as he sat waiting for death.

'Yes.' Mrs Grey's voice firmed, became positive. 'Now don't you go worrying your soul over this. Angus is a big boy now and he'll survive. I didn't rear weaklings!'

Clary managed to laugh. Her mother's matronly appearance belied the strong character which had kept her on an even keel through her husband's betrayal and enabled her to give him refuge free from recriminations when he had come back to her without prospects or hope.

'We are so looking forward to seeing you, Clary. Be happy.'

Clary hung up and turned to meet Donna's eyes. 'Well,' she said on a long exhalation of breath, 'that was a suitably expurgated version. She told me to be happy!'

'Why not?' Donna said robustly. 'I think most people are about as happy as they want to be.'

Which was easy enough to say; in the months which followed Clary found herself wondering why the situation should have the power to produce the kind of bitterness she found herself suffering. OK, she said to herself innumerable times, so you met a man who looked like an erotic fantasy and made you feel as though you were playing a central role in just that. That was all it had been, lust, passion, carnal love— only love was too kind a word to describe it. There had been no love in their reaction to each other. If she hadn't been so frightened at the primitive power of the emotion they would have coupled like animals, mating with total, sensual abandon until the flame died, as was inevitable, and then she would have despised herself for the rest of her life.

Gradually she managed to push the memories and the emotions they caused far enough into her subconscious to give some relief from the tension they brought, helped by both Crowe children who became increasingly dear to her.

About Angus their mother's letters were cautiously optimistic. He had obtained a separation order and now had only to wait out the two years for the divorce to be finalised. He was still working incredibly hard, but he had found a consortium who were definitely interested in backing his latest invention, which would be a marvellous boost for his morale. Angus made quite a good income from the patents on several of his gadgets but from what her mother wrote, this one was big-time.

Halfway through a bleak northern autumn Clary kissed Amanda and Beth goodbye, said her farewells to their parents and realised with quite intense relief that she would no longer have to see Lady Sedbury or parry her malicious little remarks. Several times the other woman had tried to get some reaction from Clary, mentioning the evening at Adrian's with delicate effrontery. Each time Clary had stared blankly at her, treating the impertinent enquiries with calm seriousness. In the end Leona had given up, but her appearance was a continual reminder to Clary of the worst evening of her life, and she was glad not to have to cope with it any more.

She made her farewells to the rest of the village with considerable regret and went on up to London with all her worldly goods in one suitcase and a pack.

She spent a hectic week getting ready for Donna's wedding to James Preston, at which she was bridesmaid. After that she shifted to a small bed-and-breakfast place and made final preparations for the flight back home. In between she indulged in last-minute sightseeing, trying to cram into a few days as many as she could of the sights she had previously missed. It was enjoyable being on her own; solitude suited her mood exactly.

The day before her plane left she was walking down the Haymarket on her way to the National Gallery when it began to rain, hard pelting drops which persuaded her into New Zealand House, where she decided to wait out the shower. There, reading a newspaper from Wellington, she met a girl with whom she had once spent a miserably wet weekend in a youth hostel in the Lake District.

After the usual surprised greetings the girl said, 'Did you know there's a note for you in the rack? It's been there a while.'

'No! I'd better check it out. Nice to see you again.'

'You too. Give my love to Enzed, won't you.'

Smiling, Clary promised to do that, then made her way to the rack which held the slightly creased envelope. The note was concise to the point of starkness. *Clary, please contact Susan*, it read, and was followed by a London telephone number.

It took an effort not to shred the paper. What prevented her was that after that last traumatic meeting she knew Susan would only try to contact her if it was vitally important.

Slowly, her jaw tightening painfully, she folded the note several times before thrusting it into her pocket. She went down the stairs and across the marble floor to the lower level which held the telephones.

It seemed an omen when one of the normally busy booths was free. Ignoring an extremely interested appraisal from the man next to her she dialled, heard Susan's voice and fatalistically pushed the coin home.

'It's Clary here. I've just got your note. Is anything wrong?'

'No.' The silence, short and tense, rang in her ears. Then Susan said, 'I'd almost given up hope of your answering. When are you going home?'

Very coolly Clary told her, 'The day after tomorrow. Why?'

'I want to see you. It's important. Not to you, I suppose, but to me.'

Clary heard the weariness which flattened her sister-in-law's voice into a monotone, and answered reluctantly, 'All right, then. Where will I meet you?'

'Can you come here?'

'Is that necessary?'

'I'm home because I'm not feeling well.' Quickly, perhaps thinking that Clary might refuse, Susan gave her the address, finishing, 'You shouldn't have any difficulty getting a taxi.'

'Taxis are for people with money to spare,' Clary said acidly. 'What's the nearest underground station?'

The shaft struck home. Susan began to say something, thought better of it and gave her the information, suggesting they meet by the ticket box.

'I'll be there in half an hour,' Clary told her.

Donna had been correct when she noted the resemblance in colouring between herself and Susan, but instead of Donna's bright curls Susan's hair was a deep rich auburn, so striking that it shone across the station like a beacon. Even with her perfect features sharpened by strain, Susan's beauty beckoned. In the utilitarian surroundings she was alluring and exotic, a glittering star.

'How are you, Clary?'

'Fine. Thank you.'

There followed an awkward moment which threatened to stretch into a hiatus until Susan turned away, saying brusquely, 'My flat is only a few minutes' walk from here.'

Once inside the small, pleasantly furnished flat Clary cast a quick, comprehensive glance about her before her gaze came back to Susan's face.

'Looking for Morgan? He's not here.'

'I didn't expect him to be.' Clary's voice was every

bit as defiant as her sister-in-law's.

Susan smiled mirthlessly. 'I know. If you'd thought there was any possibility of his being here you wouldn't have come near the place. Sit down and I'll make us some coffee. It will give us something to do with our hands while we talk.'

As she prepared the coffee she spoke of her work as a trainee beauty therapist, finishing calmly, 'It probably appears a frivolous career but I have always wanted to do it. I hated modelling.'

Clary nodded, listening to the sound of a siren ululating along a road somewhere.

'I'm really enjoying it,' Susan told her above the soft chatter of china. 'We do quite a lot of work with hospital patients, mental patients too. They get an immense kick out of being made up. Psychiatrists say——'

'You don't have to justify your career to me.' Clary spoke belligerently, angered by the soft, husky voice, smooth as Irish coffee.

'Don't I? Then why do you look at me as if your eyes hurt whenever you can't avoid seeing me? What do you think of me, really think of me, Clary?'

'Does it matter?'

'No, it doesn't.' She said no more until the coffee was made and poured. Then, staring into the dark depths of her cup, she said without preamble, 'I should never have married Angus. I never loved him as he deserves to be loved.'

'Then why did you marry him?' Clary knew that she sounded remorseless, but sentences from her mother's last letter danced in her brain, goading her on.

Angus is making a great effort, Helen Grey had written, *but he has lost a lot of weight. I don't think he is eating properly.* And later, *He has turned in on himself, become withdrawn. He looks so lonely.*

Susan cried angrily, 'Because he was so—so *dependable!* At the time that's what I needed, someone

I could rely on. And he loved me. I felt a
responsibility to him. He didn't mean to use his love
as a weapon but he made me feel guilty because I
couldn't love him as much as he loved me. I know I
should have been strong and refused to marry him,
but he made things so easy for me. He just took
charge, he was in control, I didn't even have to think!
I needed that basic, rock-deep stability you Greys
have.'

'It palled on you fairly quickly.'

Susan's face closed up, her expression becoming
smooth and bland, her eyes as shallow as green glass.
'I tried,' she said carefully. 'At least give me credit for
that. I tried and he knew I was trying and that hurt
him beyond bearing. You're all so damned *intense*
behind that matter-of-fact air you cultivate so
religiously, even your mother. Oh, Angus tried to
smother his pain and his anger, but it was only a
matter of time before the anger won out over the pain.
I knew it would happen and then all that intensity
would be turned against me. I was frightened.'

'Don't give me that! Angus wouldn't hurt——'

'You listen to me.' Susan set her cup down with a
little jarring crash, spots of colour burning high along
her cheeks. 'Angus has exactly the same temper as
you. Sooner or later that self-control you're all so
proud of would have snapped and I'd have borne the
brunt of it. I tell you, I *know*! I may be the sort of
woman you despise but I happen to have a well-
developed instinct for self-preservation. It slipped a
bit when I let him talk me into marrying him, but it
soon sprang back into life. Angus has the kind of iron
integrity which smashes lesser people; he's quite
capable of breaking anyone who fails to live up to his
standards. I know, I lived with him, I'm not the little
sister he's always loved and protected.'

Stung, Clary hurled, 'He would—he did love you,
and protect you too. You forget, I saw him with you.'

'On our honeymoon. Of course he did, then. But he didn't love me, he loved the woman he thought I was, the woman who loved him in return.' Susan drew a deep breath. 'Oh, what's the use? You're just as hard as he is. You look at the world from your lofty, self-righteous little pinnacles and wonder how in hell people manage to make such a mess of their lives. I only hope for your sake that you aren't obsessive like your father was—like Angus is.'

'That's a peculiar way to excuse yourself,' Clary said icily, her hands trembling.

Susan drank her coffee with swift, catlike neatness. When she had finished she set the cup down and looked steadily across the space which separated her from Clary, her face a beautiful porcelain oval.

'Well, what if I am trying to vindicate myself? When you saw me with Morgan you looked at me as if I were something loathsome, something disgusting you couldn't bear to see. Your eyes went dead and you didn't look at me again. You looked past me and through me as if I wasn't there, even when you spoke to me.'

'I can't imagine why my opinion should matter to you.'

The long-nailed fingers clung to the empty coffee-cup, then slowly relaxed. As if she hadn't heard Susan said slowly, 'When I met Morgan it was like moving from black and white to colour. He didn't burden me with his emotions. I was afraid of Angus, and guilty. Do you know what guilt does, Clary? It corrodes your soul, it makes you hate the person you're betraying——'

'Oh, for heaven's sake!'

'You think I'm wallowing in self-indulgent drama-tics, don't you? Well, you listen to me, some day you might want to know how ordinary people think and react. With Morgan I didn't have to worry about breaking his heart, I knew he didn't have one! He laughed and teased and made love like a god. Oh, your brother is good, but with Morgan there was no intensity, no responsibility. It was so easy, so exciting. I needed that excitement, that glamour and charm. I needed him. He brought me back to life.'

'Did he know you were married?' Clary's breath stopped in her lungs as she waited for the answer.

'Of course not, not at first.' With defensive brittleness Susan met the contempt which darkened Clary's eyes. 'A friend of mine persuaded me to model in a charity show. He was there. I didn't have my wedding-ring on. I went to bed with him that first night—it was like a bushfire out of control. My friend warned me that he had this thing about breaking up marriages, so I didn't tell him until after I'd left Angus. When he found out he was angry, but not for long.'

The reminiscent smile with which Susan made her final comment had Clary fighting down a surge of sick humiliation. She too had experienced the excitement that caused that glitter in the green eyes of her sister-in-law, had been dizzied by the desire which licked through her body at the impact of Morgan's potent masculinity. Images danced in her brain, images of Susan and Morgan entwined in each other's arms, of her own helpless response to him. Contempt for her weakness made her gentle with the woman opposite.

'It doesn't matter,' she said tiredly. 'I had no right to be so arrogant. It's none of my business.'

Incredibly Susan produced a harsh, derisive laugh. 'If you believe that, you'll believe anything. Did you know that he hasn't been out with another woman since he left London? For Morgan that's a record. He's waiting for you to get back.'

Clary's teeth closed on her lower lip. 'I'm not flattered,' she said, 'and I don't believe it.'

'I do. My friend in Auckland moves in the same circles, she keeps me in touch. I knew he'd found someone else as soon as he came back from Chase. He was preoccupied, and he made it quite clear that things were over. Oh, he was quite kind, very generous, and totally implacable. Before I knew what had happened I'd been paid off. I felt like the whore he obviously thought me. I insisted on going with him to that restaurant even though I knew he no longer wanted me with him, because I was furious, I wanted to meet his cousin, I thought I might find out who he was hunting.'

Clary could find nothing to say, no way of breaking into the agitated angry words. In a way it seemed that by revealing it Susan was ridding herself of the humiliation she had felt at her summary dismissal.

'Well, it served me right,' Susan went on bleakly, her normally modulated tones raw. 'He damned near ate you with his eyes, and he hated me for being your sister-in-law because it meant that you'd have nothing to do with him.'

Clary closed her eyes, recalling only too well the storm of emotion which had battered her that night. Long lashes flickered, then lifted to reveal nothing but a blue as intense and opaque as lapis lazuli. 'He behaved,' she said evenly, 'like an absolute cad.'

The words didn't sound amusing or old-fashioned. Not the way she said them.

Susan shivered at the complete lack of emotion in both face and voice. 'You sound like a judge pronouncing sentence,' she muttered.

Outside it had begun to rain again, this time the determined, weary drizzle of a London autumn. Silence, somehow eased of tension, spread through the little flat.

Abruptly, after a further quick glance at Clary's pale, shuttered face, Susan said, 'He knew I wanted to do this course and he arranged it. He was very kind, in a totally impersonal way. I suppose because he realised that he couldn't really blame me for being your brother's wife. He's very logical, is Morgan.'

'He's a swine.'

'Because he sleeps around? Then so was Angus. You don't really think that he came pure as the driven snow to our marriage, do you? Grow up, Clary. Are you still a virgin?'

Colour burned along Clary's cheekbones. Stiffly, keeping her eyes fixed on a small china dish on the table, she said, 'I don't see that my moral standards have anything to do with this.'

Susan was smiling, with surprise and a hint of sympathy. 'Poor Morgan,' she said unexpectedly, and then, 'poor Clary. At least I knew right from the first how it was going to end! Men like Morgan Caird do not fall in love, at least, not the happy-ever-after kind. They marry for practical reasons and fidelity isn't a part of the bargain. Romance is strictly for affairs. And I don't suppose he has ever made love to a virgin. He has his own principles.'

Clary said nothing. There was nothing to say. She knew, had known from her first glimpse of him, that he was nothing more than a predator, sleek and beautiful and dangerous.

'He rescued me,' Susan said abruptly. 'I wanted him and I told myself all the stupid things that women have fooled themselves with when they want to go to bed with a man they know instinctively has nothing more than sex to offer them.' Her voice changed as she leaned forward, capturing Clary's reluctant gaze in a painful kind of complicity. 'You'll find yourself doing it too, Clary. They come easily, all those lying platitudes. It must be love, you'll tell yourself, and at least there'll be memories. Don't be fooled by the traitor in your body.'

'I'm not so stupid,' Clary returned flatly. 'Anyway, I'm not likely to see him again.'

Susan's mouth curved in a sardonic smile. 'I'd say he probably knows the exact date you're arriving back in Auckland,' she said with the calmness of complete conviction.

'You're paranoid.' But Clary was uneasy.

Susan gave an odd grimace. 'I know the man, and I saw him in action. He's not a man to accept defeat, not in any part of his life. Just remember, when he holds you and tells you in that beautiful voice that he wants you, how it will end. I don't think you could handle an affair.'

'Any more than you could handle marriage.'

Susan flinched but took the thrust without anger. 'If you're a virgin you don't want to cut your teeth on Morgan. Men have the advantage over women. Angus will sublimate his anger in work and probably embark on a period of dissipation just to prove he's over me; I don't think any woman will mean as much to Morgan as his work. Don't let yourself be sweet-talked into an affair, Clary, why ask for pain?'

They had talked themselves out. For a moment they stared at each other, reaching a tenuous understanding, and then Clary got to her feet. 'I have to go.'

They walked back to the station under a grey, lowering sky.

'Autumn,' Susan said wistfully. 'At home it will almost be summer. Are you flying straight through?'

'I'm stopping off for a week in Hawaii.' Clary shrugged, suddenly bone-weary. 'It seemed a good idea at the time, but at the moment I only want to get home.'

'Oh, you'll enjoy it once you're there. Lie on the beach and polish up your tan.'

At the entrance to the station they stopped, and there was another awkward silence.

Moved by the hidden gallantry in the other woman's bearing Clary suddenly leaned over and kissed her cheek. 'Goodbye and good luck,' she said quickly.

Susan's astonishment was open and rather shaming. 'You too. If you can bear to, keep in touch.' She hesitated then said half under her breath, 'When the time is right, tell Angus I'm sorry. Not for leaving him, but for marrying him.'

Clary watched as she turned and swung off down the indifferent street, back straight and stiff, the glowing hair hidden by a scarf. As she went into the station she thought that just like that a woman might go to the gallows.

Not until she was back in her small bedroom did she allow herself to consider Susan's warnings. Brooding uncomfortably in the chair, she wondered if Morgan Caird really did want her enough to pursue her as Susan had indicated. The thought brought a half-excited, half-terrified thrill with it; she had to force the rational part of her brain back on course.

Viewed logically, of course the idea was absurd. What he wanted from her was obtainable easily enough anywhere. The dark promise of his sexuality was fascinating enough to attract all women but those in love with someone else. That sensual magnetism combined with his powerful personality made him almost irresistible.

Logic must force him to realise that there could be no sort of future for them. Unfortunately logic seemed to have very little place in the attraction which had blazed into life between them. As for any future, well, his affairs didn't deal with the future, they were very much of the here and now—and the past.

He was everything she despised in a man, a sensualist with a hunter's callous instincts and cold ruthlessness. If Susan was right and he intended to try to renew their acquaintance, he also had the hide of a rhinoceros. It would always be impossible for her to feel anything but contempt for the man who had caused Angus such heartbreak.

CHAPTER THREE

'HONOLULU was superb,' Clary said, hugging her mother. 'All frangipani and fabulous sunsets and mosquitoes! I loved it.'

'But you're glad to be home?'

'Thrilled. Like all Kiwis I'm convinced that New Zealand is the best place in the universe. You're looking extremely fit, mama. And so,' turning to her brother, 'are you, Angus.'

He smiled, nodding at her suitcase. 'Is that all you can show for the years you've been away?'

'And the backpack!'

They laughed, amusement temporarily replacing the cool wariness which each was striving to hide. Seen together they must look rather like clones of each other, Clary thought. All tall, all with the same colouring except that Angus had his father's darker skin and was superbly tanned; all three had eyes the brilliant deep blue of the sky at twilight, and the same features shaped each face, feminine grace altered to a harsh masculinity.

Quickly, to hide the fact that she was ill at ease, Clary told them, 'Actually I've sent a tea-chest back from London by sea. It's got all my winter clothes in it as well as my souvenirs.'

Suddenly swamped by love and pleasure, she smiled radiantly at them both. It would have been nice to link her arm with her mother's but Helen had never found it easy to show her affection physically, so Clary contented herself with another quick hug before saying eagerly, 'Come on, let's get out of here. I've seen enough of airports to last me ten years.'

Auckland glowed under the warm spring sunlight.

Tucked into Angus's aged, much-loved Jaguar, Clary relished the way the red roofs of suburban bungalows contrasted with trees and lawns. Coiled about the land were the estuaries and inlets of the two big harbours, land-locked Manukau and the Waitemata dotted with its many islands. Gardens burgeoned with flowers, the jewel colours of impatiens like gleaming eyes in the shade, tall wands of yellow and lollipop pink ixias, Dutch irises in the deepest, brightest blue in all the world, and graceful azaleas.

Even as Clary sighed with pleasure she sent a swift, secretive glance towards her brother. He didn't look as though his life had been shattered. He had an impassive face, hard to read; it was impossible to tell what went on in the clever, quick brain. Just now he seemed tired, the already harsh framework of his features emphasised.

'He's working too hard,' Mrs Grey confided that night after he had left for his flat. 'I'm worried about him.'

Clary looked up. Normally her mother would not dream of discussing Angus; it was a measure of her anxiety that she revealed this much.

Brusquely she told her mother of the meeting with Susan, ending, 'She seemed genuinely sorry.'

'So I should hope! Really, people like her make me so angry! Jumping headfirst into situations and then feeling sorry when things go amiss. Why on earth did she marry Angus if she was going to run away with the first attractive rich man who looked sideways at her?'

'She said she married Angus because she needed his protection. And because she felt responsible for him.'

'Because he fell in love with her?' Mrs Grey looked her disdain. 'It can't have occurred to her that he'd recover much more quickly from a firm refusal before things got too serious than he would from a blow to his self-esteem like this.'

Clary sighed. 'Was it only to his self-esteem?'

'Who knows? It has been a long time since I had any idea of what was going on in Angus's brain. It will be a long time before he forgives her.'

Helen's astringent common sense was refreshing, even if it couldn't encompass every situation. On impulse Clary said, 'I saw Morgan Caird too.'

Helen cast a swift, sharp glance at her daughter's smooth, down-bent face. It was as impassive as that of her brother. Repressing a sigh Helen asked, 'What's he like?'

'A dark angel.'

Her mother's lifted brows recalled Clary to herself. She laughed, covering the slip with flippancy. 'A big, bold pirate, modern style, sleek and elegant and super-sophisticated. Sexy as hell and well aware of it. A splendid male animal, but behind all the glamour there's a kind of cynicism which, speaking personally, scared me witless.'

'Oh dear.' Helen forbore to comment on this vivid description of a man her daughter had only seen for a few minutes. 'A dangerous man. I gather he and Susan are no longer together.'

'No, that's all over. He set her up in a flat.' Her mouth twisted in sudden savage sarcasm. 'He was very generous. It's a nice little place, and she is training to be a beautician, a beauty therapist. I gather he provided the wherewithal for that, too.'

'Well, she was always interested in that. I wonder what caused the break-up?'

Clary had never been able to lie to her mother. Now she didn't even try. Quietly she sat out the penetrating scrutiny until Helen said, 'I wish Angus had never met her.'

'Unfortunately he did, and he loved her and now he's lost her.' In spite of her efforts to control it Clary's voice was strained. She gave a sudden, wide yawn.

Helen got to her feet. 'My dear, you're exhausted. Go to sleep. Things will be better in the morning.'

Her mother saw too much, but she never pried. Helen believed in allowing everyone plenty of space, particularly her children.

The night passed in dreamless sleep. Clary woke late to a cloudless sky and a day of such calm loveliness that she spent the rest of the morning admiring it from the terrace at the back of the house.

Although Helen held a responsible position as a buyer in one of Auckland's department stores she made time to garden. After the death of her husband when she had moved her family into this house there had been nothing growing on the section but lawn and a scraggy old datura tree. The loveliness which gladdened Clary's eyes now was a tribute to her mother's care and hard work and skill.

'Oh, this is sheer, pure bliss,' Clary told the elegant bronze crane by the little fountain, eyeing with a connoisseur's pleasure the clustered blossoms of pink and white and crimson at its feet. Across the struts of the pergola a creeper suspended crimson-throated flowers like small pink trumpets.

A step below the balustrade the lawn spread out in smooth lushness presided over by a weeping cherry, bereft of blossom at this season, and several rosebushes heavy with scented blooms. Late bulbs sent flowers forth from beneath shrubs and perennials; a chaffinch flitted across the lawn and a blackbird called impudently into the warm air.

'Oh, it is *good* to be back,' Clary told a thin marmalade cat from over the side boundary. 'Now all I have to do is get a job.'

She hadn't expected it to be easy, but after a couple of weeks spent answering advertisements for quite unsuitable positions she began to wonder whether it would be better to go back to nursing. Most of the places she was offered seemed to entail vast amounts of work and responsibility for next to no wages, and several were extremely dubious.

'Hopeless,' she told Angus one night, describing one man who wanted a housekeeper and had made no bones about propositioning her there and then.

'I wish I'd been there,' Angus growled. 'What is the chance of getting a decent job? I thought the hospitals were shouting for qualified nurses.'

She shifted in her chair, watching him as he poured drinks, whisky for him, Cointreau for her. Mrs Grey was at the theatre and Angus had allowed himself to be coaxed into taking Clary out to dinner. It had been a pleasant evening, but now she felt tired and a little miserable. Angus was no longer the brother she had used to tease and be silly with. An old quotation— from the Bible?—came to mind. *The iron had entered his soul.* She could see why her mother worried about him.

'I don't know,' she said frankly. 'It looks as though I'm going to find out, though.'

He regarded her levelly, tasting his drink, then said, 'You'll get there. Look, do you mind if I put the television on? There's a current affairs programme I want to watch. One man in particular . . .'

The programme was good, incisive and hard-hitting, and Clary enjoyed it until halfway through when it switched to a panel discussion, and one of the panellists was Morgan Caird. Clary stiffened, her gaze flying to her brother's face; he was sitting like a monolith, gripping his glass with a ferocity that whitened his knuckles.

'I'll turn it off,' Clary muttered, scrambling across the room.

'Leave it. I've never met my wife's lover. I'd like to see just what he's got. Besides money.'

'But——'

'Leave it, Clary.' He spoke quietly but she shivered as she huddled back into her chair.

What followed was near torture. Morgan was completely at home in the studio, very self-possessed,

the cool brilliance of his mind rather awesomely
revealed. Others lost their tempers; not so Morgan.
Others rambled, tried to obscure the point, justified
themselves. Morgan revealed any shoddiness in their
arguments with a few concise, rather curt sentences
before settling back to watch them with a dispassionate,
concentrated scrutiny.

Clary forgot to drink, forgot Angus, forgot
everything but the need to keep her eyes on the screen,
drinking in the severe beauty of Morgan's features
with sheer sensual pleasure. Oblivious, her heart in
her eyes, she watched until Angus got up and switched
off the set.

'Well,' he said, draining his glass in one savage gulp,
'what do you think of him? She has good taste, my
wife, hasn't she?'

'Angus——'

'After she left me I made it my business to find out
as much as I could about bloody Morgan Caird. I
wanted to see if there was any way I could pay him
back.'

'Oh, Angus——'

'I'll do it some day,' he promised, coldly determined.
'I'll make him wish he'd never set eyes on my slut of a
wife, never slept with her. He's six years older than
me—those six years are my bank account.'

'And Susan?' When he frowned at her she probed
gently, 'Are you going to make her suffer too?'

'No. She's not worth it, the cheating, lying tramp.'

Clary bit her lip, restraining herself from asking him
to justify his attitude. She could tell him that Morgan
was not as much to blame as he thought, but a glance
at his shuttered, brooding expression revealed that it
would be useless. Now was not the time to tell him
what she had learned from Susan, or that she had met
Morgan. Angus was too much a prisoner of his pain
and humiliation to listen. The Cointreau slid smooth
and fiery over her tongue; she sipped it slowly,

watching from beneath her lashes as he poured another drink and stood staring grimly into it.

After long moments he lifted his head and said without expression, 'I've made a start. This latest gadget is going to take me to the big time, Clary. All I needed was a start; the consortium has given me that, and barring something unforeseen I'm going to fly far and fast. I'll end up as rich as Caird, perhaps richer. And when I've got the power I'll bring him to his knees. Hatred and the desire for revenge provide a really strong impetus to ambition.' At her horrified gasp his voice hardened even more. 'Do you blame me?'

'Revenge is about the worst reason for doing anything,' she said steadily, 'but I can understand how you feel. I hope you don't end up like him, hard and ruthless.'

'It seems to be the way to go,' he said indifferently. 'He started out with nothing much and now he's a millionaire. If he can do it, so can I. Anyway, it appears that not all women share your aversion to hard, ruthless men. He's had his share.'

Clary had never felt quite so inadequate. Damn Susan, she thought, searching her brother's closed, dark face. Angus had retreated, turned in on himself, urged on this destructive path by the sort of pain she could only imagine. As yet no one could help him; she could only pray that he would soon emerge on the other side of this dark night of his soul, with the madness of revenge left behind.

When he left she waited up for her mother, trying to make sense of the thoughts chasing themselves around her brain. Helen arrived home as she was making cocoa, trying to woo sleep.

'My dear, what on earth is worrying you?' Helen asked.

Mug in hand Clary turned to face her. 'We saw Morgan Caird on television. Mum, do you think

Angus is *unbalanced*? He spoke so—so wildly, yet he meant every word he said.'

Helen sighed. 'Put some more milk in the pan, there's a dear, I'll have some with you. No, I don't think he's unbalanced, just coping with a very complex, painful set of emotions the only way he knows how to. He feels very deeply, so his sense of betrayal is—well, I suppose extreme is as good a word as any. He needs time to come to terms with himself.'

Clary certainly hoped that time was all he needed. When he arrived at the house the next afternoon she scanned his face unobtrusively but carefully. He looked a little aloof, perhaps, as if he were embarrassed by his outburst of the night before, but otherwise just as he always had. Only—his eyes were like stones, opaque and flat.

'One of the men I deal with in the consortium knows a woman who's recovering from a heart attack,' he told her after his greeting. 'Apparently she lives with a son who has to travel a lot so she needs someone to take responsibility for her. More like a companion than a nurse, I gather. It's live-in.'

'It sounds all right,' Clary agreed cautiously.

'If you want it you'll have to go and see her.' Long fingers searched through pockets, finally emerging with an address. 'There's her name, and the hospital ward. She's expecting you at two tomorrow afternoon. Why don't you want to go back nursing, Clary?'

She hesitated, frowning unseeingly at the slip of paper. 'It's hard to explain, but at the moment I want something less structured.'

'Do you want to find yourself?' His tone invested the words with a mockery which had grown sharp and punishing.

'No,' Clary said softly, thinking of Susan and her unhappy face. 'I know who I am and what I am. I'm good at my profession and I'll probably go back to it fairly soon. But I need time to assimilate all that I did

while I was away. I need to wind down.' She grinned
and gave his lean cheek a teasing little pat. 'You
should know what I mean. In your spare time you
devour travel books—*Forty Years Spent Crossing The
Sargasso Sea*, et cetera, et cetera.'

His sardonic expression eased into laughter.
Hooking a powerful arm around her waist he swung
her from one side of his body to the other. '*Touché.*
I'm glad you're home, love. It's been a lonely few
years.'

And although her heart ached for him she knew that
he had said all he ever intended to say about his brief
marriage.

Mrs Hargreaves was not a big woman but she
managed to dominate the hospital lounge without any
effort at all. She watched Clary approach with shrewd,
snapping eyes, surprisingly youthful in her elderly
face, and a small smile.

'My son told me you'd be in,' she said by way of
greeting after Clary had introduced herself. 'What sort
of music do you like?'

Clary's swift, radiant smile was touched with
mischief. 'Classical, with the exception of most violin
concertos and some string quartets, opera, especially
Italian, some pop, some country and Western,
Victorian music hall songs——'

'Very eclectic.' Mrs Hargreaves' smile widened.
'And have you a sense of humour?'

'Banana-skin variety? Certainly.'

'How about a joke against yourself?'

Clary smiled rather ironically. 'Well, I can usually
see the joke,' she admitted. 'Sometimes I laugh. Once
or twice I've even thought them funny.'

'Miss Honesty. When can you start?'

Startled, Clary suggested, 'Don't you want to check
my credentials or look at my references, or something?'

'My dear, if you are inefficient or dishonest, or I

discover a secret passion for heavy metal rock in you, I'll get rid of you soon enough, don't worry. What do you know about the job?'

Clary told her. Mrs Hargreaves nodded, her eyes never leaving Clary's face. 'That's it exactly. You'll be paid a nurse's wages, you will be on call for most of the time until I can manage to convince my son that I have no intention of dying this time, and I plan to be fully recovered in three months' time.'

'I've no doubt you will be,' Clary assured her. 'I knew that the job was temporary.'

'Well, can you start tomorrow? I don't want to spend a day more in this place than I have to.'

Still bemused, Clary gave a sudden chuckle. 'Very well, but I'll leave my references and papers here and you must promise to read them before you and your son make a final decision. Am I the only person you have interviewed?'

'No.' Mrs Hargreaves' tone consigned all the other applicants to perdition. 'I don't need your bits of paper, I've made up my own mind all my life and rarely had cause to regret it, but if it makes you happier to leave them here, do so. I won't read them. Clary is an odd name. Short for Clarissa?'

'I was named Clarice after my grandmother,' Clary told her with a grimace, 'but fortunately my brother decided on Clary and it's stuck.'

'It's unusual, like you. Pretty. I like it. I'll see you at the address on that paper tomorrow at three. Goodbye.'

Torn between amusement and astonishment at being so summarily hired Clary left, stopping on the way home to buy some summer clothes. The ones she owned were a little tired and a size too big; six months ago she had been some pounds heavier. Because the Crowes had insisted on paying her a substantial bonus she had a comfortable sum of money in the bank, but habit persuaded her to shop carefully. She did not

mind paying for quality, it was just that the years
spent overseas had curbed any tendency to extrav-
agance.

A pair of sandals completed her purchases. They
were a little difficult to find but after several false
starts she discovered a pair which fitted her, although
she pulled a face at the price. Still, the position of the
straps lent elegance to her feet; women with feet out of
the norm had to pay for comfort, and hers were
narrower and longer than average.

Promptly at two-thirty the next day she climbed
down from the bus, smiled thanks to the driver when
he handed her a small suitcase, and walked briskly to
where, as promised in Mrs Hargreaves's phone call of
the night before, a car waited. At Clary's appproach a
middle-aged woman got out, her smile wide, warm
and uncomplicated.

'Clary Grey?' When Clary nodded that smile
deepened and she held out a competent hand. 'I'm
Ruth Swann, Mrs Hargreaves's housekeeper. Hop in.
Did you have a good trip up? Just as well I decided to
come out a bit early. The bus can be pretty erratic but
it's not usually ten minutes ahead of time.'

'There were no trucks holding us up on the hills,'
Clary said, deciding that she was going to like Ruth
Swann.

'It can take much more than half an hour to get this
far, although with that new stretch of motorway to
Albany things are much better now. I'm afraid this
next bit of road is the worst part of the trip. Still, it's
not far.'

She drove slowly inland down a narrow gravel road,
carefully avoiding the thick build-up of metal on the
side. Clearly she did not feel confident enough about
the road to indulge in idle chit-chat. After a few
minutes Clary decided that she trusted her driving
enough to take notice of the unfolding landscape.
About them low hills were spotted with sheep and red

Hereford cattle sheltering from the sun in the shade of trees, some still chewing at the lush grass. A little stream ran between banks decorated with the tall wrinkled trunks and spiky heads of cabbage trees. Clary inhaled as the heavy scent of the great panicles of tiny cream blossoms floated in through the window.

After a mile or so the road debouched into a valley, fertile and well-farmed, with hedges and clumps of trees providing shelter and beauty.

'Almost there,' Ruth Swann said. 'Look, you can see the homestead from here.'

Clary followed the direction of her nod and felt her heart swell. Pink and severe against the spreading green of the enormous trees behind it, the house stood well back from the road at the end of a long drive. She had seen enough Georgian houses in Britain to recognise the style immediately.

'It must be very old,' she said, her eyes fixed on it with a shock of something that was almost recognition.

'It is. When Mrs Hargreaves and her husband—that was her first husband—bought it, it was almost derelict. Over the years she's completely restored it. The garden, too. People come from all over the world to look at the garden. She's a real fusspot about details, and everything in the house and the garden has to be just so. I really don't know what she's going to do now that it's complete.'

Clary was quite sure that Mrs Hargreaves knew exactly what she was going to do. She was far too decisive not to have made plans to cover any such eventuality. She said nothing, however, watching with satisfied eyes as the car moved beneath the magnificent magnolias which lined the drive, the rusty under-surface of the leaves barely moving in the slight wind. Beneath them were rhododendrons and azaleas, past their best now but still colourful, sheltered from the worst of New Zealand's winds by a belt of native evergreens along the fenceline.

Clearly her new employer did not lack money. A housekeeper did not come cheaply, and the gardens which unfolded before her appreciative eyes were far too extensive to be kept in such immaculate condition by one woman, however vigorous.

Clary leaned back into the solid comfort of the Volvo. That there were extremely rich people in New Zealand was no secret; normally they kept a very low profile. It seemed that in the next three months she was destined to find out how one such family lived.

Her eyes roamed lovingly over the restrained façade of the house, its severe simplicity and the perfection of its proportions enhanced by the faded pink of the weatherboards.

'It took Mrs Hargreaves ages to find just the right shade,' Mrs Swann confided as she guided the car around to a complex of buildings behind the house. 'At first the painter thought she was crazy, but she soon changed his mind! In the end he was as fussy about it as she was.'

'It is perfect.'

Clearly the buildings which housed the Volvo and, judging by their area, other vehicles, had once been the stables. They were separated from the house by a wide stretch of ground which held an orchard and a flourishing kitchen garden. To one side, screens and lush plantings sheltered a swimming-pool. A large space paved with flags led into the house.

Clary took a deep breath of the warm air, spicy with the scents of stocks and thyme blossom, and said simply, 'I think I'm going to love it here.'

'I hope so,' the housekeeper said crisply. 'It can be a bit isolated if you are used to city living.'

The winged line of Clary's brows lifted but all she said was a pleasant, 'May I see Mrs Hargreaves now?'

'Well, the doctor gave her a sedative and when I left she was asleep. I'll show you to your room and on the way I'll have a peek to see if she's woken yet.'

'It doesn't seem to me that Mrs Hargreaves needs either nurse or companion,' Clary said ruefully as she followed the older woman up a superb flight of carved stairs and down a wide hall lit by the sun through a pair of French windows.

'Oh well, there's enough for me to do here just keeping the dust under control! And the doctor thought she needed someone here to make sure she didn't get back to work too soon. She's not used to sitting around. Until she had this trouble with her heart she lived for her garden. I think they thought she would get bored and restless.'

Clary gave a non-committal nod but she remembered the sharp intelligent eyes of her employer and decided that Mrs Hargreaves was surrounded by people who fussed too much. She did not seem the sort to decline into apathy. Far from it, she possessed altogether too much shrewd common sense to allow herself to become bored.

'Here's your room. It's right next to hers and there's a bell—see, here—that she can use to call you if she needs you. Now, after I've seen whether she's awake I'll make us a cup of tea while you unpack. Or would you rather have coffee?'

'Tea will be fine, thank you.'

'I'll bring it up on a tray. You must be ready for it.'

This switched Clary's stunned gaze from her perusal of the lovely room. 'Oh no, you won't,' she said decisively. 'I'm not here to make extra work for you. After I've unpacked and had a quick shower I'll find my way to the kitchen.'

'Well, if you're sure.' Mrs Swann was doubtful. 'The bathroom—it's your own little one, you don't share—is through there. We've a bore as well as good supplies of rainwater, but it is only spring and there's all the summer to get through yet, so if you could be economical with the water . . .'

'Of course.'

Mrs Swann left the room, only to tap on the door a moment later to assure Clary that her employer was sleeping like a baby. When she had gone Clary smiled and set to unpacking, putting her clothes into the drawers of a superb wardrobe—surely not *genuine* Sheraton?—which was so much more fitting than a modern built-in would have been.

Either Mrs Hargreaves or her decorator had chosen green and a fresh primrose yellow for the room, warmed by the amber of an immense Persian rug which almost hid the wide polished boards. The furniture bore the deep patina of age and care, the little davenport in the window reflecting Clary's bemused expression as she stood for a moment looking through the panes.

'Beautiful,' she told the room, her gaze lingering on the wide four-poster bed with its embroidered spread before she went into the tiny, luxurious bathroom and showered off the dust of her journey.

Half an hour later she ran her fingers through the bronze waves of her newly dried hair, smoothed the skirt of her shirt-waister and went out of the door and down the hall, following her intuition towards the kitchen.

The house was silent, all doors open to the mellow spring day. In the downstairs hall sunlight spilled across the crimson rug and the dark floorboards, and winked from a silver vase holding an arrangement of pink blossom. Clary tensed, setting her feet down carefully, as quietly as she could because there was a watchful, waiting quality to the atmosphere.

The soft thud of a door closing behind her brought her to a frightened halt. Every fine hair on her body prickled upright; her hands tightened into fists while her heart pounded as though she had just seen the monster at the core of all nightmares.

'Come here, Clary.'

She struck one clenched fist into the wall, willing

the pain to free her from the sick anger which held her captive.

'Clary.' This time there was concern in the hard pirate's voice.

'Damn you, Morgan Caird,' she whispered through bloodless lips, turning at last to face him, 'how dare you use my brother to get me here? How *could* you!'

'I would have used anyone, including my mother,' he said, his dark gaze purposeful as he reached for the hand she had maltreated. 'But in this case you can blame coincidence for your arrival here. Or the Fates.'

It was useless to resist. She watched dully as he ran his thumb over the knuckles, smoothing the tender skin with something like relief. She kept her eyes lowered but she had seen that he too had lost weight in the past months. He looked tense, wound up to too tight a pitch, the heavy-lidded eyes burning as they swept her shuttered face with possessive fire.

'Come into the office,' he commanded quietly, leading through the open door.

Once there he gestured at a chair but when she resisted the mute suggestion he opened the door of a cabinet which held bottles and glasses. He poured brandy and brought it to where she stood in the centre of the room, her whole being clamped into stiff rejection.

'Drink this,' he ordered, holding the glass to her lips.

Numbly she drank, not even choking as the warming, life-giving cognac slipped down her throat. When it was gone she stayed silent, the dark blue of her eyes opaque, every freckle standing out across the bridge of her nose as she stared over his shoulder.

'Now you can shout at me,' he said urbanely.

When she ran the tip of her tongue across her lips that flicker of relief lightened his expression once more, but Clary was too beleaguered in her own private hell to be aware of it.

'I'm going home,' she said huskily after long, silent moments.

'No.'

The monosyllable fell with heavy emphasis. She looked up into that possessive glitter she dreaded and feared.

As if awakening from death she said, 'You can't stop me.'

'I can.' He set the glass down and took her hands in his, holding them to the thin cotton of his shirt, just above his heart. The heavy beat drove into her palms, fast and irregular, a counterpoint to the turbulence of her own.

'Clary,' he said so thickly that her attention was dragged from her long fingers up to the drawn, intent passion which spread over the symmetry of his features until the sign of the predator blazed forth, fiercely intent on his own needs, his own desires.

'No!' she cried, but it was far too late. He crushed the little sound beneath his lips, smothered it into nothingness with the primitive intention of forcing a surrender.

Knocked completely off balance by his reappearance Clary lost control, drowning in a purely pagan response. Her mouth opened, every bit as savagely desirous as his; she clenched her fists into the crisp material of his shirt, uncaring that her grip might hurt.

At last the ferocious kiss ended; red lights dazzled beneath her closed lids as he muttered, 'Oh Christ, I need this,' against her mouth before demanding on a muffled half-laugh, 'Do you know how long it's been? Centuries, an aeon of waiting . . .'

Clary couldn't answer. Absorbed by the signs of arousal in the lean body pressed so intimately to hers she turned her head and began touching small kisses to the damp, slightly salty skin across his cheek until she reached the slashing line of his jaw.

Her mouth was erotically open, the tip of her tongue leaving a small trail to mark the position of each kiss. His scent of man was more beautiful to her than anything a flower could produce; it filled her nostrils. Heat bloomed to life deep within her then rioted in tendrils of sensation through her body. For the first time she realised that desire can produce as complete a self-absorption as pain. At that moment she lived solely through her senses. All thought processes ceased; she understood only the ache in every cell, the throbbing urge to submit and so to master. A groan shuddered the length of her throat as she twisted against his aroused body.

'Stop it,' he said heavily, 'unless you want me to take you here, on the floor.'

His voice was empty of emotion, as though he was producing sounds to go with someone else's thoughts, but the words struck through the sensual haze enveloping Clary. She froze, the ache in her flesh becoming an anguish of frustration before she jerked free of his hold, her set face white with self-hatred at the betrayal by her body of heart and mind.

'Oh—God!' She pressed her fists to her eyes but nothing could shut out the hardening of his expression or the triumph there.

'I don't know why, either,' he remarked conversationally, regaining command of himself much more rapidly and easily than she did. 'However, one of the many things my tough and sensible mother taught me was never to waste time bewailing facts. Like it or not, *we* are a fact. If we had met in the ordinary course of events you would have followed your inclination and not that particularly obstructive conscience of yours, and we'd have gone on from there. Now that you're here you'll be able to learn that I am not the villain you think me.'

Slowly she lowered her hands, staring at him with the flat, unwinking gaze of hatred. 'Why should I

want to know you? I know what you are. That's quite
enough for me.'

He met her eyes with an implacable determination
which reduced her defiance to fear. 'You know
nothing about me.'

'I know enough to prevent me from sleeping with
men who seduce my sister-in-law,' she whispered.

For a moment she thought she had found a chink in
his armour of self-possession. A muscle at one corner
of his mouth was pulled tight, straightening the
sensuous curve, but before he spoke it had relaxed.

'I don't suppose you have met many,' he said
calmly. 'She is not promiscuous. Or are your morals so
firmly rooted in the nineteenth century that you
consider any woman who has an affair to be a harlot?
If so, you're a hypocrite. That's no virginal reaction I
get from you.'

She hated his cynical appraisal, hated the reminder
of her flaming response to him, hated, *hated* him.
Stonily, her expression bleak, she stated, 'I'm going
home.'

'You are not.'

The even, toneless statement sent a nervous chill
through her but she lifted her chin to demand, 'And
how do you propose to stop me?'

'Quite easily.' He took a step towards her, stopping
with a frown at her involuntary tremor. His hand
dropped and he said, 'I'd rather not use force to keep
you here but if I have to, I will. Make no mistake
about that.'

'How?' she asked, hiding an icy trickle of fear with
contempt. 'You can hardly keep me in chains——'

'How much do you love your brother?'

The silky interruption silenced her as nothing else
could have. Every muscle in her body clenched in
anticipation of a blow. 'Why do you ask that?' she
whispered.

This was how he must conduct business, with a

pitiless assurance which delivered either a *coup de grâce* or an infusion of capital in the same cool manner.

'What has Angus to do with—oh!' Realisation hit her in the blow she had been expecting.

'Yes,' he said judicially. 'When Angus wanted financial backing for his latest idea he approached a friend of mine. He was interested, but unable to help him, so without giving him my name he contacted me, knowing that I'm always interested in possible exports. I investigated Angus very carefully and was impressed. While this was under way I met Susan. Her name meant nothing to me, there are plenty of Greys about.' His lips twisted derisively. 'I wish I had never set eyes on her, but she seemed to be free, she was certainly available and even you must admit she is very beautiful.'

'Is that all that mattered to you?' Clary's voice was shaking with outrage. 'That she was beautiful?'

'No. I liked her, she was amusing and intelligent. I was angry when I discovered that there was a husband, but by then she had left him. She never spoke of him, so it came as a shock to discover that he was my genius inventor.'

He hesitated and Clary said as nastily as she could, 'The opportunity to make money being more important than any woman, however good in bed she is?'

'Strangely enough, no.' He spoke mildly, patiently, as though she was being very obtuse but she rejoiced in the gleam of anger beneath his lashes. 'Your brother's invention has the capability to save lives, Clary. And, if it is developed here, to earn the country a considerable amount of money. As soon as I made the decision to back him I set up the consortium, covering my tracks so that he doesn't know that I *am* it. Solely, entirely. I can withdraw my support any time I like. Angus was too eager to get the backing to worry about terms. It will be almost impossible for him to go anywhere else for development funds.'

'Why?'

He told her, reducing the technicalities to a clear statement that Angus had more or less handed over the marketing rights to the consortium. 'Which means that there are few financial sources open to him. Anyone who provides funds for development will only do so for the rights to market it.'

'Did you do this deliberately?' she asked, white-lipped.

He hesitated. For a moment she scanned his implacable face with painful intensity.

'It's standard procedure,' he said at last, dark lashes hiding any emotions he felt. 'He's a genius, your brother. As for today ... I knew when you were coming home, but it never occurred to me that you wouldn't go back to hospital nursing. My financial frontman mentioned my mother to him after Angus had told him how difficult you were finding it to get a job.'

'But you knew before I came here today.'

'I knew before you went to see her.' Again he hesitated, the fractional pause so at odds with his normal self-assurance that she stole another look at him.

In profile he was just as beautiful as full face; she wondered with an aching heart why she had never considered any other man to be beautiful. Yet allied to the symmetry of features and the subtle harmony of colour, gold of skin, green of eyes, delineation in black of brows and lashes, warm tawny tint of hair, there was strength and character. It was the character which was in evidence now, a certain grimness which straightened the finely moulded mouth into harshness.

He looked up, catching her helpless scrutiny, and his eyes darkened, one hand going out towards her. For a moment their glances locked; then he shook his head to clear it and said abruptly, 'I didn't expect contacting you to be this easy, but it's happened, and I'm not letting you go.'

'How can you stop me?'

'I can still pull the money out.' He nodded at her startled gasp. 'I told you that he was eager to get the backing. If I do that, as well as having no wife, he will find it extremely difficult to perfect the one thing that is keeping him sane at the moment.'

'How do you know that?' she cried in a hard hoarse voice, turning away from the inexorable strength and purpose of the man.

'I know,' he said. He smiled, but there was no amusement in the bright depths of his eyes.

'All this because of a woman?'

'All this because of you.' He corrected her bitter question with the patience of a hunter who is confident of his chance to kill. 'So what are you going to do? Tear back to Auckland in high and righteous dudgeon, or stay here?'

Outside the sun beamed down on newly-mown lawn, calling forth that indescribable, delicious perfume of freshly-cut grass. A thrush not long out of the nest hopped importantly about underneath the long leaves of a bush. Clary's eyes followed the brilliant flash of colour which was a parakeet as it sped towards the orchard so fast that the red and blue and green of plumage was a blurred streak. Its loud 'quink-quink-quink' fell in familiar cadence on her ear.

'I won't expect you to give yourself to me as a sacrifice for your brother,' he remarked, investing the statement with an insolent mockery which tore at her nerves, 'I won't insist on anything. When you come to me I want it to be a willing surrender. All I ask is that you give us time to get to know each other.'

He came across to where she stood motionless, putting a hand on her shoulder to turn her towards him. 'For example, until my mother told me yesterday, I'd have said that Victorian music hall songs and you——' The smooth voice was cut off as his finger lifted her blind face. 'Clary,' he muttered, holding her close to the warm length of him, 'don't, darling, please don't. I don't want you to be unhappy——'

'Will you let me go?'

'If I do, will you go out with me?'

Her eyes flew open to meet the grave question in his. 'No,' she whispered.

He gave himself no time for thought. 'Then my answer is the same. No. You stay here.'

'You have yourself a bargain.' That dreadful unseeing anguish was gone. With a dignity which made her suddenly formidable she disengaged herself from his grasp and he, perhaps recognising that she had reached the limits of her control, let her go, although his brows shadowed his eyes in a frown.

'Very well,' he said crisply after a tense moment. 'I don't want either your brother or my mother to know about this.'

She bit her lip. About Angus she could only agree; her heart quailed within her at the thought of his reaction if he should find out any part of the truth. Slowly, as if considering the matter, she said, 'I could try a little counter-blackmail.'

'Threaten to reveal my perfidy to my mother?' He was smiling, genuinely amused. 'My darling, my mother entertains no illusions about me. Anyway, she would think it a perfectly rational way to behave. I told you she was tough, and very practical. Much tougher than you, because you couldn't do it. You're far too conscious of your duty to your patient.'

Her shoulders slumped as she made a small defeated gesture. 'Too soft, I think you mean,' she said tonelessly. 'Luckily for you. May I go? I did promise Mrs Swann that I'd have tea with her.'

CHAPTER FOUR

THEY met again in the small drawing-room before dinner, Clary still pale but hiding her maelstrom of emotions with an air of cool poise which she hoped only she knew was barely skin-deep.

She was standing in the long window watching a kingfisher on the top of a melia tree, admiring the brilliant blue and buff of its plumage against the cloudy lilac flowers. She had dressed carefully for this confrontation in a rose-pink skirt and matching shirt, looping a silver chain about her neck. It was not her custom to wear much jewellery, and when she did it was always silver. Gold tended to look obvious against the sheer translucence of her skin.

When the door opened her nerves tightened, warning her of Morgan's entry. She refused to look around.

'How did you find my mother?' He spoke quietly, pleasantly, but there was an inflexible quality to his tone which forced a careful answer. Clary realised that he loved his mother very much.

'She appears to have suffered no ill-effects.'

'How did you manage to persuade her to stay in bed?'

Clary shrugged. 'You implied that she's a realist. I merely pointed out that if she over-exerted herself now she'd almost certainly pay for it tomorrow.'

'What are you staring at so desperately?' He spoke from just behind her, his silent passage across the room startling her. 'Ah, our local *kotare* in his favourite hunting spot.'

'I thought they ate fish.'

'As an occasional treat. I've seen kingfishers with

mice and lizards in their beaks, but mostly they prey on insects and worms. He'll have a hole full of hungry nestlings in some bank quite close by. Ah, there he goes.'

A flash of the bright blue to which he gave his name, then the little hunter rose from the lawn with encumbered beak and sped back through the trees.

'And now,' Morgan said very softly, 'would you like a drink before dinner?'

Up in her room as she dressed Clary had made a very firm decision about this man. She had decided that she would treat him with the courtesy due an employer and her host, and she would, in all her dealings with him, assume an aloofness which would keep him effectively at bay. She would be polite and reserved and answer him when he spoke to her; she would not volunteer information or conversation, and she would make sure that he never got the chance to touch her.

Her strange and probably irrational conviction that she could trust him, at least when he said he did not want to force her to do anything other than stay here, had helped her make that decision, although not without a surge of fury because he had made that concession in the arrogant belief that he had the power to persuade her easily into his bed.

The long months since they had met had not diminished her body's perverse hunger for him, but she had forgotten its strength. Now, with him only inches away, his subtle male fragrance taunting her senses, she realised sickly that the ease with which she made decisions in her room was belied by the violence of her reaction to his presence. It was going to take all her will to control the leaping response in her blood.

His suggestion of a drink brought relief. It would get him away from her long enough to stop the fine trembling in her limbs.

'Yes, sherry please,' she said, her voice abrupt with strain.

'Dry, of course.'

Mockery, of course.

'I like all sherry,' she told him politely as she followed him part of the way across the lovely room. Beside a glass-topped curio table was positioned a lone chair. Pretending to be fascinated by the mementoes so carefully arranged beneath the glass, Clary sank on to the cushion.

'A truly civilised appreciation of the wine.' Morgan's voice was urbanely sardonic as he set a glass on a table beside a luxurious sofa.

For a moment they were perfectly still until his hard handsome face broke into an ironic smile at the swift mutiny in Clary's expression.

'I don't want to have to shout across the room,' he said softly and held out a hand to her.

Eyes clear as the sky on a summer midnight measured the crystalline glitter of his, clashed and held in fierce silent battle. When Clary rose it was a defeat made more bitter because she had been fighting her own instincts. Behind his worldly mask lurked a throwback to more barbaric times. He would not have forced a physical surrender; he did not need to, because they both knew that once in his arms she lost all sense of personality and became a slave to their mutual passion.

Still smiling, he came across and lifted her to her feet; she had to suffer the small punishment of his hand at her elbow until she sat in the place of his choosing. Lesson one, she thought drearily. Do as the man says.

The wine was pale and dry. At first it made her shudder, but in a very short time she learned to appreciate the austere flavour. With her face in three-quarter profile she gave polite non-committal replies to his polite non-committal statements.

He hadn't sat down beside her. His point made and taken, he chose a chair opposite, and watched her. The impact of that survey stretched every nerve on a rack, but she set her teeth and endured it stoically as he commented on the headlines, told her a little of his mother, and a little more of this place which was to be her prison.

'Very prosaically known as Hunter's Valley,' he said. 'The first settler was one James Hunter, who arrived a hundred or so years ago with a pregnant wife and all the paraphernalia necessary to live the life to which he'd been accustomed, that of an English gentleman. Unfortunately common sense wasn't part of his equipment, nor adaptability, nor, I regret to say, any inclination for hard work. He took one horrified look at the valley, half swamp and half bush, and fled to Auckland where he lost his money in unwise speculation.'

'Careless man.' Clary concentrated on relaxing her muscles before their tension became painful. 'Did he sell the valley?'

'No, no one wanted it. Eventually his son, a much more far-seeing and practical young man, decided to do something about rebuilding the family fortunes. When he was eighteen he left his parents to their genteel poverty in Auckland and came up here. He built a *nikau* hut where the homestead is now and set to work bringing in the land.'

Unwillingly she had become interested in these pioneers. 'Was it he who built the house?'

'Yes. It was as close a replica as he could get to the ancestral home. You must have seen quite a few of the originals in your perambulations about Britain.'

'Yes.' Seen them and loved them, loved the way the timeless felicity of their severe proportions, solid yet graceful, acted as the perfect complement to the gentle loveliness of the countryside they adorned.

She said as much and he nodded, watching her from beneath his lids. 'We like to think it suits our landscape as well. A very adaptable style.'

'Mrs Swann said that your mother had restored the house and the gardens as well.'

'It's her hobby. Unfortunately there's very little for her to do here now.' He cast a glance around the serene, gracious room. 'When my parents bought the station both the land and the house were in very poor heart. It took them years and an immense amount of money and hard work to get it back into shape. My father died before it was done.'

Why was he telling her this? Intuition gave her the answer. He was trying to establish links between them, encouraging the exchange of information. It was difficult to hide her resentment at this attempted manipulation, but she was well-schooled in manners and appropriate responses seemed to come without thought.

'How old were you then?'

'Eleven.' He smiled, the hard mouth rueful. 'Old enough to be a damned nuisance by considering myself the man of the house. My mother packed me off to boarding school.'

'That seems a little harsh.' She spoke tentatively, for a moment forgetting all her reasons for mistrusting this man in her compassion for the child who had lost his father so young.

'I told you she was realistic,' he returned coolly. 'I thoroughly enjoyed school, as she knew I would, and left determined to try some other way of earning my living than farming. The financial world fascinated me. By then my mother had married Geoffrey Hargreaves, so it was just as well I'd decided my future lay in Auckland.'

'Didn't you get on with him?'

'Not particularly.' He sent her a smile of cynical tolerance. 'I was quite prepared to like him, but he felt that his extra years and his position as my stepfather gave him certain rights. Rights I wasn't prepared to concede. I was young and rash, he set in his ways and conventional.'

'That's—rather sad.'

'Oh, we didn't quarrel. Nothing so undignified. We just didn't see much of each other.'

'When did you come back here?'

He looked at her. 'When he died.'

The answer told her a lot, even delivered as it was without inflection. He had resented those years in exile, but the hard practicality which was one of his legacies from his formidable mother had helped him accept that they were necessary.

'I went to university,' he said, watching the changing emotions in her face with hooded eyes. 'Then with an enormous amount of cheek and a stake inherited from poor old Geoffrey, I took on the financial establishment. I enjoyed it immensely, the wheeling and dealing, pitting my wits against all comers, the incredible deals—it was like riding in an exhilarating circus, but by the time I reached thirty I decided to turn respectable.'

She couldn't prevent the laughter which bubbled forth at his wide, shark's grin. However hard he tried to 'turn respectable' there would always be something of the pirate in him. Something she had better not forget, she thought, appalled at how easy it was for him to make her laugh. As she snatched the smile from her face she reminded herself that this man had seduced her sister-in-law, and was not above using blackmail to get his own way.

'You look much prettier when you smile,' he observed, not bothering to hide the lazily caressing note in his voice or the slow appraisal which accompanied it. 'When you're angry your eyes light up but you go white around the mouth and your face gets a pinched look. I want to see you smile a lot while you're here.'

'Oh, I can grimace like a trained chimpanzee,' she retorted. 'But that's all you'll ever get.'

That shark's smile altered in quality, all of his

ruthlessness and the cold intelligence which fuelled it displayed in the handsome face. 'You'll do what I want,' he told her calmly. 'Dance, smile, talk——'

'Make love?'

'Not unless it's what you want,' he answered, the green-gold eyes completely confident as they rested like a kiss on the controlled line of her mouth. 'You've set up barriers in your mind, but I can wait until they're down. I don't go in for rape.'

'What is this you are doing to me if it's not some sort of rape? You force me to stay here, to acknowledge you——'

'That's what frightens you, isn't it?' He moved into the attack with the smooth deadliness of the predator he was. 'You don't want to see me as a man, no more nor less than any other man. To you I'm an ogre, the beast who stole your brother's wife and is forcing you to stay in my lair. But you're running scared because when I touch you you become mine. In fact, I don't even have to touch you. Look at me.'

As if they were dragged upwards her lashes lifted. She stared into his narrowed eyes, her skin prickling with instant heat as he deliberately let his gaze drop from the length of her throat to the curves beneath the rose-pink shirt, and thence to the long legs tucked gracefully against the sofa. By the time the sensual assessment was over her mouth was dry and her body feverish, her expression twisted by shame.

'All I have to do is look at you,' he said, no mercy softening the deep voice, 'and you become mine. Every response of your body belongs to me. And that is what scares the hell out of you.'

Her tongue touched the centre of her top lip. His gaze lingered on the small betrayal and tension roared across the space separating them like the lightning she had once seen blow a tree apart. It had all the casual inevitability of a primal force.

'It's the same for you,' she managed to return

raggedly. She was barely able to form the words but
something had to be done before she was dragged to
her feet by this almost irresistible desire and went to
him in silent surrender.

'Yes,' he replied, his voice uneven, 'but I'm not
fighting it, Clary. I know what I want and I'm going
to get it. You'll find that desire eats at your guts until
it becomes an obsession. Do you know I haven't had a
woman since I saw you? I haven't even wanted one.
Have you slept with anyone since then?'

The question hit her like a fist smashing glass.
Mesmerised, she shook her head, seeing too late the
triumph which blazed over the hard features. At that
moment she crashed to a full realisation of the power
and potency of his masculinity. Her eyes dilated as he
came towards her; she could not move, her whole
being trapped by such naked hunger that she was not
surprised to hear his breathing, the feral sound of a
man forced by passion back to his primitive self.

This time he did not just extend a hand. His fingers
fastened on to her shoulders and he pulled her to her
feet, his chest rising and falling as though he had
climbed a cliff to reach her. His eyes were slits, his
face drawn and famished but he held her away from
him until she signified defeat by closing her eyes and
swaying close to the lean strength she craved.

She expected the crushing brutality of their last
embrace, was prepared for it, would have welcomed it.
Indeed, his arms closed about her like a vice but
instead of taking the soft mouth held for him he
buried his face in the hollow where her neck joined her
shoulder as if her warmth and closeness was enough.

Clary's hands moved slowly, pulling his shirt free
from his trousers. They ached to touch his skin yet she
could not hurry them; they seemed enclosed in some
medium thicker than air which impeded movement
and sensitised her skin.

When at last she slid her fingers beneath the

material of his shirt his mouth moved convulsively against the heated silk of her throat. Trembling, she stroked the sleek warmth of his back, her shudder answered by his; a small, bland smile as old as the first woman pulled at her lips and forced the lashes down to cover her blank, unfocused eyes. Beneath the slow exploration of her hands his skin was on fire, smooth and silken over the taut framework of his body, magnificent, perfect to her.

A little gasping noise rattled in her throat. She turned so that her mouth came in contact with his neck and she pressed an open kiss there. Untutored, guided purely by instinct, her hips began to move, seeking relief from the burning ache which consumed her.

'Oh *God*!' he muttered, responding ferociously to the provocative, unconscious movement. His arms tightened as his hands slid down to her hips and brought her hard against him.

Clary went up in flames, welcoming the fierce thrust of his loins with an ardour as potent as it was explicit. She had no experience, no comparison to make. In the past there had been occasions when she had fought her way free from embraces as ardent as this, but they had caused her nothing but an uncomprehending disgust. She had forgotten them.

There would be no forgetting this, no convenient banishment of the sensations running untamed and free through her body, the straining, desperate urgency which had her reciprocate in kind. Her arms clung tightly across his well-muscled back, her mouth nuzzled into the part of his face or neck which was nearest as she tried to press closer, seeking that unknown, ultimate ecstasy with every movement.

'If I kiss you I'll take you.' The words were thick, rough, and they made no sense.

Clary didn't know that she was whimpering, strange, wild little noises expressing nothing but her pleas to have this pain assuaged, this hunger sated. The man holding her released her, then just in time to prevent her falling he grabbed her shoulders, shaking her with a violence which snapped her head backwards.

'Clary,' he groaned, more clearly this time, and again.

Slowly her lashes lifted, revealing empty, brilliant eyes. Colour burned along her cheekbones and her lips were parted, the tip of her tongue just visible.

Morgan's dark face was under such savage stress that it looked like a mask carved from dead wood. Strong white teeth clenched in agony; as awareness returned to her his chest rose and fell abruptly, the breath breaking harshly through his lips. He was not looking at her, he stood staring above her head. Clary tried to move away but her steps faltered. Already painful fingers gripped her more tightly, bruising her flesh.

In a voice she did not recognise she asked, 'Has this ever happened to you before?'

'No. Never.'

As the urgency of passion began to seep away, cooling her blood and taking with it the terrifying demands of a need she did not understand, she began to shake with reaction and self-contempt.

'Why?' she whispered. 'Why you, of all men?'

He smiled bitterly at the white hatred in her face. 'Why not? One of Fate's little jokes, my lovely. Can you stand upright without support yet?'

She needed to hide from his knowing gaze but her feet only took her as far as the nearest chair. Huddled into it, she watched as Morgan drained the rest of his drink and brought hers across. It was no consolation to see that his fingers trembled slightly, or that dusky colour still burned beneath his skin.

Her body was racked with unfulfilled longing. Hastily she drank the wine and sat hunched over the empty glass. 'I don't believe it,' she said blankly. 'It doesn't happen that way. I don't believe it.'

'Refusing to believe it in the hope that it might go away doesn't work. I spent some months trying.'

She barely heard him, her mind trying to make sense of the whole situation. Slowly, as if they might get hurt in the process, her eyes drifted towards Morgan. He sat down, the muscles in his thighs flexing and then relaxing as he stretched his legs in front of him. Another wave of heat scorched through Clary as she remembered those strongly-muscled thighs against hers and the exquisite sensations they had engendered.

'It's impossible,' she protested jerkily. 'It's *indecent*.'

He met her accusing stare with a great burst of laughter. His head went back in open enjoyment while Clary watched in impotent and fuming silence.

'I wonder what your definition of decent is,' he teased when his amusement had faded.

She shook her head, more affected than she dared admit by his laughter. 'You know what I mean.'

'Yes, I do. Doesn't it make you wonder, the fact that we can almost read each other's thoughts? No, I can see that you're going to try to close your mind to that too, just as you've refused to accept anything else about this situation.'

'All that you want me to admit is that I want to go to bed with you!'

'I know that you do, I've always known it. And so have you, from about two seconds after we saw each other across that pony ring. No, I want much more than your reluctant admission of desire, Clary.'

'You want me to be your lover,' she said angrily.

His soft laughter held a caressing note which tightened the skin over her cheekbones, across her breasts. 'That's inevitable,' he said with cool arrogance, 'but that won't be enough. I want all of you. All the intelligence and spirit and character, all of the warmth and the kindness—everything. All of it, just for me.'

Horrified, she stared at him. The freckles across her nose were like tiny exclamation marks on her pale skin.

'You're crazy,' she managed at last.

'Ambitious, perhaps; not crazy. You see, not only do I want you—I've had to face the fact that I must have you.' He gave a twisted, enigmatic smile, the classically perfect features rendered suddenly as harsh as a hawk's profile. 'Which was a considerable shock——'

'You might well end up wishing that you'd never seen me,' she interrupted. 'What if I demand the same of you?'

Arrested by the fierce challenge flung at him like a glove in the face, Morgan's expression revealed his surprise. Then it was replaced by that imperturbable mask which so successfully hid his emotions.

He replied, 'I think I would be disappointed if you accepted less. You're welcome to take what you want of me.'

'Be careful it's not your soul.'

Later, eating strawberries in the dining-room, she watched his lean hand lying motionless, half-curled on the dark polished wood of the table and wondered with shame just what had possessed her to succumb to a dramatic urge.

An excess of emotion—of sensation. Even now she felt the nagging bite of unsatisfied passion. How easy it would be to rouse again the tiger which slept so lightly within her.

A swift upward glance revealed Morgan's face, remote with the implacable beauty of great sculpture. Deep inside Clary, hidden tension dissolved in a surge of unidentifiable emotion.

It terrified her. *He* terrified her. She knew exactly

how the defenders of some great fortress must have felt when the walls they trusted to save them proved useless against the assault of treachery. Naked and bereft, betrayed by an enemy within.

The glowing crimson strawberries were tasteless in her mouth. Nervously she swallowed, forcing her mind away from the frightening present to the immediate past, to Mrs Hargreaves.

'Don't look at me as though I'm a patient,' she had greeted Clary when she had gone in to see her and found her awake. 'Tomorrow I'm getting up.'

'No reason why you shouldn't, if you remember that over-exertion now will set you back tomorrow.'

The shrewd eyes, more hazel than her son's but with the same straight brows, were fixed on Clary's face. 'Oh, I shan't overdo things. I don't intend to die for quite a few years yet. I'm going to see my grandchildren before I go.'

'An excellent ambition, and one quite easily attained if you do as you're told until you are over this,' Clary had replied, but her shock must have shown in her face because Mrs Hargreaves chuckled.

'It's time Morgan settled down. He's had a good innings, now he's ready to indulge his dynastic urge. You met in London, I believe?'

She couldn't have made her satisfaction more obvious if she had come right out with her blessings.

'Just outside,' Clary said hastily. 'At Chase.'

'Nice place, isn't it? Pity my cousin is such a stupid man. Still, his wife is even more stupid.' Mrs Hargreaves dismissed the Sedburys with open contempt. 'Do them both good to have to work for a living. Do you think you're going to like it here?'

Clary thought bitterly of that obsessive desire which carried within it the seeds of its own destruction and said carefully, 'Yes, I'm certain I shall. It's a lovely place.'

'But the people don't appeal so much.'

It was on the tip of Clary's tongue to tell her just what she thought of one of the people there, but she remembered Morgan's threat, and her own sense of responsibility forbade her to disturb the woman in the bed. So she said merely, 'I'm afraid it takes me a little while to relax with people I've just met, but everyone has been very helpful. Very nice,' she finished lamely.

'Of course they have,' Mrs Hargreaves said with relish. 'Both Morgan and I like living with nice people, probably because we're not very nice ourselves. Do you believe in the attraction of opposites?'

Clary avoided the shrewd gaze of the older woman by straightening the flowers on the bedside table. 'I'm afraid I've never given it much thought.'

'Try it some time. Thinking, I mean. It's amazing how few people are actually capable of thinking, as opposed to using their emotions as reasons for their actions. Morgan has a very good brain, he's always used logic as a basis for his actions. So far it's worked extremely well for him, but although he probably doesn't realise it, he's vulnerable because he doesn't know how to cope with the sort of emotion which goes beyond logic. Now, off you go and get dressed for dinner. I don't want to see you again tonight. Ruth Swann is going to get me up to date on the Valley gossip.'

'I'll come in before I go to bed.'

At this juncture there was a slight tussle of wills, which Clary won. Now, drinking excellent coffee, she wondered at that remark about grandchildren. She had assumed, in the most egotistical way, that it was aimed at her, but perhaps Mrs Hargreaves had some other woman picked out to be Morgan's wife. Savaged by a jealousy so intense that it hurt to draw breath, she had to set the coffee-cup down. It made a soft chinking noise as it reached the saucer.

'What is it?'

His voice startled her into looking across at him.

Something in her expression gave her away, for he got to his feet and came to crouch by her chair, taking her hand in his.

'What is it?' he repeated half beneath his breath, his thumb finding a pulse which fluttered wildly. 'Do you feel ill?'

'No, it's nothing.' She tried to free her hand but his grip tightened. Seen so close his eyes were actually a green as deep as the sea; from the dark pupil the green was irradiated by rays of gold like a sunburst.

Beautiful eyes, superbly shaped and placed in the sculptured framework of his face, heavy-lidded, with long curling lashes. Very slowly she reached out a finger and traced a straight black brow, the haughty aquiline blade of his nose, the sweep of cheekbone, until her exploration reached the autocractic jaw. Still staring into his eyes as if lost in their depths she followed the line from his ear to the thrusting strength of his chin. She was overcome by a strange tenderness which mingled with the effect of his closeness to become inseparable from it.

'You are magnificent,' she heard her own voice whisper as if she had discovered the answer to the riddle of the universe.

He didn't smile. Like her he seemed astonished, almost awed at the newness of this experience, but the glitter of gold in his eyes flared to a radiance she could not meet.

'And you are perfect,' he said at last, his voice husky.

It was then that the barking of several dogs roused them from their absorption in each other. Beneath her fingers Morgan's lips moved as he said something she was glad she didn't quite catch, then he was on his feet, listening as the noise of a car engine increased, idled, then stopped.

It was a man to see him on business of some sort; they spent an hour in the office, emerging as Clary was wrestling with the intricacies of a country telephone exchange.

'Wait,' Morgan said curtly to her. 'I'll be back in a moment. Use the phone in the office.'

'I'm quite capable——'

But he was sweeping the rather surprised visitor away with him, only to reappear almost immediately.

'Look, you needn't bother——' she began angrily as he opened the door into the office.

'It's no bother,' he returned, his mocking amusement only too obvious. 'As your host it's my duty to smooth your path whenever possible.'

'You're not my host, you're my employer.'

He smiled. 'Is this the number you want?'

'Yes. It's my mother. I'll reverse the charges.'

He lifted his brows. 'My dear girl, we can afford a call to Auckland.'

Clary frowned, and he leaned forward and said, 'I've spent a lot of time these last months wondering how you'd look when you smiled. You don't do it enough, but the reality more than lives up to the best my imagination could produce. Actually, I've been living a rich fantasy life since I met you. I've derived an immense amount of pleasure imagining you in all sorts of ways——'

'Stop it!'

'—laughing, smiling that funny little smile you give when you try to hide the fact that something has amused you, naked and eager in my bed, in my arms——'

'Morgan, shut up!'

His voice overrode her shocked protest. He stood by the big desk, one lean hand on the telephone, and effortlessly held her rooted to the floor by the sheer power of his words. 'And afterwards, when you're sated, I know how you're going to look then, too. All that self-control you wear like armour will have disappeared, and you'll be open to me. Your skin will be flushed and your lashes will curl down over your eyes and that lovely mouth will be fuller, still red from my kisses. And your beautiful body will be warm and lax, and mine, all mine . . .'

Fascinated, terrified at the punishing surge of desire roused by the slow, erotic words, Clary's tongue touched her lips. The brilliant gaze which held her prisoner caught fire at the involuntary little movement. He took a step towards her, his intention plain, and then stopped.

'No,' he said raggedly, 'this is not the time, or, damn it, the place. When we make love we're going to have all night to do it and a bed to make it comfortable. Otherwise you'll end up so bruised that you won't be able to move for days.'

'You are incredibly conceited if you think it's going to be that easy.' She didn't really know what she was saying. She was too busy trying to conjure up some self-control so that she could subjugate the unruly sensations which went brawling through every nerve and cell in her body.

'Face facts.' His voice was dry and sardonic; by now he had his emotions well under restraint. 'I can take you any time I want to. I don't even need to touch you to have you completely willing. But you must be ready too, because once we become lovers it will be too late to change your mind.'

'Just make sure that I don't make you wait too long.' Yes, that had the right note of contempt to it.

He looked very levelly at her, meeting her accusing stare with a touch of her own contempt. 'I can be patient when I want something as much as I want you.'

'I'm not a *thing*!'

The broad shoulders lifted slightly. Clary watched as he strode behind the desk.

'I'm sorry.' He sounded tired. 'No, you are not a thing. You are all woman. My woman. But I like my fruits mature, not sour and unripe. So I'll wait.'

CHAPTER FIVE

HE did not leave the room while she spoke to her mother. He lounged on the other side of the desk with a moody expression which intrigued while it irritated her. Halfway through the call it was replaced by a smile, taunting and amused. She had to suppress her savage desire to slap it from his face. Only worry at his possible reaction and the shaming knowledge that she was quite incapable of resisting him, whatever he did, kept her hand by her side.

The extremes of emotion and sensation he induced in her were mind-boggling. Never before had she felt anything like this anger which fountained through the top of her head, and she had not known that it was possible to suffer such erotic tension. The only thing that eased her bewilderment was the knowledge that Morgan too was dealing with something outside his experience. And that was a dangerous path for her thoughts to take. She could not afford to weaken. His need for her surrender was all that kept her safe. If he came to her room at night she would accept him as her lover and while they were together she would give him everything he desired.

But afterwards she would hate him and hate herself, and he knew it. Because he was the man he was, possessive, dominant, he needed more than the begrudged gift of her body. *All of you*, he had said, and he meant it. He wanted capitulation, to take over her life like a conqueror. So he would not press her to sleep with him, not yet.

Submission was impossible. If she allowed him any sort of victory she would lose herself. Exactly as her father had, as Angus had. She was terrified of becoming an emotional cripple like them.

When the call was over she slammed down the receiver, glaring at him.

'Very cool,' he said, those penetrating eyes sliding over her angry face. 'Are you always so matter of fact when you speak to your mother?'

'We aren't a demonstrative family,' she snarled, then bit her lip.

'No?' The single syllable said it all, but in case she had missed the point he hammered it in. 'I know one of you who is—very demonstrative. Excitingly so.'

'That's sex,' she scoffed. 'Not emotion. I've seen what emotion can do.'

'Angus?'

'And others.'

He came around the desk and slid his fingers around her wrist. 'So you are afraid.'

'Aren't you?'

'Yes. I knew that sort of emotion existed; my parents were devoted to each other. I never thought it would happen to me.'

Stunned, she pulled her wrist free, twisting to stare up into his face. 'Are you implying that you are in *love* with me?'

'How do I know? I've never experienced it before. You'd be pleased if I loved you, wouldn't you, because it would give you power over me.' Her eyes blazed, and he smiled without humour. 'You'd pull the world down around our ears and glory in it, if you thought it would free you from me.'

In the days that followed she expected him to press his claim but although he insisted on her company whenever he was home he didn't touch her except with those bold, disturbing eyes.

In an odd way she enjoyed herself. Mrs Hargreaves was well on the way to complete recovery and her astringent common sense made her an entertaining if occasionally intimidating companion. After one sharp enquiring glance she made no comment on the tension she picked up when Clary and Morgan were together. When she wanted her face could be as impassive as Morgan's.

After the first uncomfortable few days Clary found herself taking pleasure in the times when all three were together. Accustomed as she was to her mother's calm practicality, the unsentimental frankness between Morgan and his mother pleased rather than shocked her. Nor did she make the mistake of underestimating their affection for each other. She listened without horror as Mrs Hargreaves told Morgan exactly which sort of tree she wanted her ashes buried under.

'A Charles Raffil magnolia,' she told him firmly, ignoring his smile. 'The one with those superb rose-pink flowers. Plant it down by the water-lily pond. The empress tree will be too big by then, it will have to come down before its roots block the drain. I can't think what possessed me to plant it there. Not that it matters, as I've planted another by the tennis court.'

'I wish you would make up your mind,' Morgan complained cheerfully. 'That's the fourth one you've chosen in the last year. Every time a new catalogue comes out you fall in love with a different tree!'

'Ah, but I always go back to my lovely magnolia. It is, I think, one of the most beautiful trees in the world. Just think, every year you'll be able to go out and tell each other how well I'm flowering!'

Repressing her surprise at being coupled with Morgan so blatantly, Clary said, 'Or that it's a blooming good year for mothers.'

This brought forth some satisfactory groans as well as a crop of puns from the other two, each worse than the one before, until she clapped her hands over her ears and cried peace.

Mrs Hargreaves busied herself with one of her catalogues, making a list as she scanned the pages. It was Saturday and Morgan lay sprawled on a lounger, reading the newspaper. They had just finished morning tea beside the pool. The sun beamed down with the fresh, hopeful strength of early summer. Both women sat in the vine-wreathed shade of the pergola but neither the heat nor the dancing, glinting light from the pool seemed to bother Morgan. He didn't even wear dark glasses.

Clary had been watching him for some time before she was aware that she was taking in the shadows cast by those long lashes, the loose-limbed grace of his relaxed body, the way the muscles in his leg moved when he pulled up one knee to balance the sheets of newspaper. The beautiful morning had coaxed him into wearing shorts and a loose cotton shirt, but he looked as elegant in them as he did in his severe, well-tailored business suits.

Desire tightened into a coil in the pit of her stomach. Before she could look away his lashes lifted and his eyes met hers; in them she saw a reciprocal passion. The peace of the morning fled.

'Come for a swim,' he said, too calmly.

'I only swim at the height of summer, when the water is lukewarm.'

'The solar panels on the roof keep it that temperature all year round.' He recognised the excuse for what it was and gave her no quarter.

'I haven't a bathing suit.'

His smile slid over the edge into mockery. 'We always keep spares. Ruth is easily shocked, so we prefer that no one swims naked.'

He got to his feet and came across to where she sat, feet pressed side by side, knees and thighs primly clamped together, her whole body tight with rejection. 'We're sure to find one that fits you,' he insisted and pulled her gently from her chair. 'I'd like to see if skin as white as yours ever tans.'

His touch burned into her arms. She said, 'Mrs Hargreaves . . .?'

Without lifting her head the older woman said, 'Go and swim, Clary, or he'll pester you until you do. Morgan always gets his own way. It's very bad for his character, but that's the way he's always been.'

'So come on.' The silky voice laughed at her impotence, but there was an intense hunger in his gaze which seemed to fill an emptiness in her.

'Very well,' she said under her breath.

Like children they walked hand in hand past the huge room which was used, so Ruth had told Clary, for informal parties. It was furnished in cane and light wooden furniture, rough yet elegant and comfortable, and had its own kitchen facilities and the same quarry-tiled floor which formed the terrace around the pool.

The changing-room was just as luxurious. Clary surveyed the shower cubicles, the wide bench which served as a vanity, and the enormous mirror. There were plants here as well as in the party room, great leafy things which emphasised the impact of dark wood and more quarry tiles. It could have been a grotto beside a pool in some lush, tropical jungle.

'Here,' Morgan said, opening one of a bank of cupboards. 'See what you can find. If you aren't ready in five minutes I'll come in to get you.'

She opened her mouth to protest but he was already halfway to the door. Frowning to hide the piercing excitement in her blood, she eyed the bathing suits carefully stored in the cupboard. Her frown deepened as she pulled our various scanty pieces of swimwear, holding them up before discarding them. Bikinis would expose far too much skin to Morgan's bold appraisal, yet the only maillot which was long enough in the body and big enough in the bust for her was one with exceptionally high-cut legs which she disliked.

A quick glance at her watch made the decision for her. Even as she hissed with dismay she tore off her clothes and climbed into the clear yellow suit. It didn't need her swift look at her reflection to reveal that the suit hugged her body far too lovingly. Ordinarily it would not have worried her to wear such a maillot; what tensed every muscle was the fact that Morgan had definite effects on her body and she was at enough of a disadvantage without letting him see just what he did to her.

So she headed straight for the pool and dived smoothly in before setting off for the other end in her efficient crawl. Morgan was already in the water and, like her, he seemed content to do lengths until they had both worked off some of the pent-up sexual energy which pressured them.

At last Clary hauled herself up on to the bottom step and pushed her hair back from her face. As if she had given a signal Morgan followed her, the sheen of the water accentuating the powerful grace of his body. He wasn't panting but Clary could see the rapid beat of his pulse in his throat and knew that her own was a similar betrayal.

'That suit,' he said gravely, 'could make old men's homes redundant.' He grinned at her astonishment and continued, 'They'd all die of heart attacks, or rocketing blood pressure or just sheer chagrin because you're the same age as their granddaughters. I'm rather thinking of having a heart attack myself. Fortunately I don't have to worry about the chagrin, because you're just the right age for me.'

'How old are you?' It was inane, but it was all she could think of to say while his narrowed devouring eyes were telling her that she was beautiful, that he wanted her beyond all reckoning.

He smiled. 'I'm thirty-three. And you are twenty-five. As I said, just the right age. Are you cold?'

'Yes,' she lied. His satisfied laughter followed as she showered and dressed. His confidence bordered on egoism, she told herself savagely, but the fact that he had every reason for that confidence made her cringe.

Angus, she thought stubbornly, and into her brain

there flashed an image of Morgan and Susan, the tanned litheness of his body blending into the sinuous grace of hers in the closeness of passion.

It seared savagely through her but she kept it in her mind, forcing herself to remember that even if she was so weak as to give herself to him, it would be impossible. The pain he had caused Angus with his casual lust for Susan stood between them like a poisoned sword.

'Angus,' she said through the soft hissing of the shower, repeating his name like a charm, like a warning.

When she re-emerged into the sunlight Morgan was lying on his stomach on the lounger, apparently asleep, still clad in his brief black bathing suit. Her eyes swept the length of his body from the sleekly-muscled shoulders to his lean flanks and the strength of his thighs. He lay deceptively relaxed like a great cat, with an underlying alertness which was probably never dormant. In spite of the caution she had given herself her mouth dried. For a moment her face was illuminated by such naked need that it seemed to flame forth.

She felt ill, especially when her eyes slid to meet his mother's. It did not help that there was sympathy in the hazel gaze so openly watching her. She felt cheap as well as sick. Did Mrs Hargreaves think that Morgan and she were having an affair? It humiliated her to be classed with the women who had shared his bed. She wanted to shout, 'I am special, he said so,' and immediately wondered if he told them all that.

And as immediately she recognised that her cynical little thought was unfair. Morgan was just as astounded by the depth of attraction between them as she was. He had not lied; she would have known if he had.

After lunch, when she was alone with her employer, she said hesitantly, 'Mrs Hargreaves, I am not Morgan's mistress.'

'I know that.' Mrs Hargreaves's acerbic voice softened as she went on, 'If I have learned anything in a life spent dealing with cantankerous, bull-headed, unreasonable humanity it's never to interfere and never to take sides.'

Clary said carefully, her eyes very dark in her white face, 'I didn't want you to think that there was anything going on behind your back.'

'You're a well-brought up girl. Thank you. However, Morgan is not intimidated by me. If he'd wanted to install a mistress here he'd have done it quite openly.'

'And you wouldn't object?'

Mrs Hargreaves's thin shoulders lifted. 'Why should I? Hunter's Valley is Morgan's, he can invite anyone he likes here.'

'Oh, I thought—I'm sorry, I assumed it was yours.'

'No, his father left it to him.' The older woman smiled reminiscently as she looked back down the years. 'His father was another one like Morgan. He bought the station when it was so run down nobody would come near it. The previous owner made his living by chopping the *manuka* scrub and selling it for firewood. Once we'd paid for the place we had no money for development, so we had to do it the hard way.'

'How old were you when you came here?' So interested was Clary that she didn't even consider the rudeness of her question.

'Seventeen, straight from school.' Mrs Hargreaves laughed at Clary's stunned face. 'I knew what I wanted; my parents tried to coax me into waiting by offering me a trip around the world, but I said I'd wait until John and I could go together.'

'And did you go?'

'No. He died. My splendid, vital John, gone in three weeks with a cancer he never knew he had. I'm glad I refused to wait until I was twenty-one before I married him.' Remembered pain showed briefly in Mrs Hargreaves's expression, was as swiftly banished by a definitely mischievous twinkle. 'Not that I really had much choice. John was eight years older than I, and like Morgan, he didn't wait around once he'd made up his mind. He was hard, he made a bad enemy, but he was the best husband in the world for me. And a good father to Morgan, although they had some almighty clashes. Even when Morgan was a child they were too much alike to live comfortably together. I used to wonder how I was going to cope when Morgan was growing up.'

She looked across at Clary with a grim little smile. 'But John wasn't there to see his son grow up. He would have been proud of him. Instead there was Geoffrey Hargreaves, who was shocked by Morgan's hard-headed attitudes even though he liked and respected him. Geoffrey was always more than aware that in Morgan's eyes he didn't measure up.'

Clary would have dearly liked to ask why Mrs Hargreaves had married again when she had so obviously buried her heart with Morgan's father, but she didn't dare.

'Because I liked him,' the older woman answered the unspoken question with a subtle little smile. 'And because I was lonely; because he had loved me since he first met me fifteen years before. For several reasons, but mainly because the thought of never loving again terrified me. We had a good marriage, even if Geoffrey failed lamentably to tame my wild son.'

There was nothing to say to that. Clary pushed a curl back behind her ear and twitched the coverlet straight.

'You're going to have to develop a little toughness yourself if you want to deal with him,' Mrs Hargreaves astounded her by saying. 'You have the same streak of wildness, well camouflaged of course——'

'Wildness? Oh, come on now . . .' Clary laughed, her hand indicating her shirt and skirt, restrained, almost prim.

'I said it was well camouflaged. You had better accept it,' her employer said drily, 'otherwise you're going to be badly disadvantaged in this game you're playing with my son. One of Morgan's strengths is his ability to home in on weaknesses. It doesn't matter whether he's dealing with a company or a conglomerate or a man. Or a woman. He's not above using those weak points to get the results he wants, either.'

'No.' Clary was almost tempted to confide in her. She went so far as to look her way with a hint of entreaty, but even before she met Mrs Hargreaves's bland gaze she knew that she would not beg for help. She doubted very much whether it would be granted; if it was she would refuse it. She was, she had to be, strong enough to fight for herself and win. The exhilaration of battle flamed in her expression, transforming it.

'Yes, you have plenty of courage,' Mrs Hargreaves decided in a satisfied voice. 'Learn your strengths and don't underestimate your weaknesses. That's the only advice you'll get from me. Now, away you go. I'm going to rest. You can go out, if you're feeling housebound. Take the little car if you want to explore; Ruth tells me you're an excellent driver. And she will keep an eye on me, so you can have a few hours off without it hurting your conscience.'

Clary no longer worried about her patient. She was progressing well and not given to foolishness. In fact, with Ruth in the house no nurse was needed. Clary had suggested to the doctor the previous day that she was superfluous, only to be told rather austerely that as Ruth was not confident enough to take the responsibility and Morgan spent most of his time in Auckland, her presence was very necessary.

Morgan's time in Auckland was news to Clary.

Since her arrival he had slept every night at Hunter's Valley, even those on which he stayed in town for dinner and didn't arrive home until late. His deep if unspoken love for his mother was the most endearing thing Clary knew about him. It made him a little more approachable.

He did not look in the least approachable when he emerged from the office as she was going past; he looked tired and angry. However when he saw her he smiled, his eyes roaming her face with open appreciation.

'That's a very determined expression. I like the way your chin lifts in a delicate little defiance when you see me. In fact, I like all of that chin. Especially that cleft. Very provocative, I find that cleft.'

'Oh, to to hell!'

He laughed, his teeth very white in his tanned face. 'I suppose it's always a possibility. Come for a drive with me.'

'No, thank you.'

'But I insist.'

She measured glances with him, her chin very much in evidence until he smiled and said, 'I promise I won't touch you. Not unless you ask me to.'

He doesn't have to *touch* you, her brain told her and she read his knowledge of that unspoken admission in his face. He knew that even the thought of him was enough to set the blood running wildly through her body.

Yet she said, 'Where—what will I wear?'

'You look stunning as you are. I've been neglecting my friends lately, but yesterday I was pinned down by one for tonight. You'll like the Oxtens. They live at Orewa.'

'Your mother——'

'Thinks it a marvellous idea. It's been over a week since you had a day off. We'll be there for dinner but it will be a barbecue, so if you want to change, something casual.'

Casual chic, no doubt, not the sort of thing Clary owned much of. However she did have a shirt-waister in dark blue cotton which was not too elegant for a barbecue. With a wide grey belt to make the most of her slim waist and interesting pewter buttons, it could go almost anywhere.

In her room she changed and was pulling a comb through the tumbled mass of her hair when her door opened and Morgan strolled in as though he had every right.

'You damned well knock!' she flung over her shoulder.

'I did, but you were too busy muttering to yourself to hear me. What's the matter?'

'Oh, it's just my hair. It's so thick it drives me crazy.'

He came across to stand just behind it. 'I like it,' he said, looping a finger through one soft curl. 'It's like silk. I love the way it swings when you walk, and I find it intensely erotic against my cheek when I kiss your throat. But,' quite matter of factly as he released her, 'I find everything about you extremely erotic, as I'm sure you must be aware.'

'You've made it more than clear.' She had to get away. It took an effort of will to put the comb down and walk across the room to slip on a pair of dark blue sandals.

'Not going to reciprocate?'

She recognised the lazily insolent note in his voice and shook her head, caution warring with anger. 'Don't torment me, Morgan.'

'Why not? You and your inhibitions torment me.'

The words frightened her, yet she couldn't subdue the primitive pleasure which welled up in her.

'Yes, you like that, don't you?' His eyes narrowed as he surveyed her face. 'Beneath that cool restraint you're a tease, my lovely. I don't mind, in fact, I enjoy watching you spin your plots, but remember one

thing. You are not going to renege on this hand. I'll
collect when we're both ready for it, and the payment
is going to be wild and sweet and loving for both of
us.'

'Loving?' The word splintered between the syllables
but she retained enough control to flash scornfully,
'You don't know the meaning of the word.'

He said quietly, 'Making love is what it's called.'

'*Sex* is what it's called.'

Beneath the fine cotton of his shirt his shoulders
moved in a dismissive shrug. 'Have it your own way.
Call it sex or making love, it's those and more, but it
comes to one thing in the end. You are going to admit
that you need me as much as I need you.'

'You'll be waiting a long time.'

He looked suddenly demanding and possessive. 'I
can stand it if you can.'

The statement made her bristle, but behind the
arrogant words she heard the same aching hunger
which made her nights restless, the days long and
tense. Her lips trembled; she turned her head so that
all he could see was a remote profile.

'In the meantime,' he said coolly, 'I tantalise myself
by imagining things.'

Her head snapped around before she could stop it.
He was laughing at her, mockery gleaming beneath his
lashes. 'So far we've made love in every different way
there is, and several which are probably only described
in Kama Sutra——'

'I will not be used as material for your sordid
fantasies!'

The amusement was wiped from his face as if she
had slapped it. 'I don't like the word sordid. Making
love may be sordid to you—to me it is an affirmation
of love and life, something valuable and beautiful.'

She bit her lip but came back gamely, 'I suppose
you were in love with every woman you've slept with!'

'No,' he told her, 'but I have liked and respected

each one, and making love has always been a part of that. Now, Miss Prim, on your way. I love that pretty blush but we'd better get out of here before I start translating an occasional fantasy into reality.'

CHAPTER SIX

THE Oxtens lived on the cliff to the north of the long pale sweep of Orewa beach, overlooking both Orewa and the equally lovely though much smaller Hatfield's beach. Before them lay a wide, shimmering expanse of the Hauraki gulf, flecked by the multitudinous sails of a part of Auckland's fleet of pleasure yachts.

The house was modern, starkly crafted so that it seemed to hover between the enormous voids of the sea and the sky. It was impressive and very lovely, but Clary found the Hunter valley homestead's elegant suavity more satisfying. However, the Oxtens were more than happy with their house, and were certainly delighted to see Morgan.

He introduced Clary as his mother's nurse and companion, which effectively changed the knowing look in Sam Oxten's eyes into a slightly startled glance, one which he shared with his wife. Clearly they were accustomed to meeting Morgan's girlfriends, but were not too sure how to treat a woman who was not in that category. The little hiatus lasted only a second until Fay Oxten remembered her duty as a hostess.

'How is Mrs Hargreaves?' she asked as she led them into a huge room which appeared to have as two of its walls only the sea and the sky.

'Fine,' Morgan said briefly, adding with a dry lack of expression, 'you know my mother. You could, perhaps, do her some damage with a hammer if you really tried.'

'Incredible, isn't she?' Fay's voice revealed genuine awe. 'Now, Clary, meet Karen Graham and Tony— you two know Morgan, of course, but this is Clary Grey.'

The Grahams were both statuesque blondes, the woman only an inch or so shorter than her brother. From her Clary received a pleasant smile and greeting, but Karen Graham's attention was fixed on Morgan and there was that in her glorious eyes which made Clary furious. Not another one, she thought savagely as she smiled and exchanged greetings with Tony Graham.

Appalled by the violence of her angrily possessive reaction, she didn't notice the warm admiration in Tony Graham's expression until she was sitting beside him on a very expensive and rather uncomfortable sofa.

'. . . long at Hunter's Valley?' he was asking.

'I've been there since Mrs Hargreaves came home from hospital, and I'll go when the doctor decides she doesn't need me any more.'

His smile flirted openly with her. 'Where are you from?'

'Auckland.'

'So am I.' He made it sound as if it was an incredible coincidence.'

'As it's the biggest—the *only*—city around, I don't find that altogether surprising.'

'Don't be like that,' he implored. 'I was trying to forge a bond between us.'

'Consider it forged. We both come from Auckland. We're both human beings. We both speak English. Lots of bonds if you look for them.'

Using his body to shut out the rest of the room he complained, 'You're not taking this at all seriously! If you're going to be frivolous and flippant how can I possibly convince you by the time you leave tonight that you know me well enough to go out with me?'

'You can't,' she said promptly, smiling because though he was a fast worker he was rather endearing. All open and on the surface, with nothing of Morgan's dark danger. 'Now, behave yourself. It's bad manners to turn your back on the rest of the room.'

'Not when the rest of the room has Morgan Caird in it,' he grumbled, but he moved back obediently, saying with a long-suffering note in his voice, 'I suppose you're just like all the other women I meet, including my very persistent sister. You're crazily in love with the man.'

Morgan's voice was amused as he brought a long glass of some white concoction over to her. 'Alas, I wish she was,' he said lightly. 'The lady is very much her own person.'

'Oh, well, if your celebrated charm hasn't worked, go away and let me try,' Tony commanded with cheerful rudenes.

'I'm still here,' Clary said very gently, the merest edge of steel sharpening the words.

It was enough to startle Tony. 'Was I being rude? Sorry——'

'You were both being rude.'

Morgan's eyes gleamed with sardonic appreciation as Tony said earnestly, 'You're beginning to remind me of the lady who taught me when I first went to school. She had flaming eyeballs and stood fifty feel tall, and she had a nasty knack of stripping your skin at a hundred and fifty paces. Was she a relation?'

'Almost certainly,' Morgan drawled, holding out an imperative hand to Clary. 'Leave this amiable clown to his drink and gladden Sam and Fay's combined hearts by admiring their view.'

It was an order, and one she obeyed as she realised that the others in the room were paying a considerable amount of attention to them. He released her hand immediately, but not before his fingers closed around hers in a sudden fierce warning. Colour touched her cheeks; she knew she should not have let Tony corner her like that, so she walked meekly across the ceramic-tiled floor to the enormous walls of glass.

Her gasp of delight was all that her hosts expected. 'Oh, this is superb,' she breathed as her eyes took in the scene below.

The house was built back from the edge of the cliff and there was no garden, just a grove of *pohutukawa* trees, flashing green and silver in the slight breeze. Beyond them were the waters of the bay backed by Hatfield's beach and directly opposite sprawled another headland like their own, pine- and *pohutukawa*-clad, with tiny beaches at the base of rusty, cave-spotted cliffs. On the other side stretched the long gentle curve of Orewa, on this hot day thick with sun-worshippers. Past it Whangaparoa peninsula probed into the waters of the gulf. Most if it was as heavily built-over as the flat land behind Orewa beach, but the maritime park at the tip and the island beyond that were still green, as were the hills behind Hatfield's beach.

'It must be like living in the gondola of a balloon,' Clary murmured at last.

Fay nodded enthusiastically. 'Or on the bow of a ship. At night it's superb. We love living here.'

'It reminds me a little of Greece,' Clary said. 'The stark hills and the pines—only here they're much thicker and the hills are greener than I ever saw in Greece, but the olives have that silvery gleam, like the *pohutukawas*, and the atmosphere is almost unbearably the same. I drove a funny little van up a goat-track in the south of Paros and got out and cried amongst the thyme and oregano and cistus because I was so homesick.'

'Did you?' Karen was openly incredulous. 'I never got to Paros, but I adored Mykonos. I never wanted to leave it.'

Everyone chimed in with their favourite holiday spot, everyone but Morgan, and Clary, who felt rather embarrassed at her revelations. She tried to concentrate on what was being said, but her attention was almost totally captured by the man who stood beside her, outlined against the sun by an aura of light. She looked blindly at whoever happened to be speaking but she comprehended only the full oppressive weight of his watchfulness. Slowly, as inevitably as it always was, her body responded with an expectant, vivid awareness.

'How about you, Morgan?' Karen favoured him with her lovely smile. 'You've probably travelled more than the rest of us put together. What is your favourite place? Some secluded hideaway in the Seychelles? A ski-lodge in St Moritz?'

'A little village not far from London,' he drawled.

'Don't be infuriating. Tell us why.' Karen's smile was a nice blend of encouragement and languor. She was a very pleasant woman, but at that moment Clary could have pushed her out of the window without an atom of regret.

'I have a remote cousin who lives there,' he said with a tantalising smile. 'It's very pretty in the English style, but my favourite spot is one field where they hold pony-club events.'

When it became clear that he wasn't going to continue Fay Oxten pleaded laughingly, 'Oh, go on, Morgan, you great tease. We're all dying to know why.'

Speak for yourself, Clary thought, rigid with tension. What was he going to tell them? She kept her eyes fixed unseeingly on the splendid view, waiting.

He grinned at his hostess, saying with infuriating blandness, 'I first saw the love of my life there, of course.'

The laughter which greeted this was guarded, as though they weren't sure whether he was joking or not.

'Truly?' Karen said sweetly, recovering from her initial astonishment. 'Who's the lucky woman?'

'You'll have to wait for that information, I'm afraid. I'm having a little difficulty convincing her that she is lucky.'

They clearly didn't believe this. No wonder he's conceited, Clary thought viciously, knowing that she was wrong, that his arrogance was the result of a naturally commanding personality with the strength and authority to back it up. Amid a chorus of teasing remarks about this incredibly blind and deaf, not to mention invisible love of his, remarks he parried with wit and good humour, they moved out on to a courtyard sheltered by the wings of the house.

'I know the sea is only ten minutes down the cliff,' Fay admitted as she caught Clary eyeing the swimming and spa pools with astonishment, 'but the path down is steep, and the sea is always much cooler than the pool. We like our creature comforts.'

'Sybarites.' That was Morgan, affectionately mocking.

Fay grinned at him. 'Oh, we all know you swim in icy-cold bush pools, but even you, iron man, have the pool at the homestead heated. Do sit down, Clary. Have you shown Clary your own very private pool yet, Morgan?'

'Not yet,' he said lazily, joining Clary on a wide, brilliantly patterned sofa.

He kept his eyes on Fay; she was smiling at him as though she had discerned a secret. Perhaps she had but no sign of it appeared in her voice as she said, 'You must. It's so beautiful, a pool on a wide ledge halfway down the big hill behind the homestead. It's surrounded by bush and it has a waterfall feeding it and about a hundred feet of rapids at the outlet.'

'Down quite a steep cliff covered with trees and thick with rocks.' Sam Oxten smiled reminiscently at his wife. 'Up which I had to push you, if I remember correctly. I know Morgan refused to help.'

The two Oxtens and Morgan exchanged smiles. Karen demanded, 'Where is this pool? Why haven't I been shown it? Morgan, you've been holding out on me.'

'It's difficult to get to,' Morgan said coolly.

'The only reason we went is that Morgan told Fay he'd learned to swim in it and she's insatiably curious.'

Sam winked at Clary. 'And when we got there—at last!—nothing would induce her to even dip a toe in it.'

'I should think not! It looked freezing!' Fay was laughingly indignant, wrinkling her nose at her husband's mockery. 'And I wanted to go up because Morgan said there were native orchids in the bush there. It is so lovely, with a huge *titoki* tree on a grassy bank which has a long rope suspended from a branch so anyone who's brave enough to swim can swing right out over the pool and drop into it from a great height!'

She shuddered; Clary's eyes met Morgan's amused, uncommunicative gaze and she knew who that rope was for. He used the pool at the homestead to keep fit, swimming lengths for over half an hour each day. Now she wondered how often he climbed the cliff to that other pool and used the rope as he had when he was a reckless daredevil of a boy.

The conversation drifted, became a discussion on an exhibition at the Art Gallery in Auckland, a selection from the Queen's collection of da Vinci nature drawings, including the superb 'Deluge' series.

Clary listened silently to the comments and observations. Karen was enthusiastic but not knowledgeable, the others spoke with understanding and delight. From art the conversation moved on to sailing and some mild gossip, thence to a projected visit by one of the great English ballet companies, the best way to deal with an entire smoked marlin, and a new potter Fay had discovered.

'She's marvellous!' she assured them all fervently. 'Her work has a lovely sculptural quality, and she's done some fantastic things with glazes. I bought one of her bowls which is a symphony, a poem; as miraculous as a sunset!'

Karen teased her about her enthusiasm, but Morgan asked the name of the potter.

'Yes, I thought you'd be interested. She's Jennet Hollingworth.'

'Rafe Hollingworth's wife?' This did interest Karen.

'That's her. You know Rafe, don't you, Morgan? Weren't you and he at school together? He's an absolute dish with a fabulous station up north. Jennet was his step-sister. She was an actress in Australia before she came home and married him. Melissa Addison is her half-sister.

'Trent's wife?' Karen leaned forward, her expression alert and, as her glance touched Clary's face, just a little smug. It was as if she was staking her claim to inhabit a circumscribed, exclusive little world. She gave an artificial laugh and rolled her eyes heavenwards. 'Oh, but Trent is a gorgeous man, a real brigand. We all went into shock when he married the first time.'

Morgan must have noticed that taunting little glance, for he calmly told them what all but Clary must have known. 'He started off in electronics—he's quite brilliant in that field. Eventually he gained control of the Durrant group and pulled it out of the red. His first wife is Sir Peter Durrant's granddaughter.'

'That marriage was a very odd business.' But Karen met with no encouragement to expand and finished lamely, 'I wonder what happened to her. Last I heard she was in London . . .'

They were off again, chatting about people most of whom were just names to Clary although occasionally she recognised one which turned up in the news, sometimes in the financial section, as often in reviews of art or books. Between them they seemed to know everyone of any importance in the country. Apart from Karen they were not trying to make Clary feel inadequate; the conversation was light and amusing, but if anything was needed to hammer home the difference between their life-styles and hers, it was this idle way of pleasantly filling in an idle afternoon.

Apparently content to sit and listen, Morgan said

very little, occasionally dropping in an explanatory remark or lifting a brow at some of Karen's more outrageous gossip. Clary watched the ice melt in her drink, a delicious concoction of fruit juice and white rum, and pondered on the peculiar differences between the class system in New Zealand and that of Britain. And all the while she was conscious of every breath the man beside her took, the slight movements of that magnificent body, her attention focused on him in a way which almost excluded the others.

More guests came to dinner, pleasant people who laughed and flirted and ate the delicious food and drank Sam's drinks with enthusiasm. Clary enjoyed herself. She was not beautiful like Karen, nor exuberant and funny like the only other unattached girl, who on arrival had cast herself into Morgan's arms and kissed him with considerable vivacity, but she could conduct a mild flirtation as well as the next woman, and hold her end up in an intelligent conversation.

She was well looked after. Fay was an excellent hostess, always alert to see that none of her guests felt neglected, and Tony hovered, flirting and flattering. The few times when she could have felt a little alone, Morgan was soon beside her; clearly he was watching. She felt protected, a sensation as unusual as it was pleasant.

While all this happened the sun set slowly in a regal display of golds and scarlets. With its departure a cool little breeze sprang up.

'Cold?' asked the man with whom she had been discussing the possibility that protea flowers would be the country's next big horticultural breakthrough. He spoke quickly, the words blurring together. 'I'll warm you.'

Hemmed in between a slatted screen and an oleander in a large tub, Clary was unable to avoid the arms which suddenly groped for her. Belatedly she realised that he had had just enough to drink to turn his mind from thoughts of exports to flirtation. A pity. He'd been quite interesting to talk to.

She said pleasantly, 'If you'll let me by I'll get something warmer to wear.'

'I'll keep you warm,' he said obstinately, his mouth searching greedily across her cheek.

'I'm afraid I don't want you to,' she retorted, standing stiff and unresponsive in his grasp. 'In fact, if you don't let me go I'll be forced to knee you in the groin. And while you're rolling around in agony I'll explain to everyone why I did it.'

The icy distaste in her voice finally got through. He dropped his arms and stepped back, peering owlishly at her. 'No need to do that,' he said warily, backing further away.

No, not a nasty man, merely one who turned amorous when he'd had a little too much to drink.

'Dean, your wife is looking for you.' Morgan made no attempt to hide the steel in his level voice. He loomed up behind the hapless Dean, who gave him a startled look, muttered something and headed, none too steadily, back to the rest of the party.

'Thanks.' Clary was warmed by the realisation that he had come looking for her.

'Think nothing of it.' The steel was naked and cutting. 'You coped admirably, but do try not to be manoeuvred into any more corners. Tony is waiting for the same opportunity.'

He was *furious*. Clary flinched and put out a tentative hand to touch his forearm. Beneath her fingers the muscles were rigid with tension. Unwittingly she stroked across the firm warm skin and his other hand came over and covered hers. Only then did she look up into his face. He was frightening, the skin drawn over its beautifully moulded framework, his eyes blazing gold.

'I don't like to see anyone touch you,' he said

tonelessly. 'It hurts me. I've known Dean for years—
he's a nice chap—hell, even his wife laughs at his
amorous tendencies—but I could have killed him then.
Come on, it's almost time we left.'

Shaken as much by the leap of her pulses as by the
realisation that she had escaped only narrowly from
danger, she went back with him to where the lights
bloomed and people provided a measure of safety.

'Ah, there you are.' Fay gave them a shrewd look
before smiling beguilingly at Morgan. 'If you'll
relinquish Clary to me I'll show her that piece by
Jennet Hollingworth. I keep it in my bedroom where I
can gloat over it.'

'Off you go, Clary.'

Morgan's voice was smooth but Clary took a deep
breath before following the older woman into the
house.

'He's an overpowering man, isn't he?' Fay remarked
lightly, ending on a questioning note so faint that
Clary probably imagined it.

'He's angry with me. I got bailed up by Dean
Somebody-or-other and Morgan arrived on the scene
as I was disentangling myself.' There, that should
convince Fay that nothing had happened. Morgan
would be furious if she caused gossip; she had noticed
his distaste at some of Karen's wilder flights.

'Oh dear, Dean is a nuisance! I'm so sorry. One
thing, he's easy enough to choke off.'

'It was hardly discreet of me.' Clary's voice was wry.

'My dear, you weren't to know. Morgan is not such
a chauvinist as to believe that you encouraged Dean,
he knows him. He was probably cross with him for
harassing you. There, what do you think of my bowl?'

It was a superb thing, the pottery almost as thin as
porcelain, with a red-gold glaze which held all the
depth and fire of a volcano.

'Go on, touch it,' Fay urged, and watched with a
satisfied smile as Clary caressed the lovely thing.

After some minutes of admiration Fay led the way back to the terrace. They arrived just in time to see the vivacious little blonde who had embraced Morgan so ardently when she arrived launch herself on to his knee and cover his smiling face with kisses before pressing her mouth to his.

A chorus of whistles and light-hearted jokes greeted this display. Morgan's lean hands came up and grasped the girl about the waist before, revealing incredible strength, he stood up with her and set her lightly on her feet.

A primitive, shattering jealousy held Clary in stasis. Ignoring Fay's amused comment, she had to force herself to bend as though she had caught something in her sandal; when she straightened Morgan was smiling down into the blonde's pouting little face before he turned her away with a pat on the shoulder and a remark which made those around roar with more laughter. The blonde swung back and shook her fist at him, but she was laughing, too, leaning for a moment into him with a familiarity which spoke of more than friendship.

Recalled to her duty as hostess Fay said, 'Oh, that Vicky! You can't help liking her, even though she gets away with murder. Probably that's why she gets away with murder. You need another drink, Clary. Let's see what Sam can produce,' but Clary didn't follow her. Here, in the semi-gloom of the eaves, she was safe from observation. Out there the lights were bright enough to reveal Karen's face, naked in its misery, all beauty fled.

Morgan replied to his petite companion's comments with another devastating smile and a kiss on the cheek before he turned and without looking her way made his way to where Clary stood half-hidden, her whole being locked in a rigor of desolation.

'Don't eat me with your eyes,' he said, his sardonic glance missing nothing, 'or people will begin to wonder if you're not more than my mother's nurse.'

'And that would never do, would it? I should imagine they're probably wondering why your mother's nurse isn't with your mother.'

The cold words were heavy with self-contempt. The sight of Karen's unhappiness had forced her to realise just what she was courting if she allowed him to bulldoze her into loving him. Disillusionment and pain; exactly what Angus was suffering for daring to love where wisdom failed him. Move out of the circle of your own experience and you deserve what you get, she told herself, holding her face averted from his penetrating gaze.

'You look like a Fury,' he said deliberately, 'beautiful and terrifying and stony-hearted. My friends are not so unreasonable that they will think there's anything odd about even the most dedicated nurse taking an occasional afternoon off.'

'And of course they are accustomed to seeing you with a woman in tow. In fact, they'd think it strange if the irresistible Morgan Caird——'

'If you want a fight I'll indulge you in the car. Until then, curb your tongue—or I'll do it for you. And then everyone *will* have something to talk about.'

The threat was no less effective for being delivered in a cool, almost indifferent voice. Clary swallowed to ease the obstruction in her throat before obeying the economical gesture of one lean hand which propelled her towards their host and hostess.

Ten minutes later they were on the road back to the Valley, the snarl of the Ferrari echoing Clary's emotions. Rebelliously she stared through the windscreen as the headlights cut a shocking swathe through the swift-falling darkness, pinpointing various creatures of the night, a hedgehog, the startled flight of some small bird in front of them.

Almost immediately they abandoned the tarseal of the main highway, turning inland along one of the back-country roads. The powerful engine made short work of the steep gradients as they wound through hills and along a narrow valley. Against her will Clary found herself admiring Morgan's driving. He seemed to know by instinct how to get the big car without fuss or drama around tight corners and through the drifts of gravel which could have made the road dangerous.

'When I was in Italy,' she said quietly, 'I drove some friends across the mountains in the north. We came to a rather hair-raising section and halfway up a mountain discovered that bits of the road had slipped away, leaving a one-way stretch with no edge. It looked as though the other half of the road could go any minute.'

'And?'

'And the van was pretty shot, we didn't know if it would ever get to the top if we stopped. There was no room to turn around in and it was pouring with rain. I was terrified.' She gave a small sigh, remembering just how frightened and lacking in confidence she had been. 'Not as terrified as the others, though. The boys bit their tongues trying to give me advice without flustering me and Donna had her eyes shut all the way. You remember Donna, she was with me——'

'I remember her,' he said with finality. 'Are you such a bad driver?'

'No, I'm a good driver, but both men were convinced that a woman is automatically inferior to almost any man when it comes to driving. Or most things,' she finished, remembering them.

'They sound very young.'

'A little older than I was.'

'How long were you together?'

She shrugged, uneasy at a metallic undertone to the question. 'Three months. Not nearly long enough to see everything I wanted to see in Europe, but at least I knew the places I wanted to go back to.'

Tension seeped from her bones as he began to talk of various places he had visited in Europe; once more she was surprised at how easy it was to talk to him. He had a dry, almost cynical attitude which should have repelled her yet beneath it she discerned an essential humanity. He spoke warmly, respectfully, of a farming family in Greece, admiring their tough pragmatism and the kindness which went with it, then told her a hilarious anecdote of a meal in a small cliff town in France where the cook had wept into the soup and confided his marital troubles in language which was rich and Rabelaisian, as salty as his tears and the soup.

Clary astonished herself by giggling, before capping it with the time she had been kissed on the neck by an amorous Italian waiter in one of the most famous cafés in Rome.

'And what did your boyfriend think of that?'

A note of—coolness? contempt?—in his voice sobered her. Rather stiffly she returned, 'The boys laughed, of course. What do you think they should have done? Hit him?' She invested the last word with a delicate scorn which should have made him feel like the barbarian he was.

'I would have.'

Flat and dangerous, the observation sent a cold thread crawling up her spine. She turned her head to scan his profile, cruel in its aquiline strength against the pale backglow of the lights. It was probably useless to try to explain but she did it just the same.

'It was purely light-hearted. He was a real tease. It was sheer high spirits on his part. And neither of the boys had any right to object. We were travelling companions, no more. For mutual protection. Oh, what's the use!'

'None. None at all. My mother tells me that I've been possessive since before I could say, "Mine!" I don't share, especially not my women.'

'But I am not one of your women!'

'No. You are the woman. And there's nothing I can do about it.' Incredibly, he laughed, although there was no humour in the sound. 'Shattering. If I'd been warned that I'd fall victim to love at first sight I'd have scoffed to high heaven. Then it happened, just like that. One look, and I knew we belonged together. I'd finally found my woman.'

'Love?' she asked smoothly, fiercely, repressing an atavistic thrill at such a blatant statement of ownership. '*Love*, Morgan?'

'Call it what you like, it exists.'

'I call it lust,' she bit out. 'Concupiscence, lechery, carnality, greed. That's what it is. The blind urge to reproduce, if you want to be polite about it. What——?'

The car slid to a halt. As the note of the engine died Clary stared around, realising that they were stopped in a wide area sheltered from view of the road by an enormous heap of gravel.

'They're going to straighten and realign the road,' Morgan told her conversationally as the lights flicked off. 'That's why this convenient stockpile of metal.'

The click of the seat-belt clip resounded in the silence. Now that her sight was attuned to moonlight Clary could see the harsh purpose which hardened his features.

Nervously she asked, 'Why have we stopped?'

'Oh, Clary,' he mocked, unclipping her belt with a swift sure movement.

She grabbed at the strap as it moved past her body. 'I warn you, if you think you can——'

'Darling, I'm just going to clear up a misconception or two,' he said as he opened the door. 'I think honesty in a relationship is vital, don't you?'

Sarcasm sharpened the words into an unanswerable statement. Biting her lip, she wondered what on earth he was going to do, watching suspiciously as he swung around the front of the car. When he opened her door she protested, but he gently extracted her from her seat and draped his arm about her shoulder.

'Uncomfortable things, cars,' he observed. 'Still, beggars can't be choosers.'

'You promised you wouldn't touch me.' It was futile to struggle against that rawhide strength but she did. He merely tightened his grip, being careful not to hurt her.

'Clearly I can't be trusted.' He was mocking her, the even, taunting words breathed into her ear as he bent to open the rear door. 'I think a demonstration is the only way to prove that you're wrong.'

He foiled her attempt to escape by sliding into the car first and pulling her in after him. She ducked to avoid the roof and ended up in his lap in a tangle of arms and legs and anger, and a slow deep excitement which came from the depths of her soul.

'This,' he said deliberately, pulling her head back with a cruel hand in her hair, 'is lechery. Take note, or I might find it necessary to repeat the lesson.'

What followed was a calculated humiliation. Even as his mouth crushed hers, forcing it to open to a crude, suffocating invasion, his free hand slid the silken length of her thigh, hesitated long enough for her to flinch, and then moved to her breast, finding with accuracy the aroused tip. Clary writhed in shame, hating him, hating the reckless treachery of her body which responded even to this callous subjugation. Desperately she struck at him. More by luck than aim her open hand connected noisily with his cheek.

He lifted his head, surveying her furious face with glittering eyes. He smiled, a slow, dangerous curving of that ruthless mouth.

'Do you like to receive pain as well as inflict it, my lovely?'

Strong white teeth closed, not gently, on her throat for a second before moving to hover above the full curve of her breast.

'You dare,' she breathed, a cold fear beginning to replace anger.

Again he smiled. Lean fingers roughly flicked free the pewter buttons of her dress, quelled her renewed struggles with a ruthless economy of movement which forced a breathless whimper from her. His remorseless hand wrenched at fragile lace and her bra fell agape.

'You've ruined it!' she spat, hiding her fear behind clenched teeth.

'Ah, lechery enjoys destruction.' Beneath the thick screen of his lashes blazed a cynical appreciation which was an insult in itself.

On her exposed skin his breath was warm and potent but the mouth which fastened on to the shadowed bud of her breast was heated and avid and her anger fled, lost in sensual submission.

'Don't,' she whispered, hot tears blinding her eyes when at last she lay quiescent in the hard prison of his arms.

'Why not?' The words were slurred, but the predatory note in them made her feel sick. Heat stung her skin, became transmuted into an icy lethargy as his hand swept from the high warm peak of her breast to settle threateningly on her thigh.

'Why not?' he repeated. 'Lust takes no notice of pleading, or prayers for mercy. Lust says the devil take you and your needs, your desires. Why should I stop, Clary? Why should you expect me to stop? If this is mere carnality you should know not to expect anything more from me than my own self-gratification.'

She bit her lip, determined not to give him the admission he was trying to wring from her.

'Desire, now, desire is different. Desire encompasses consideration,' he murmured, and the cruel hands gentled, caressing her skin with loving care. 'Desire can be gentle or fierce but it is always tender. Desire is between two people ... desire is for lovers ...'

CHAPTER SEVEN

His voice wooed her. With gentle ardour he kissed the pale satin of her throat and a certain spot where her jaw met her ear. He was not rough but he was persistent, and the knowledgeable expertise of his love-making made her shiver, and turn her face into the hard wall of his chest in complete surrender.

'Desire is sensitive,' that disturbing voice continued, 'and exciting . . . Desire gives as well as takes . . .'

Clary groaned as his mouth inscribed slow, lazy circles over the smooth skin he had bared so violently only minutes before. The soft friction of his cheek on her flushed skin was unbearably stimulating; she rested her chin against the textured warmth of his hair, inhaling the faint natural scent of him with trembling delight. Shudders of exquisite pleasure ran through as his mouth found its goal. The soft, tugging sensation seemed to sear through her body, almost more anguish than rapture. Her hand curled against the lean jaw, her palm and fingers appreciating the tiny movements of the muscles he used in this delicious torture.

A strange inertia weighted her limbs. A soft little moan caught in her throat and her burning, shaking hand quested down the strong line of his neck to its juncture with his shoulder. Beneath her fingers the tendons were strung taut as wires; emboldened by the deep, rasping breath which lifted his chest she explored its width, finding through the fine tangle of hair and heated skin that every muscle was flexed and tense.

And all the while she imbibed his fragrance and learned the contours of his torso his mouth pleasured

her until she flamed for him, their mutual passion
igniting a blaze which forced stumbling, unheard
words from her tongue.

'Morgan,' she whispered. 'Oh, God, Morgan ... I
want—please ...'

A rigor shook her. She responded to the burning
frustration the only way she could, arching her body
in a provocative, involuntary movement, every cell
screaming for fulfilment, aching and acceptant.

His dark head lifted and he kissed the mouth which
opened in sensual invitation to him, penetrating the
sweet depths in a blatant evocation of another more
powerful and fundamental penetration.

For long moments they strained together like lovers
on the brink of the abyss. Then he dragged his mouth
from hers and held her with tormenting gentleness, his
trembling lips against her temple, until the violent
thudding of their hearts eased and reality began to
douse the conflagration his expert seduction had
ignited. At last, his ragged tones revealing just how
much control he was being forced to exert, he said,
'And desire can be restrained. It is not greedy, it is not
frightening.'

Clary could have wailed her frustration to the
peeping moon. Instead, she drew a hiccuping breath
and with a control which matched his, muttered into
his shoulder, 'What do you want, for heaven's sake?'

'I've told you. Everything.'

'I'll give you everything,' she whispered through a
fog of unsatisfied passion. 'Now, if you want it. Why
are you torturing me like this?'

He gave a curious breathy laugh. 'It's not just you
who is suffering. Can't you feel how I hurt?'

'Why? You could have taken me.' It humiliated her
to admit it yet it was stupid to pretend. His
lovemaking revealed his experience; he knew exactly
what he had done to her, and how easily.

'I gave up making love in cars years ago,' he said,

the words threaded with the same irony which muted
his smile.

'You're asking the impossible,' she said dully. 'I
shouldn't even be living in your house. Angus is too
dangerously close to the edge for me to do anything
that might push him over. I won't have an affair with
you—sooner or later he would find out. You might
just as well try to persuade me to marry you!'

'Marriage is irrelevant.' He scanned her defeated
expression closely. His face was etched with a kind of
stern remoteness which was so unlike his usual
confident sophistication that she felt she was talking to
a stranger.

Not for anything would she have admitted that she
winced. 'I know. It's just as irrelevant as an affair.'

He pulled the gaping lapels of her dress together,
lingering a moment to cup the warm weight of her
breast.

'What is relevant,' he said quietly, 'is your fear of
losing control. Why, darling?'

She sat up and with shaking hands fastened the
buttons over the remnants of her bra. Gravely he
watched her, making no further attempt to touch her
but when she was once more covered he pulled her
back into the haven of his arms. The tightly wound
tension in him was communicated to her. She was
afraid of this weakness in her; she could deal better
with the mindless world of passion he made for them
than this dangerous gentleness. She summoned up an
image of Susan, her beautiful face dazed with pleasure
as she lay with him in ecstasy, Susan who probably
still recalled with sensual enjoyment the hours she had
spent in his bed.

Clary's teeth clamped on to her lower lip. She
fought to banish the picture of them clasped together
in voluptuous delight. It made her feel sick and angry
and betrayed.

Perhaps that was better than feeling frightened. She

had thought that Morgan's threat to her was purely physical, that she was endangered only by the flaming incandescence of their sexual need for each other, but his last comment was altogether too perceptive. She huddled still, feeling the steady beat of his heart, and hoped that it was just a shot in the dark.

His next comments proved her wrong. 'You were afraid right from the start,' he pursued. 'I thought at first that it was because you had never felt such an attraction, and I was pleased, because I have never wanted a woman as I want you. But it wasn't entirely that, was it? You were—you are afraid of the emotion itself, not just of me. What made you decide that men could only hurt you, Clary?'

Why not tell him? It was easier to give in than continue resisting. In a voice that held no emotion she said, 'In our family we don't fall in love, we run to obsessions. When I was seventeen my father became besotted with a girl about three years older than me. He left us and went to live with her.'

'That was tough, but it happens.' The wide shoulders lifted in a shrug. 'It happens all the time. The Americans call it a mid-life crisis.'

'Is that what it was? It killed my father. She was a bitch. She lived with him for a year and in that year she went through every cent he had. He even sold the house, put my mother out on to the street.' She choked back a sob. 'Not quite literally, but she had to find a flat, and a job. I was at boarding school but there was no money for me to finish there. When his lover had gone through his money she left Dad for another, richer man. He had nowhere to go, so he came back to us and sat down and willed himself to die.'

He made no reply and she looked up into the stark perfection of his features, limned by moonglow. Harshly, so quickly that she stumbled over the words she finished, 'He couldn't face life without her. We had to watch as he deliberately killed himself.'

'And do you think the same thing might happen to Angus?' He spoke in formal, even tones, revealing nothing.

'I don't know.' She was appalled at having her most secret fears put so bluntly into words. Nervously she ran her tongue over her top lip. 'He worshipped Susan and she took all that he had and flung it back in his face. She said—she s-said——'

He held her closely while she wept out her anger and fear, making no attempt to comfort her until she choked into a silence broken only by the involuntary sobs of over-indulgence. Then he tilted her face and wiped it with his handkerchief and kissed her brow and her wet eyes.

'My poor little love,' he said very gently. 'All that worry and fear! For what it's worth I think you've underestimated both the depth of your brother's feelings for Susan and his powers of recuperation. I happen to believe that love is only love when it's reciprocal. And Susan didn't love Angus, so whatever he felt for her, intense though it might have been, was not love. No, I know you won't believe me, but do believe that he's over the worst. The front man who deals with him is quite relieved because he no longer looks and behaves as though he's heading for a nervous breakdown. As for your father——' he paused, before ending calmly, '—I think your father died of pride.'

'*Pride?*' She reacted fiercely, sitting up with a swift movement which catapulted her from his embrace on to the seat beside him. 'He had no pride left!'

'Exactly.' Morgan stilled her twisting hands in his warm, firm clasp. 'She hit him in his pride, made him look a fool, and he couldn't cope with it. Never underestimate the power of pride, Clary. It's killed as many people as sex or greed. He died because he wasn't strong enough to face a world which found him ridiculous. Angus is not so passive.'

He looked down into her astonished face and gave a tight smile. 'I'm looking forward to meeting your mother. I presume that's who you and your brother take after. Because you aren't weak, Clary, you're like spider's silk, fine and clear and strong as steel. In your innermost heart you don't class Angus with your father, either. I can hear the pity in your voice when you speak of your father, but there is no taint of it when you mention Angus.'

She could not respond but as they drove home in a silence which held an oddly peaceful wordless communion she wondered whether Morgan could possibly be correct in his assessment of her father. And she hugged the memory of his kindness, so unexpected, yet not out of character. He had the gentleness of the strong.

Slowly, in that silent drive, she realised that what she felt for him must be love.

Just like that, she mused later as she made herself ready for bed, going mindlessly through the familiar rituals. She had looked across an English field and fallen in love, deeply, irrevocably—hopelessly. For although he had spoken optimistically of Angus he must know, as she did, that no man would be able to bear his sister marrying the man who had, however innocently, seduced his wife away from him.

If seduction could ever be called innocent.

It's not *fair*! she thought, too anguished to appreciate how inappropriate the childhood lament was. Why had it been Susan who was so alluring that the two men Clary loved had wanted her?

Not that it really mattered. Pride and her moral code—and Clary's sense of self-preservation—would not permit the complete capitulation Morgan needed. He might say now that he had never felt this way before, but was it a difference in degree or one in kind? And if—*when*—he lost interest in her there would be absolutely nothing she could do about it. It would be agony, and she would have no right to feel this savage sense of possession.

It was then that she realised how much she had allowed herself to be seduced into hoping that perhaps this time, this emotion he felt for her might be different, that it might last.

'Oh, you fool!' she whispered to her angry reflection. 'You great idiot!'

And watched as all colour fled from her pale skin, leaving the freckles standing out like blotches beneath eyes almost black with mocking self-derision.

Resistance had not been enough. Whatever happened now, Morgan had marked her for life. If she held out against him she would always be eaten by the savage frustration of unsatisfied desire. And she would hunger for him until the day she died ...

Perhaps the idea was born then, fretting at the edge of her conscious mind, teasing, elusive. Perhaps it burgeoned in the following week which Morgan spent mostly in Auckland, not arriving home until late, twice staying the night in his apartment.

Not that the idea ever emerged full-blown into her head. By the time she had to admit its existence she realised that she had been subconsciously examining it for some time.

The process of making a decision was not easy. To start off with, the idea ran directly counter to the way she had run her life. Always, it seemed, she had been afraid of emotion, obsessed with a kind of terror at the power it could unleash. She had built defences and crouched behind them. Not even her family had been allowed too close. She had told Morgan they were not demonstrative and it was true, but in her case a fundamental fear of being hurt intensified a natural reserve.

But pain had come. Pain caused by the bitter treachery of body and heart. It was with the only unbiased part of her that she assessed her idea and it was her mind which finally gave her permission.

Looked at logically, there was no reason why she should not take Morgan for her lover. All of the reasons she had given him were the products of her fears. When the passion between them burnt out she could go on her way, scarred perhaps, but not maimed for life. He wanted her submission. Very well then, he should have it. The leopard could not change his spots, so it was unfair to expect him to be otherwise than he was, a man of powerful magnetism, having a connoisseur's appreciation of women.

And remembering more of Susan's remarks Clary smiled with painful cynicism and told herself that at least she would have memories to feed her hungry heart—told herself all the lies which gave a gloss of respectability to her decision to seduce him.

It should not prove too difficult, this seduction ploy, even for a woman as completely inexperienced as she was. Recalling how the electricity had arced through him when she touched him, she smiled a sultry woman's smile which would have shocked her had she been able to see it.

Perhaps the struggle her decision caused her showed. After a long night her employer looked sharply at her and asked, 'Are you sickening for something?'

'No. I didn't sleep well.'

Mrs Hargreaves appeared to accept the evasion. 'Feel like driving the car?'

'Yes, of course.'

So with Ruth they drove out to the coast and there Mrs Hargreaves bought an old, dilapidated Victorian villa which she clearly couldn't wait to get into and redecorate. It was, she announced to an equally enthusiastic Ruth, the perfect place for grandchildren.

Once more Morgan didn't come home that evening. After dinner Clary found herself roaming about the garden, quite blind to the pictures Mrs Hargreaves had created there. She was filled with an intolerable restlessness, a corroding hunger which ate into the fabric of her composure until she was almost distraught. She knew what it was, of course.

In a gesture as graceful as it was unforced, she looped an arm around the trunk of an Australian frangipani and cooled her hot cheek against its bark while the sweet-spicy perfume of the yellow flowers gave tangible expression to her erotic yearnings.

'Oh hell,' she muttered furiously and strode back inside to meet a somewhat agitated Ruth just inside the door.

'Clary, I think you'd better take a look at her.' Ruth indicated the stairs with her head. 'She's excited——'

'Ruth, between you and me and the newel post, I'd say that I'm more likely to succumb to over-excitement than Mrs Hargreaves.' Clary gave her a conspiratorial grin. 'A charge of dynamite might just manage to carry her off, but I'd lay odds on her even then. Are you really worried? You know her better than anyone except Morgan.'

'Better than he does, too.' But the worry had eased from the housekeeper's expression. 'Yes, I know I fuss, and I'm not really concerned, but I would feel better if you checked her out. She's up there drawing plans!'

'Why did she decide to buy a new house? I thought she loved the Valley.'

With a somewhat astonished look which made Clary flinch Ruth said, 'Well, Morgan is going to marry sooner or later, and the Valley is his home. The flat in Auckland is lovely and big, but it's no place to bring up a family, and his mother knows perfectly well that no bride is going to take kindly to a resident mother-in-law. Besides, she just loves doing places up, she'd have made a superb decorator, but there's nothing left for her to do here. Oh, the new place will give her a wonderful new lease of life.'

There was no doubt about that. Up in her bedroom

Mrs Hargreaves was making notations all over the surveyor's report. When she looked up she gave Clary a smile which revealed that she knew exactly why she was there.

'Ruth's an old fusspot,' she declared. 'I haven't felt as good as this for years.'

'Well, perhaps not, but it might be a good idea if you went to bed a bit earlier than usual.'

'And what about you? Feeling restless, are you? I saw you flitting about in the garden. Why don't you go for a walk?'

'Oh, I'll stick around——'

'In case I die of excitement? You can't possibly devote yourself to me night and day. It's not sensible!'

'I was employed——'

'Oh, rubbish!' Mrs Hargreaves looked as though she would have preferred to use a stronger term but she went on reasonably enough, 'Now, tell me the truth, is there any reason to suspect that I might be struck down tonight or any other night by another heart attack?'

'Well—of course not. You know your doctor is very pleased with your progress.'

'Of course I do. I'm not an idiot. But you are starting to act like one. I told you once before that I'm waiting for my grandchildren, but that's not the only reason I'm living, believe me! If it will make you happier, Ruth can stay with me until you get back. Now go away, you're as restless as a dog in a thunderstorm; it's bad for me to have to watch you prowl about as if the end of the world is just around the corner. Go on, away you go!'

Clary laughed and risked a quick kiss on her patient's cheek, much to their mutual astonishment. 'Oh, very well, then. Just don't you do anything energetic,' she warned, tossing over her shoulder, 'or get too excited over Ruth's scandal!'

Her nurse's instinct told her she had no need to

worry over her patient but once through the door Clary hesitated, her expression almost haunted. She clasped her hands between her breasts in a vain attempt to still the rapid beating of her heart; her skin was over-sensitive, reacting too violently to the oppressive heaviness of the atmosphere.

It should have denoted the approach of an electrical storm, but although the sky was filmed by cloud there was no sign of any thunderheads. The sultry sunlight was smoke-orange in shade, reminding her that there had been bushfires in Australia. This must be the smoke from them, carried thousands of miles across the Tasman Sea by the westerlies of the past week. Fortunately this time no one had died in the fires but she felt immeasurably sad as she thought of the destruction and the wreckage of people's lives left in their wake.

Wearily she made her way to her bedroom. Perhaps she should just go to bed. Discarding the idea even as it was born, she made a sudden decision, changing into a pair of stout shoes. She met Ruth halfway up the stairs and told her that she was going up the valley to the pool. Morgan had not had time to take her there, but he had pointed out its location and she was confident that she could find it.

'You'll get hot and sticky,' Ruth told her prosaically. 'Still, if you've got excess energy to burn off it's as a good a way as any, I suppose. Better take a torch.'

She did get hot and sticky, but the scramble up the steep face gave her tension something to feed on, dissipating its strength by substituting hard exertion for foreboding.

By the time she reached the top it was dusk and she was almost exhausted. From beneath the *titoki* tree she watched a sunset as dramatic as any she had seen in all her wanderings, an inferno of crimson and scarlet and hot oranges and pinks, fading at last behind the dim veils of night. Before the magnificent spectacle vanished the moon arose behind her, an enormous globe like a muted, mysterious sun. The air became marginally cooler but it was the stifling burden of the atmosphere which caused Clary to shiver. The pool glimmered, beckoning, alluring. She removed her shoes, revelling in the cool softness of the grass against her hot feet. The little dell beneath the *titoki* tree was now a cup of shadow; she stood looking about her while tears stung her eyelids.

Angrily, scarcely aware of what she was doing, she put the torch down and began to tear at her clothes, freeing herself from their clammy embrace until she stood slim and naked in the strange hazy glow of the moon.

The rope Fay had spoken of dangled invitingly over the water. Clary ran up the steep little bluff and jumped, snatching at the rope with a ferocity which helped ease the tension coiled within her. Out she swung in a long arc over the water; at the furthest and highest point she let go and dived gracefully into the black pool. It welcomed her with the sensuous sweep of water about her heated body. Abruptly her head emerged into the forest-scented air in a spray of glittering droplets as she shook it to free the clinging curls of excess water. She swam rapidly back and forth, still driven by her demons, until something impelled her out. When she rose to step up on to the bank water streamed from her in veils of gold and silver, inextricably blended, shimmering the length of her lithe nakedness. Again she shook her head, then ran her hands from her breasts to her thighs in a gesture which was unconsciously provocative, hating the tight bands of tension which wound through every nerve and cell in her body.

CHAPTER EIGHT

'CLARY.'

Her initial shock of terror fled as soon as she recognised the speaker. Although all she could see was his silhouette, big, almost menacing as he waited by the tumbled heap of clothes, she recognised him. With the departure of fear came the resolution of that other tension which had plagued her. She smiled, and came out of the water like a naiad of old confronting the mortal she had chosen for her lover.

'Morgan,' she said and her intention was clear in her voice, her carriage, the explicit promise in her smile. She stopped in front of the tall, unmoving figure and raised her finger to outline his mouth, so intriguing with its blend of austerity and passion.

'I was waiting for you,' she whispered.

The last wary remnants of the cautious Clary of the past fled as she admitted that her only chance of freedom lay in the forbidden pleasure he represented. Eventually, when she was sated by a surfeit of carnality, she could leave him.

So she said his name again and the tip of her forefinger slid between the straight line of his lips and met the soft edge of his tongue. Frozen, she by shyness, they stood motionless. Then his tongue curled around her fingertip and she felt every nerve in her body blaze into excitement.

Nervously she jerked her hand free, lowering her glance to his chest. She began to undo the buttons of his shirt. She felt the harsh in-drawing of his breath but was not ready for the way his hand covered hers, trapping them against the warm, heavy beat of his heart.

'Are you sure?' he asked.

The thick, ragged note in his voice restored her confidence. Smiling again that blind primal smile, she nodded.

Still he hesitated, so she moved into him, leaning her gleaming, almost dry body against him in obedience to the prompting of age-old instincts. Her mouth found the tense line of his jaw and she whispered throaty little endearments until the potency of her feminine seduction broke his resistance.

He groaned as his arms enfolded her. For long moments his mouth crushed hers, giving no quarter, demanding submission. Clary gave it to him with a fierce driven hunger. After an aeon he lifted his head, muttering against her tender lips, 'I'm sorry, I'm sorry, I hurt you . . .'

Clary was totally given over to her long-repressed sensuality. The famished pressure of his kiss should have hurt, but if there had been pain it was lost in the seething tumult of sensations which surged through her.

What followed was erotic fantasy, a dream-like drama of passion and surrender played out beneath the eerie smoked orange of the moon. Laid down on to the sweet-smelling grass Clary was a slender white houri, possessed of knowledge gained by all the generations of women who had preceded her in love. With hands and mouth and throaty, smoky voice she adored the masculinity of the man she loved, and Morgan responded with such fevered skill that she was transported into another plane of existence. His touch roused trails of fire across her skin, igniting that other fire within her until she was aware of nothing else but the sensations which overwhelmed her, the scent of aroused masculinity, the sound of her heart as it tried to burst through the confines of her breast, the deep husky note of his voice when he whispered his appreciation of her offering.

And as she discovered the secrets of her body and

his, her heavy-lidded stare never wavered, noting the contrast of bronze skin against white, the dark colour which burned along his cheekbones, the incredibly erotic brush of his cheek against her breasts and the delicious savagery of his mouth around the tender aureoles which welcomed him so ardently.

Those primeval women who had been her forebears told her when to arch her back so that the length of her body pressed into the aroused strength of his, showed her how to circumvent his efforts to make their love-making a leisurely sophisticated affair. Here, beneath such a moon, he was on her territory, captive as she was of the age-old pulse of sexuality and the endless circle of birth and death, of life.

So Clary resisted his practised, civilised seduction with every bit of woman-magic she could call upon, and knew of her success when he groaned into her mouth and obeyed the demands of her body with the sudden, brutal invasion of his.

And that was right too, the pain and her acceptance of it, the melding of light and dark, strength and beauty, male and female, the sensual driving abandon until the ultimate ecstasy, the explosion of sensation which left them spent and trembling, all strength drained away.

It was right too that they sleep, bodies entwined beneath that glowing moon, beside that still pool; but only for a short time.

Clary woke gently, relaxed as never before. Her lashes flicked, then lifted and she was looking straight into the face of the man who had just taken her. She should have been appalled, disgusted with herself, shocked at her capacity for passion and the barbaric ferocity of their coming together. Instead, she felt an immense tenderness for him, and for her a kind of profound and lethargic smugness.

And a slow but unmistakable resurgence of the hunger which had precipitated all this. Tiny shivers of sensation heated her skin as his hand cupped her breast, testing the weight with possessive intimacy. He was smiling, the triumphant, rather astonished smile of a man who has been given more than he expected.

'I knew it would be incredible for us,' he said softly. 'I didn't realise just how incredible. As wild as a force of nature.'

'Sex is a force of nature.' She didn't begrudge him his triumph—was it not hers too?—so her voice entirely lacked tartness. It was, she decided dreamily, quite easy being a seductress. Tomorrow she might start to worry about things again, but tomorrow seemed a long way away.

In the meantime she lay sheltered in his strong embrace as his hands rediscovered the contours of her body. Soon, very soon, his dark profile would harden in the absorption of desire and that elemental fusion would happen again, and for a few minutes they would be freed by rapture from the confines of the world.

Lazily she turned her head so that she could press open-mouthed kisses into his shoulder, revelling in the rapid hoarseness of his breath, the way his muscles flexed in a sudden involuntary movement. It gave her an indescribable sense of power to be able to overset the controls of that clever brain, to make him as much a prisoner as she of the primordial forces hidden in them. His sophistication could not withstand the allure of her sensuality.

Suddenly his hand stopped that sensuous silky stroking.

'What the hell—?' he muttered, and turned her on to her back with an abrupt twist. Taken by surprise she rolled laxly, landing with a grimace.

'Blood,' he said harshly. 'You *bled*!'

She nodded unconcernedly. He was still staring at his hand. Slowly, as if he could not believe the evidence of his eyes, he reached out and touched the stain on her leg.

'You were a virgin.'

Again she nodded, smiling rather ironically at the gathering anger in his face.

'I don't suppose you've taken any precautions at all.'

Is that all that he was worried about? A thread of anger wove through her voice. 'Wrong. I'm on the pill.'

He closed his eyes briefly, perhaps in relief, and she decided not to tell him that her use of the pill was necessary because of the irritating irregularity which had used to bedevil her.

'OK,' he said between his teeth, 'but you were a virgin.'

Smiling, Clary lifted her arms to link them behind her head, knowing that this tightened and emphasised her breasts. She didn't want to discuss her virginity. She wanted him.

'Couldn't you tell?' she teased.

'What's the hell's got into you tonight? Lunacy?'

She sat up, turning towards him to run a provocative hand from his chest to his lean hip, her expression pensive. 'Oh, call it a return to the past,' she said lightly. 'A full moon, a virgin sacrifice, a ritual mating to ensure prosperity for the crops—we have all the ingredients.'

He made to speak but when she bent over him and kissed his mouth tenderly, his body shook. Lifting her head she smiled, sure of him once more, but he twisted away from her to his feet, and he was suddenly no man to be seduced for her pleasure but a menacing intruder in a moonlit idyll, man the aggressor, anger transmuting his lean grace into a threat.

Shivering, cold without him, Clary stared up at his averted face. 'What is it? What is the matter?' They were stupid questions, revealing the weakness which was the flaw in the fabric of her woman's power, especially when asked in a voice which quavered on the last word.

'For your information,' he gritted, leaning down to haul her to her feet, 'yes, I did realise that you were different, but as I've no experience with virgins I didn't recognise the proof of it. At that exact moment I wouldn't have cared if the world had shivered into nothingness around us.'

'Then what *is* the matter?' This time Clary demanded rather than asked, and there was no betraying break in her voice. 'Do you always snarl at your lovers after sex? If that's the case I'm surprised that you keep them.'

He replied harshly, 'No, I don't. And don't try to reduce this to the usual affair, either. We both know that this is something entirely new—for both of us.' When she didn't speak he finished angrily, 'I wish I knew what was going on in that lovely head of yours.'

'I don't see your problem. You've been trying to get me into your bed since you saw me. Well, you've done it. I think you should be pleased. Or else blasé. That's the usual course of events, surely?'

She had spoken coolly, but beneath the objective words there was provocation and she expected him to retaliate. Instead his hands tightened about hers and he said indistinctly, 'Nothing about you has followed the usual course of events. Oh, Clary . . .'

His mouth on hers was warm and searching. She sighed and relaxed against him, borne once more on the hot tide of passion which began to flow through them again. But Morgan tilted her face between his strong hands and scanned the dazed submission he saw there with unreadable eyes.

'When can you marry me?' he asked.

Clary's brain, already clouded by desire, went into a complete spin. She felt her mouth gape and closed it, swallowed and wished that she could break free of that shrewd, hard gaze.

'No, you hadn't given marriage a thought, had you? What did you have in mind for us, Clary? A *relationship?*' His voice invested the words with scornful contempt and his eyes seemed to bore into her soul. 'I'm not interested, thanks. I can't be content with a nice simple affair, quick and easy, still friends when it's over, no bones broken. I need more. I want you to marry me.' She shivered at the determination in his tone, and he said tersely, 'For God's sake, put your clothes back on.'

She obeyed, scrambling into the crushed garments with an icy anger which made her wrench them into place. When she looked up he was half dressed, his shirt slung over a tanned shoulder, his brows drawn into a frown.

'What happened tonight, Clary?' he asked quietly, the strange glow of the moon sliding over the strong angles and planes of his face. He looked magnificent, like a severe god, filled with power and authority.

Wearily Clary shook her head. 'It doesn't matter,' she said with a painful attempt at carelessness.

'Why, darling? A virgin as determined as you were doesn't throw all that self-imposed restraint to the winds on a whim. What happened?'

'Oh, blame the moon.'

Her flippancy made his lips tighten but that perceptive gaze still searched her face. 'Tell me, Clary,' he insisted.

'I gave in,' she flung at him. 'It's as simple as that. For once I decided to do what I wanted instead of the sensible thing. Is that so dreadful?'

'If it's the truth, no. Your sensuality is as much a part of you as your family loyalty and your intelligence, and that warmth you don't even know you have. And the way your eyes gleam with sly laughter when you make one of your appalling puns. But I don't think that was the entire reason, was it? Why did you give me everything I asked from you and then refuse to marry me?'

'You mentioned the family loyalty,' she retorted brutally. 'If I married you I'd be betraying Angus.'

There was a taut silence. The moonlight spread its warm spell over the beautiful chiselled mask of his face, the strong neck and wide shoulders. Clary felt a clutch of sensation as her wanton brain recalled just how it had felt to have those shoulders block out the moon and the stars. Obstinately she repressed it. She had no regrets about what she had done, but such abandonment to passion was providing to be every bit as debilitating as she had suspected. Now all that she wanted to do was forget everything, Susan, Angus, her own turbulent thoughts, in the heated world of the senses into which he had initiated her. Why couldn't he accept what she was prepared to give so freely?

'If there were no Susan, no Angus, would you marry me?'

It was a loaded question but she faced it, and told him the truth. 'Probably, although with quite a few doubts.'

'What doubts?'

She shrugged, searching for the words. Finally she said, 'You keep telling me what you want, you need, like some emotional vampire. I don't hear much about *my* needs.'

He flung up his head as though she had hit him, and stared at her, his expression totally without emotion. She could not see through the thick fringe of his lashes to his thoughts; she did not know whether he understood what she was trying to get across to him.

At last he said in a shaken voice, 'I dare not. If you decide that you do not need me, do not want me, then I have to have face the fact that I will always be alone. I am a coward.'

She whispered his name and he said, 'No, I mean it. I have never needed a woman before. I don't know how to cope with it.' Incredibly he smiled, rueful and tender. 'I tried to rush you into some sort of commitment. I knew you thought I was the worst bastard unhung; I wanted you to change your mind and the only way I could do it was to keep you with me. So I blackmailed you into staying. I behaved like a fool, but I was desperate. And then I compounded my foolishness by trying to impress on you how much I needed you. I thought you might relax your guard a little. You have a compassionate heart.'

'Oh, Morgan!' She didn't know how to repond to his incredible admission. 'My dear, is that what you want from me? Compassion?'

'I'll take whatever I can get,' he said, suddenly confident, laughing, his teeth very white in the darkness. He caught her wrists and kissed her on the forehead then slid his arms around her in a shatteringly tender embrace.

Clary stiffened but the warmth of his body and the faint scent of him soothed her and she leaned her face into his throat, listening dreamily to the heavy regular beat of his pulse.

'The trouble with you,' he said into her ear, 'is that emotionally you're still seventeen. That was the year your father died, wasn't it?'

A kind of panic held her motionless. When she spoke it was barely audible. 'Yes.'

'After a year spent with his lover.'

She nodded and he said, 'I love the way your curls tickle. How did you feel about him, Clary? What were your emotions when you looked at him?'

Surprisingly she couldn't refuse him. 'At first I hated him. But he just *sat*, grey-faced and despairing, and died by inches, and all I could feel was pity and——'

'And?'

'And a kind of distaste.'

His mouth touched her fragile temple, warm and loving. 'And was that when you decided never to fall in love?'

She pushed at him but his grip was too tight. 'Don't you try psycho-analysing me like some cheap pop guru! Can't you accept that there is no future for us?'

'No,' he said implacably, 'I will not accept that. I have more respect for your brother than to believe that he would rather see you my mistress than my wife.'

'He'd be furious—and sick—if he knew that I was even staying here,' she hissed. 'He's not a sophisticated man of the world like you, swapping women with your friends and——'

'You had better stop right there,' he said icily.

She stopped. For a moment she had felt naked aggression in him, sensed the struggle he had to restrain it, and sighed, a tiny lost sound, when he regained control of his anger. 'I'm sorry,' she said in a small voice. 'That was below the belt.'

'And not true. I make no apologies for not living a celibate life before I met you, but my sexuality is satisfied by normal——'

'I know that,' she interrupted.

'Very well, then,' he said deliberately. 'Clary, I love you.'

Panic almost smothered her. 'I don't believe you,' she whispered, striving desperately for a steady voice. 'I won't marry you. Don't ask me.'

He laughed and kissed her, hard, and then as her mouth opened for him, with all the erotic mastery he possessed. When he lifted his head she was sighing, her body pressed ecstatically against his as her hands clenched on the smooth taut skin of his back.

'I'm not going to take you as my mistress,' he said deliberately into her throat. 'If you want this, you're going to have to marry me to get it.'

As she turned her face into the strength of his shoulder she smiled. Beneath her long lashes her eyes were slumbrous, the eyes of a confident temptress. This dark desire which held her captive bound him too in chains of sensuality. A short time ago she had experienced the power of her woman's body. He would be unable to resist her; she did not underestimate the strength of his will but she knew now that willpower was little defence against a passion as intense as that which they generated.

The smile widened as he whispered mockingly into her ear, 'I'm going to enjoy it when you try to make me change my mind, darling.'

She bit into the salty skin, felt his answering shudder and looked up at him, her face mysterious and beckoning, a siren full of dangerous allure. His iron-clad assurance made her long to penetrate it, show him just how susceptible he was to her feminine fascination. He was so beautiful, she thought achingly, so perfect in every way. Not just physically, either. He intrigued her, he made her think and laugh—she wanted to know just how that cool, clever brain worked, it was a seduction in itself.

Why had he slept with Susan? Had she too gazed at him like this, still hungry for the superb sensations he wrung from her body? Yes, of course she had. How many other women had tasted the pleasure of paradise in his arms, experienced the strength and grace of his body, then wept when he went on his way? More than enough to give him that superb technique, she thought acidly, hating the visions of him shuddering with the same pleasure in Susan's arms, in the arms of a horde of beautiful women. But almost certainly not one of them had driven him beyond the bounds of that technique into the driving desperation to which he had succumbed in her arms.

Abruptly, wishing to hurt him, she said, 'I won't marry you, because it would kill Angus if I did,' and stepped away from him to turn towards the place where the track wound beside the rapids away from the pool.

He caught her up before she had gone more than a few steps; he had pulled his shirt back on and was doing up the buttons.

'I can see that he would dislike it at first,' he said logically, 'but he's a reasonable man. He must realise that I didn't know she was married. If he doesn't, I'm sure I could convince him. You're using him as an excuse because you are afraid of committing yourself.'

Self-preservation forced her to ignore his accusation. 'He was—still *is*—in love with her, damn you! How do you think he'd react if if every time he thought of me—and you—all he could see was you and Susan in bed together? With calm good sense?'

'Oh, for God's sake, Clary, he must have known that things were not right with his marriage! One of the few things she said about him was that he came along at a time she needed a refuge. A man would have to be totally insensitive not to know when his wife felt like that.'

'What difference does that make to his loving her?' She turned to face him, her eyes as hard as his had ever been. 'How would you like it if I went off with—with that man we met at the Oxtens'? Tony Graham? How would you feel?'

'I'd kill him,' he said simply.

So quietly ferocious was his voice that she gaped. The implacable words sent a shiver of fear through her but she pushed on. 'And me? Would you kill me too?'

'You?' His teeth were bared in a simulacrum of a smile. 'Oh, no, I wouldn't kill you. Never. But I'd make you wish for death over and over again, Clary.'

'You're crazy,' she whispered, mesmerised by the primitive ferocity of his face. He was all barbarian, transfixed by a basic and ungovernable possessiveness. And then, as she watched, the rage was replaced by an appalled astonishment.

'No,' he muttered, extending a hand to stop her as she took a backwards step. '*No*, don't look at me like that. Oh, Clary, what you do to me! I'm sorry, darling. I'm sorry. God, all these threats . . .'

He brought her hand to his mouth and held it against his cheek as though it was a lifeline. His eyes were closed. He looked anguished. After a moment he said, 'That, I'm afraid, was the uncivilised reaction. I know that you wouldn't betray me as Susan did your brother. You have courage and honesty. And you belong to me. You knew what you were doing when you took me into yourself back there.'

The stark intensity of his words curled nerves the length of her spine. What had she awoken, with her antics under the moon?

'You shouldn't play with forces you don't fully understand,' he told her, watching from beneath lids that drooped to hide the blazing glitter in his eyes. 'Did you really think that you could unleash something as elemental as sex and not let loose all the other primitive emotions too? This is not a game, Clary.'

She jerked her hand free, whipping up anger. 'It has been until now, for you!'

'I'm glad you appreciate that this time it's different for me. And it was never a game. A pastime, perhaps, but I've always liked and respected my lovers. Don't try to change the subject, my lovely. You know that this has nothing to do with the pleasant liaisons I've enjoyed in the past. This is a compulsion, a bewitchment. We saw each other and we recognised each other, it's as simple as that. If you hadn't known it you wouldn't have reacted so violently when you saw Susan and me together, you wouldn't have allowed yourself to be blackmailed into staying here with me . . .'

She swung away again, afraid and angry, her face chalk-white beneath the moon, and began to run down the path, careless of the rocks and trees, fleeing from herself as much as him.

The hand clasping the unlit torch cracked against the rough trunk of one of the tree ferns and she drew a harsh, sobbing breath but did not stop her flight until she was out of the bush and running across the sweet grass of the paddock. Then, the haze of panic fading, she slowed down and he caught up with her in one smooth step. All that way he had been so close behind her, yet she had heard nothing.

'What did you mean, I wouldn't have stayed here? You made it impossible for me to go. You blackmailed me.'

'And did you bother to check with your brother to see whether my threats had any foundation?'

Dumbfounded, she stared up into the merciless cast of his features. He wasn't even breathing fast, she noted vaguely, and the sensation of being hunted struck her again.

'Didn't your blackmail have any basis?' Lassitude and a deep weariness flattened her voice. She allowed him to urge her across the damp grass with an arm about her shoulders because there seemed nothing else she could do.

'Yes, I'm afraid it did.' He sounded almost regretful. 'I don't make threats I can't carry out. But when you let me get away with blackmail I knew you had accepted that we belonged together. The modern woman doesn't allow herself to be blackmailed.'

'I love Angus,' she said defiantly.

He nodded, began to speak, then apparently thought better of it. After a few seconds his arm tightened across her shoulders. 'You love Angus, but you belong to me. You called yourself a virgin sacrifice—well, I've accepted your sacrifice. All that you are, all that you can be, you gave to me freely, without conditions. You can't play with myth and magic under the moon and expect to get away unscathed.' He chuckled softly. 'All enchantresses have to discover that, just as you do.'

It was nonsense, she knew that, but beneath the mockery in the deep voice was an uncompromising determination which silenced her.

The house was dark when they saw it. Clary said, 'Oh lord, I told your mother I wouldn't be long,' and tried to quicken her step.

'It's all right, you can't see her window from here. She's probably still up, it's not very late.'

It seemed as though an age had passed since she had left the house, but a glance at her watch revealed that he was correct, it was not late at all. In spite of that he locked up, and half-supported her up the stairs. She was glad of his strength; she felt waves of exhaustion wash over her.

'I'll check her,' he said softly as she looked towards his mother's door.

She let him persuade her and walked on, stopping to whisper a low good night outside her room.

He laughed beneath his breath and and caught her close to him, his mouth meeting hers in the softest of kisses.

'No,' she whispered.

'Yes.'

If he had been rough or cruel she could have borne it better, but he held her face captive between his hands and taunted her with little kisses until she swayed towards him, eyes closing. Then he enfolded her gently and pressed a chain of kisses from the cleft in her chin down the heated silk of her throat while one hand stroked the sensitive nape of her neck. By the time he lifted his head she would have followed him naked across mountains, and he knew it. Her dazzled expression gave her away as clearly as if she had spoken the words.

'Now off to bed,' he commanded roughly, as though it hurt him to speak.

She sighed and raised a languid hand to touch the place in his throat where his pulse beat. 'Are you coming?'

'No, my beautiful witch, I am not.' But he could not hide the longing in his voice as he opened her door and pushed her through it. 'Good night.'

The next morning she stretched herself awake, wincing slightly at the protests of over-used muscles.

Colour washed the smooth contours of her face and throat but she was not afflicted with the guilt she had expected. She felt marvellous, sleek and languorous and satisfied, all physical tensions resolved. A reminiscent smile curled the corners of her mouth as she stretched again with feline pleasure, examining her body for the faint bruises of passion. They were there, but surprisingly few, considering the ferocity of their union. Morgan had not been a gentle lover, but then, neither had she! He too would bear bruises, both teeth and finger marks. Afterwards, when she realised how she had marred his skin, she had searched for and kissed each small angry mark . . . She smiled again and slowly got out of bed.

Some time during the night the sky had clouded over and towards dawn rain had fallen in several heavy, sharp bursts. Now there was a mist over the garden and the valley, an ethereal Chinese vapour which shifted capriciously with the faint flurry of a wind from the north. Birds foraged for worms across the lawn, ignoring the two large cats that lay coiled together in the warmest part of the garage. The open door revealed that Morgan's car had gone. Clary turned away, fighting disappointment. He might at least have said goodbye, she thought dismally.

Over breakfast, Mrs Hargreaves told her that he wouldn't be back for several days. 'He's on the way to Tokyo,' she said. 'Didn't he tell you last night?'

'I—we talked about other things. He must have forgotten.'

It was a day of frustrations. After breakfast a telephone call, answered by Clary, turned out to be from Karen Graham. She asked for Morgan.

Not without an ignoble satisfaction Clary said cheerfully, 'I'm sorry, he's not here.'

'Oh. Who is speaking, please?'

'Clary Grey.'

A slight silence before the pleasant voice said, 'Of

course, we met at the Oxtens', didn't we. How are you? I'm afraid I have the world's worst memory. I've just realised that today is the day Morgan flies to Japan. He told me a couple of days ago that he was going but time seems to have flown by so fast!'

She finished with the graceful hope that they would meet again before Clary's job was over. And that was that. But the knowledge that Morgan had been seeing her, however innocently, made Clary raw and angry. Under her employer's direction she attacked weeds in the garden with such vigour that she broke two nails and cut the palm of her hand.

'Wear gloves,' Mrs Hargreaves said unsympathetically, 'I always do.'

'My hands don't work so well in gloves.'

'You get used to them. Do you mind driving me to the doctor's tomorrow? Ruth has to go to our local doctor so she won't be able to. I could use Morgan's driver but it seems unnecessary.'

'Of course I will. Once you've driven in Rome Auckland has no terrors.'

Mrs Hargreaves grinned. 'You're a good driver. I'm having lunch with Phil after he's checked me over, so you'll have a couple of hours to fill in. Do you want to ring your mother and arrange lunch with her?'

'She's away at Waitangi at a conference. I'll ring my brother.'

The telephone was not immediately answered; indeed, she was just about to hang up when the receiver was lifted.

'Angus?'

He sounded abstracted but he recognised her tentative voice. 'What is it, love?'

She told him of her free time and he said instantly, 'We'll have lunch together, shall we? I'll take you to—no, how would you like to go up One Tree Hill and have a picnic? There's an exceptionally good delicatessen down the road and I've been looking for an excuse to try some of their more exotic goodies.'

'That would be lovely,' she said, laughing because she found his love of picnics one of his endearing traits.

So it was arranged. The following day he picked her up in his gleaming old Jaguar from outside the specialist's impressive suite of rooms and drove her through the busy city streets until they reached the quiet, lovely open spaces of Cornwall Park with its little extinct volcano rising in grassy terraces above the houses. Angus found a sheltered spot beneath a wide jacaranda tree with a splendid view of the western reaches of Auckland, and while she spread out a rug he removed a hamper from the boot and ordered her to sit down so that he could have a look at her.

They surveyed each other, and said both together, 'You're thinner,' then laughed a little, because it had been one of their childhood tricks, this identical reaction and comment. It eased the slight awkwardness which had fretted at Clary's nerves.

'I gather from Mother that you like your Mrs Hargreaves,' he said, unpacking the hamper with deft swiftness.

'Oh, she's a darling. Very forthright and practical. My job is really a sinecure, she's no more ill than I am.'

'Then why the fine-drawn look?' he said, handing her a glazed chicken wing and a wholemeal roll.

She said nothing, stripping the meat from the bones with delicate greed before asking, 'Have you been working too hard?'

He smiled rather cynically. 'Yes.'

'How is it going?'

'Quite well,' he told her politely, piling cottage cheese and tomato on his roll. 'What's the matter, love?'

She almost told him then, but he looked so strained

that she couldn't bring herself to add to his burdens.
Instead she said bluntly, 'I saw Susan in London.'

'Did you?'

She loved him, but the days when she could read his
mind were long past. Strong white teeth bit into his
roll; with no apparent reaction he chewed and
swallowed, then asked calmly, 'And how was she?'

'She'd lost weight too.'

The irony wasn't lost on him. He even smiled a
little. 'Good,' he said pleasantly. 'I hope the slut
wastes away to a wraith. Then perhaps I might get
some peace.'

'*Angus!*' It was hopeless, of course it was hopeless.
Morgan had been wrong; where Susan was concerned
Angus was not reasonable. The tiny shoot of optimism
she had nurtured withered and died. 'Oh, Angus,' she
said helplessly.

His wide shoulders moved in an indifferent shrug.
'What do you expect? I'm not the forgiving sort. I
could perhaps be persuaded to relent if she'd fallen out
of love with me and into love with bloody Caird, but
clearly she only saw me as a convenient way station on
her road to wealth. So, if it comes to that, was he, but
he had the sense not to fall in love with her.'

In spite of the warmth of the sun Clary shivered.
'You sound so bitter,' she said stupidly.

He lifted eyes as darkly shadowed as her own, blue
as the icy depths of the polar sea. 'It's either bitterness
or Dad's way of coping with the same situation. I
prefer bitterness. Don't ever fall in love, Clary, it's not
worth the pain.'

'Does it have to be like that?'

'For me it does.' He finished the rest of his roll
while she ate a cherry tomato, then asked, 'Who was
she sleeping with when you saw her?'

'I don't think—she was in a little flat——'

'So he dumped her.' He laughed sardonically.

'She's going to some college to learn how to be a

beauty therapist.' Pleadingly Clary put her hand on his wrist, wishing quite desperately that she had never mentioned Susan. 'Angus, she said that she was sorry, and I really believe that she is. Do you have to hate her?'

His hand turned and gripped hers so ferociously that she had to bite her lip to keep from crying out. 'At the moment,' he said strangely, 'I do have to.'

She was silent at the bleak misery in his face. He needed the stimulus of his hatred to feed on. And that hatred was extended to Morgan. It was not rational, but love corroded by betrayal and jealousy is never rational.

'I'm sorry,' she said softly.

'Have I frightened you?' He leaned over and kissed her cheek, releasing her maltreated hand to give her shoulders a quick squeeze. 'Sorry, love, but I can't be sensible and sophisticated about either of them. She's a bitch and he's a swine and the only thing which keeps me going is my intention to one day prove to both of them that I am not the weak cuckold they believe me to be.'

CHAPTER NINE

THEY ate the rest of the picnic in near silence, letting the peace and the silence soak into the tension between them. After a while Angus began to tell her of his new invention and the plans his backers were making for its marketing.

'Could you have done it by yourself?' Clary asked casually. 'Without their backing?'

He shrugged. 'Perhaps, but it would have been a lot more difficult.'

When he saw that she was interested he described the processes needed to get even such potentially life-saving equipment as this on to the market as quickly and cheaply as possible.

'I'm no businessman,' he said, 'but I'm learning. These people have contacts all over the world, access to information and money I would have had to struggle for. They've saved me an immense amount of effort and time. And that's valuable, because the sooner this piece of equipment is used the sooner it's going to start saving lives. Every major airline in the world wants it!'

'My brother the genius,' Clary murmured, hiding her deep unease with a teasing inflection.

He grinned. 'Hardly. I'm very much a novice in the business world, but it's been fascinating to see how business gears up for something like this.'

'Any ideas about the next invention?'

'Lasers,' he said briskly, and delivered a lecture on their uses and prospects which fascinated her even though she understood very little of it.

'I see,' she said untruthfully when he finally ran down.

His smile was tinged with affectionate mockery. 'I don't suppose you do, but you're an excellent listener. Come on, finish that coffee or we'll keep your dragon waiting.'

'She is not a dragon. I like her enormously.'

'She sounds like a dragon. And someone is draining the colour from your face.' He packed the remnants of their lunch, putting the hamper back in the car while she folded the rug.

'I enjoyed that,' he said as they left the park. 'You are the most restful woman I know. We must do it again. When does this job finish?'

'Can you step on things a bit? We're late,' Clary said, adding, 'I promised to stay for three months.'

'And then?'

'Back to nursing, I suppose. I'm thinking about it.'

He realised that she didn't want to discuss her future, and so they chatted about inconsequential things all the way back to the specialist's rooms.

'Pull into the car park at the side of the building,' she directed when they were a few hundred yards from the rooms. 'Our car's there.'

So was the specialist's, a famous name who drove an equally famous vintage Rolls out of which he was helping Mrs Hargreaves.

'There she is,' Clary said cheerfully, giving her brother a swift kiss on the cheek. 'Goodbye, take care.'

He didn't reply, or more probably she hurtled out of the car so quickly that she didn't catch his answer, but after a moment she heard his car begin to turn out of the car park. She waved and smiled over her shoulder as she walked rapidly towards her employer.

Back at Hunter's Valley she recalled Angus's hard profile as he drove away; so bleak, so lonely. She could have wept for him.

And herself. That night, desolation murdered sleep; for hours she lay in her dark, beautiful room, staring with aching eyes at the ceiling as she forced herself to accept that she could not marry Morgan. She could not take her happiness at the cost of her brother's. He would see her love for Morgan as a betrayal equivalent to Susan's treachery, and he was in no mood to be rational about anything to do with Morgan. He had really frightened her with his ferocious desire for revenge, almost manic in its intensity.

What if he discovered that Morgan was behind the so-called consortium? No, there was little chance of that. Morgan must have buried his involvement very deep because Angus was no fool, if there had been any trace of Morgan he would have found it.

Wearily the thoughts chased themselves around her brain. Angus was fighting because, as Morgan had pointed out, he was not passive, he was a battler, but her loving eyes had seen beneath the aggression to his pain and she could not bring herself to do anything which might add to it. Perhaps, when his anger had faded . . .

But that might take years. And would Morgan wait that long? She still did not know whether he really wanted to marry her, or whether he saw it as a symbol of surrender. Perhaps he resented her affection for Angus. It was not impossible, although she had seen no signs of the sort of twisted possessiveness which that implied. He seemed unable to appreciate the depths of feeling he had roused in Angus; possibly because he had never loved as intensely as the younger man.

No, she thought, remembering, that was not so. His was no pallid desire. But he was not romantic, as Angus must be. She could not imagine Morgan suffering so bitterly if she left him, except in his pride. That, of course, was where he thought Angus had been hurt. Clary had not considered this before. Now, during the long night, she examined the idea with a gradual wonder, only to feel that she was hampered by the fact that she had never been in love before, so she could not recognise love in others.

You are in love now. How did she know? How did she know that what she felt was more than the lust she had wanted it to be? As she lay awake in the four-poster bed and the stars turned in their courses in the dark sky, she probed the depths of her emotions, teasing out the strands of affection and desire, tenderness and fear, respect, interest—the multitudinous threads which weave together to form love. Towards dawn she discovered that if marriage to Morgan would harm him, she would not do it. She wanted him to be happy. It was as simple as that. And it *was* love.

But when she tried to apply her new understanding to her brother she suffered from an even greater handicap. Except on that fleeting visit to London on their honeymoon she had never seen Susan and Angus together; she had no idea of the dynamics of their marriage. She knew only that Susan had entered into it for the wrong reasons and left Angus because she had been smothered and frustrated. Clary could not approve of the method she had chosen to put an end to it, but slowly she was forced to accept that her sister-in-law had the right to search for a more satisfying life. And that Angus's reaction bore all the hallmarks of outraged and possessive masculinity, thwarted and furious. Not of love.

But having accepted that, there was still nothing she could do about it. Angus thought he had loved Susan, so he was suffering just as much as if he had. And he would bleed if his sister married the man who had lured Susan away from him.

The day stretched before her, empty. She felt desperate, as though she had to reach some decision before Morgan came back from Japan. She thought she knew him well enough now to be able to ignore any threats of blackmail; he had almost admitted that such tactics had been a serious mistake, born of desperation.

All day, as she weeded, helped Ruth clean silver and learned the intricacies of making cape-gooseberry jam, she wondered whether there was any way out of the situation which did not involve a wait of years until Angus had had a chance to get over his disillusionment. She frowned as she picked dead blooms from the yesterday-today-and-tomorrow bush, her eyes drifting unseeingly over the white and lilac and purple flowers, and was still frowning when she emerged exhausted from the pool after swimming endless laps in an effort to get rid of her frustration. She had never felt so impotent in her life, and it galled her and frightened her.

After dinner she played three games of patience on the exquisite little loo-table in the drawing-room, winning all of them, then, gazing pensively at the muted shades of dusk, went out through the french windows into the garden.

Ruth's voice summoned her back. 'Telephone,' it said succinctly.

It was Morgan; so clear was his voice that at first she thought he had come back.

'Where are you?' she asked stupidly.

'In a hotel room in Tokyo. Missing you.'

'Oh.' After a moment's pause she said, 'Your mother is well. I took her to——'

'I've already spoken to her. I want to know how you are. Not pining for me, by any chance?'

'Of course not,' she said too quickly, and had to endure his low, satisfied chuckle.

'I like it when you try to slap me down to size. It tells me I'm too close to that prickly heart of yours. What have you been doing today?'

She told him and he asked, 'Do you like gardening? Don't let that bulldozer of a mother——'

'I've always liked gardening. My mother is an expert.'

'Good. She and mine will have lots in common.

Does yours want to be buried under a tree of her own choosing too?'

Clary choked her crow of laughter but he heard it and chuckled, before asking, 'So you aren't bored? Normally, of course, there's far more happening around the homestead than at present.'

'I know, Ruth's told me. Quite a few of your mother's friends have called in to see her. They don't stay long, but they entertain her.' She described one elegant and haughty dowager, realising only when she had finished that he might not appreciate acerbic comments about his mother's friends, however amusing.

His amused voice reassured her. 'Marvellous, isn't she? Her husband is the bane of her life, a diamond deliberately and defiantly in the rough. They fight like cat and dog and thoroughly enjoy it. You'll like him when you meet him, and you will be meeting him. You'll be meeting all our friends. How was Angus?'

'How—oh, your mother, I suppose.' She frowned at the realisation that Mrs Hargreaves had told him about Angus, but continued tonelessly, 'He seems well. I'd say he's lost a stone he needs, but he appears to be coping.'

'I find it rather reassuring that such an aloof creature as you should be so devoted a sister. Is it because it's a nice, safe relationship?'

'I love my mother too.'

The frosty words didn't impress him. 'Another safe bond, easily managed. So Angus is coping. Good.'

'He's very bitter.'

'Bitterness provides a convenient prop when things go wrong. He'll grow out of it.'

She bit her lip. 'I hope so. I'm afraid you underrate his capacity for emotion. It doesn't seem to me that it's a prop, it's more like an incentive. He wants to prove . . .' Her voice trailed into silence as she realised her disloyalty.

He picked up her meaning, of course. 'Does he, indeed?' he said thoughtfully. 'My poor little love, I think something will have be done about Angus.'

'*No!*'

Tension sizzled through the short silence that followed until he said in measured tones, 'I'm not actually into the business of bumping people off, Clary. Or forcing them into bankruptcy, if that's what you were thinking in that rather commonplace mind of yours. You've been too long overseas. In New Zealand we don't do things that way.'

'No. Blackmail, of course, is perfectly permissible.'

There was another ominous silence before he said lightly, 'You don't intimidate easily, do you? I'm sorry.'

'So am I. I over-reacted.'

She could hear his smile in his voice, and knew exactly how it would crease his lean cheeks, could see the gleam of mockery in his narrowed eyes. 'The story of our relationship. Never mind, I've become inured to the way you automatically assume the worst about me. Such as that I'm prepared to bump your brother off. I can only hope that closer acquaintanceship disabuses you of such misconceptions.'

He was being deliberately provocative, the formal polysyllables distancing her, but beneath the amused sarcasm she heard anger and hurt.' She didn't want him to hang up thinking that she believed him capable of the sort of ruthless behaviour her impetuous denial had indicated.

'Morgan?' she said tentatively.

'Clary?'

'I'm sorry. I didn't really believe—I know you wouldn't do anything to Angus.'

Another little silence before he drawled, 'I have every intention of doing something to Angus, my lovely. I consider him a damned nuisance. I can't even promise that it won't cause him some pain. However, I intend to use the universal excuse, that it will be for his own good. More to the point, it will be for *my* good. Most importantly, it will be for your good. I've had enough of seeing you torn two ways. Promise you won't leave before I come back.'

She hesitated, her finger lightly touching the dial on the telephone, picking out the numbers which would connect her to her mother. Then she said, 'No, I won't leave.'

The trouble was that she knew his capacity for ruthlessness. Everything about him proclaimed a hard relentless authority. A man who could swashbuckle his way through the financial jungle to build himself an empire needed to be tough as well as clever; it had been no weakling who had used blackmail to keep her with him. He had not liked it, he regretted it, but he had not flinched from using it.

Yet he had made no attempt to blackmail her into his bed. He had waited until she was ready. He could be kind, and shatteringly gentle, and his matter-of-fact attitude towards his mother failed entirely to hide his deep love for her.

After she had hung up Clary traced the outline of a fine Parian-ware Venus on the console table in the hall. It was humiliating to have to admit how much she missed him. That little smile she had never seen on herself curved the corners of her mouth. A Venus smile, the smile of a woman who knows how to seduce. When he came back she would show him how much she missed him—how much she ached for him.

The roar of a car being driven far too fast up the drive brought her head up, changing her expression to one of alarm when she recognised the note of the engine. An icy sensation expanded in her stomach, was reflected in the sudden pallor of her face as she ran to the door.

Angus was already halfway across the courtyard, his lean body moving with dangerous purpose. Her eyes suddenly swallowing her face, Clary stopped abruptly, then forced herself on.

'What is it?' she demanded, running down the steps. 'Mum? Has something happened to Mum?'

He grabbed the hand that was shaking his arm and pivoted around, dragging her across to the car. 'No, she's fine,' he snarled, almost pushing her into the passenger's seat.

As he strode around to his side she realised that somehow he had discovered everything. Nervously she protested, 'Angus, I'll have to let someone know that I'm going.'

'Who? Morgan Caird?'

She waited while he put the car into gear, biting her lips at the scream of maltreated tyres. When they were almost to the end of the drive she said, 'No, he's overseas just now.'

'A pity. It means I can't smash his face in this time.'

She risked a quick look at him, her heart quailing at the implacable cast of his features.

'Where are we going?' she asked almost inaudibly.

'Off his land.'

She said nothing more until she could tell him that they were past the boundary. He appeared to take no notice but at the next suitable spot he pulled off the road and cut the engine, staring through the windscreen at the rapidly darkening countryside ahead of them.

Clary remained silent until he asked silkily, 'Now tell me why you are living with him, Clary.'

'Because his mother, Mrs Hargreaves, is recovering from a heart attack.'

'That's the woman Jim Patten mentioned? The one I told you about.'

'The same one.' Her voice was very steady but she had to deliberately relax her fingers to prevent any tell-tale tension from showing.

He still refused to look at her but she sensed a slight relaxation in his taut frame. 'I see. And why, when you realised who she was, didn't you leave?'

'Because I promised her I would stay.'

'Because you were sleeping with her son.'

'No.' Her instinct was to cry her innocence to the stars, but she dared not admit emotion to the subject. She knew this dangerous quietness; it meant that he was barely in control. Very clearly she said, 'She is my patient, Angus. If I had known who she was I would not have taken the position, but I didn't know, and once I'd agreed I couldn't back out just because she's Morgan Caird's mother.'

It sounded reasonable. As he cursed Morgan with monotonous fluency she sat tensely, waiting.

'Are you sleeping with him?'

'No.'

The word fell into the frightening silence, clear, cold, tinged with impatience. A lie, yet not entirely untruthful, because there would be no more lovemaking.

'When I realised where you were I felt as though you had betrayed me. I couldn't bear it. I should have known better.'

His voice trembled. She said wretchedly, 'Oh— Angus!' and leaned towards him. For a moment he resisted, then bent his head so that the hot tears scorched into her shoulder.

She ran her fingers through the bronze hair so like her own in colour and texture, whispered soft endearments and comforted him as best she could while the light faded from her world.

At last he muttered, 'Sorry,' and moved away, embarrassed and wary. 'God, I hate him,' he said thickly. 'Did you know he's provided the money to back me?'

For a moment she wanted to lie but she did not trust her voice to do it again. So she nodded.

'Taunted you with it, did he? Well, there's no way I can get out of it, but I'll make the swine pay——'

'How?' When he didn't answer she said urgently, 'Angus, how? You mustn't do anything stupid.'

He turned his head and gave her a travesty of a smile, so cynical she could have wept. 'Don't worry, I know that nothing would give him greater pleasure than to get rid of me. I'm not so stupid as to give him the opportunity. He's a clever bastard and he's got me this time. He must have laughed like a hyena when the fish took the bait he dangled so temptingly.' One big fist hit the wheel. 'Well, he's had his fun with me. I'll take all the help he can give me and when I've enough power I'll cut free and he can go whistle for some other poor fish to cuckold.'

His agony hurt Clary profoundly, but although she shivered at such unbalanced, naked hatred she didn't dare try to present a more reasonable appreciation of Morgan. Angus needed his hatred to blanket the anguish of losing Susan. When that eased, as such pain always does, then surely his hatred would fade too.

'I'm sorry I came on so heavy,' he said after a while. 'I must have scared the hell out of you.'

'You did, rather,' she admitted. 'Now you know why I didn't feel I could tell you.'

'When I saw his mother yesterday I nearly passed out. I recognised her from a newspaper photograph—I'd forgotten she had married again. Then I remembered it was Jim Patten who had mentioned that she needed a nurse, and I did a bit of delving.' Suggestively his hand flexed, forming a clenched fist. 'He didn't want to tell me but I persuaded him in the end.'

Clary's blood ran cold. 'How?' she breathed.

'Oh, don't worry, I didn't hurt him. After I'd pointed out that I couldn't pull out now even if Caird was up to his elbows in it, he told me. He's not into heroics.'

'When was this?'

'A couple of hours ago.' He looked across to where she sat huddled into her seat, white-faced and cold. 'I thought he'd won again, that not content with stealing my wife he'd taken my sister. What do you think of him?'

The raw jealousy in his voice made her wince. She didn't dare take time for thought. 'He's very attractive,' she said remotely. 'Hard. Ruthless. What do you want me to say?'

'That you hate him, I suppose.'

'That's not true.'

If he suspected anything he chose not to pursue it, contenting himself with a long, difficult scrutiny. At last, when she thought she might break down and tell him the truth, he said quietly, 'I'm sorry, I have no right to expect you to join in my battles. I'll take you back.'

'A good idea. You look as if you could do with some coffee . . .'

'I don't feel like setting foot inside his boundaries, let alone accepting the smallest amount of hospitality,' he said in that expressionless voice she had never heard him use before.

Nobody had missed her, or if they had noticed her abrupt departure they hadn't been bothered by it. Ruth was with Mrs Hargreaves in her bedroom; as Clary walked listlessly through the garden she could hear the soft sound of their voices on the cool, sweetly-smelling air. Busy with plans for the new house, no doubt. They were both having a high old time.

The monument to Mrs Hargreaves' perfectionist attitudes was all about Clary as she wandered across lawns wet with dew, past borders bright with summer flowers, beneath trees chosen for their grace and form. The villa by the sea would be as perfect in its way as this, but it was unlikely that she would ever see it.

Surely the saddest sound in the world is the

croaking of frogs! In the lily pond a chorus of them sang a mournful little bracket and the tears came, bitter as wormwood. She collapsed on to a seat beneath a weeping willow and sobbed into her hands as if she had lost the only thing that had ever mattered to her.

It was stupid to grieve because she had wanted a romantic dream and it had been smirched. Real life bore no resemblance to fairy tales. It never had. That was why romance was so popular; it gave the greys of everyday life a colouring of glamour.

Late though it was when she came in, Ruth was still up. She gave Clary a rather too intent glance and said, 'Did you have bad news? Your brother . . .? That was him in the car, wasn't it? Mrs Hargreaves said . . .'

'Yes, it was him. And no, there was no bad news. I suppose I'm homesick.'

'Ah well, it hits us all. Hop up into bed and I'll bring you a cup of tea.'

'That's sweet of you, but don't bother, I don't really need it.'

'You look as though you need something stronger than tea,' Ruth said gently as she went towards the kitchen.

Mrs Hargreaves did not mention Clary's state, although she must have noticed. After she had showered and gone through her usual beauty routine, Clary came back into her room to find a tray with a small pot of tea waiting for her.

Her nose wrinkled at the pleasant scent. Camomile tea, just the thing to encourage sleep. Ruth must have been quite concerned about her! No wonder. Her mirror had revealed a drawn, tired face, still faintly pink about the eyelids and nose, the tiny lines at the corners of her eyes accented.

By morning they had faded into their normal obscurity, but during the next few days Clary learned several things about herself. One was that it was possible to appear quite normal when desolation seemed an actual physical weight in her chest. The other was that it helped to be as cheerful and as pleasant as she could; it took the edge off the pain and lessened a tendency to self-pity.

The hardest thing to cope with was her infinite capacity for recollection. Now that she had made the decision to turn away from what Morgan offered her, she was tormented by a hunger so intense it was like starvation. With it came total sensory recall, so that in those timeless moments between sleep and awareness when the conscious mind relaxes she relived her seduction over and over again, her feverish senses stimulated anew by the memory of his ardour and her surrender, the heated, eerie atmosphere, his mastery of her senses as he had taken her with him into that unexplored realm of passion.

When she closed her eyes she saw his face as it had been during that long initiation, by turns tender and hungry and fierce, culminating in the taut, agonised rictus of ecstasy when his body had shuddered into hers.

Night after night she twisted restlessly in her chaste bed, afire with the memory of the exquisite sensations his hands had created, the way he had used his mouth to force her into a dimension of sensuality she had never imagined, and the final pulsing rapture which had torn an unrestrained cry from her throat.

That was bad enough. What was worse were the dreams, some filled with that same voluptuous sensuality so that she woke trembling, sobbing with frustration. And the others, when she watched helplessly as his long powerful body lay against Susan, against Karen, entwined with women whose faces were mistily obscure but always enraptured.

They were the worst. Deep in her personality an intense possessiveness was outraged by his behaviour before he had known her. A wildness in her responded to and matched his unshackled masculinity; what her conscious mind found difficult to accept, her subconscious admitted freely. They were two of a kind and he had sullied that spiritual communion by his careless misuse of his sexuality.

Common sense told her that she was wrong. He had played a game with clearly defined rules, intending no hurt. What had happened before she met him was no concern of hers. She did not even have to ask herself if he had touched another woman since he had met her; she knew that he had not. It was beyond foolishness to expect a virile man in his thirties to be inexperienced, especially a man like Morgan, whose authority and incandescent sexuality was so attractive to women.

Yet she felt betrayed. She had waited, why had not he?

'You don't look as though you're sleeping at all well,' Mrs Hargreaves observed over breakfast one morning, adding without pause, 'we're going into town. Pack a nightdress and something pretty to wear out to dinner.'

After the peace of the homestead Auckland was noisy and brash and wearying. Morgan's apartment was in an exclusive tower block built hard by one of the little green volcanoes which dotted Auckland's isthmus.

'Ten minutes from town yet quiet,' Mrs Hargreaves said with satisfaction. 'How do you like it?'

It couldn't have been a greater contrast to the homestead. That had the comfortable ambience of antiques and another age; the apartment breathed an opulent modern discretion, with superb Italian furniture, a sophisticated interplay of fabrics and surfaces in dark blue and bronze backed by pale, cool suede wall hangings which reminded Clary of the thick petals of a magnolia flower.

'Did you do this?' she asked, not attempting to hide her pleasure.

Mrs Hargreaves chuckled. 'No, this is Morgan's. He had it redecorated when he got back from the United Kingdom last year. He had a good decorator to do it, but she did more or less as she was told.'

'It's beautiful.'

'I'm glad you think so. I assume it was designed to set you off. Your hair is the exact colour of that bronze over there. Can't see myself what he sees in it, I don't appreciate work that's not representational, but it certainly suits the room. And the blue is the colour of your eyes. He's like me, he can carry a colour in his head. It's quite a rare knack. Now, unless you want to wear jeans out to the airport, you'd better change.'

'The airport?'

'Yes, didn't I tell you that Morgan is coming back today?' She smiled rather wickedly. 'I should, I suppose, let you go out to meet him by yourself, but I enjoy airports. And if I know Morgan, there'll be a small deputation there to meet him. Or with him. We've got ten minutes to get ready before his driver comes to pick us up.'

Clary changed into the blue shirt-waister she had worn to the Oxtens' place, slipped on shoes and renewed her lipstick. She felt rather numb; sleepless nights and unhappiness had the effect of barricading her off from the normal emotions. For a long moment she looked into the mirror at her reflection, then, with a sensation of walls closing around her, went fatalistically out.

As always the airport was busy, but Clary took no pleasure in her favourite sport of people-watching. It was ridiculous, but she was terrified that the big jet from Tokyo would crash on landing. From the windows in the lounge they were led to where there was a good view of one of the runways; she sat ignoring it, her eyes seeing nothing.

Even there the fruitless spiral of her thoughts tormented her. Angus was too precious to her, his mental health too precarious to jeopardise. It might be years before he recovered enough to accept Morgan as a brother-in-law. She did not dare become Morgan's mistress because in his arms she became witless. Once he realised that he wouldn't hesitate to persuade her into marriage.

But oh, his hunger excited her, and her heart sang and light flared in the depths of her eyes.

'Here he is,' his mother said tersely.

He came in through the door, tall, vital, commanding. Clary's backbone seemed to melt.

'Mother,' he said, and kissed her before turning to where Clary was trying to efface herself behind a couple of eager executive types who waited for him.

'Darling,' he said deeply, and as if he couldn't help himself his hand curved around the nape of her neck and his mouth bruised hers in a hard, stinging kiss which hurt even as it pleasured her.

Branding her, she thought vaguely, opening her eyes.

'Been good?' he asked softly, his smile tinged with a blend of mockery and desire, eyes blazing green in the dark lineaments of his face.

Clary became aware of a paralysed silence about them. 'Have you?' she retorted crisply, pulling away, but there was a throbbing note in her voice which had never been there before and mockery changed to triumph as he released her.

After that his entourage treated her with a stunned respect which told her that no other woman had been greeted in that way before them. She shivered, feeling the walls close even more narrowly around her.

CHAPTER TEN

THE entourage travelled back to the city in another car, no doubt speculating all the way, except for one man who had impaled Clary with one sharp, not unkindly glance and then avoided looking her way. He sat in front beside the driver, but spoke over his shoulder to give Morgan a swift rundown on events within his organisation.

In the middle of the back seat Clary tried to hold herself away from too close a contact with Morgan. He knew what she was doing, of course, but beyond a taunting smile seemed content to allow her this small freedom.

I must be mad, she thought as his personal assistant's voice droned on, when even the touch of his arm against my shoulder drives me insane with desire.

It wasn't having the same effect on him. She dared not look into his face but he seemed totally relaxed. One hand lay on his thigh, the long fingers loose, as he made crisp pertinent comments, his brain outpacing the older man's. Clary found herself listening closely. This was a new Morgan, and she was greedy, she wanted to understand all aspects of his complex personality. Frowning slightly she concentrated, appreciating for the first time just how penetrating and subtle that acute intelligence was.

He and his assistant spoke a kind of verbal shorthand which at first confused her, but after some minutes of close attention she comprehended enough to be impressed and a little awed.

Deep down she admitted to another emotion. It was shameful, but she basked in the knowledge that she could suspend the operation of that formidable intellect, overturn that force of will with nothing more than the promise of her femininity.

Barbaric, she thought, trying to whip up contempt for herself. If her power was great, so was her responsibility to use it wisely. And if she did not then she was no better than the temptresses of old, the Messalinas and Loreleis who had used their sexuality to lure men to their doom. There was certainly something pagan and dangerous about her emotions; that, she thought wearily, was why she was so afraid of them.

Her gaze kindled with blue fire as she lifted it to the beautiful severity of his profile. He turned his head with a sharp little movement so that their eyes met. At the naked possession she saw in his glance Clary's breath caught in her throat.

Dimly she heard the voice of his personal assistant; Morgan answered and all she could think of was the sensuous movement of his lips, the contrast of his strong teeth against his skin.

Her own skin tightened and chilled, then heated into fire as he took her hand. She was aware of a slight faltering in the older man's speech, but Morgan turned his head to answer him, deep voice crisp and controlled, and Clary wondered if she had imagined the tremor which seemed to run from him to her when their hands first touched.

He didn't break the sweet contact until they arrived in the basement car park of a large central city building.

Then he said, 'I'll be home by seven,' and was gone, followed by his entourage, some of whom were a little less than subtle in their efforts to see who was in the car.

Clary said just above audibility, 'He looks like a shepherd, sweeping them off with him.'

'In a way I suppose he is. They're all very competent men, but he's the one who holds them together. Now, let's have a little saunter through the shops.'

Mrs Hargreaves's idea of a little saunter embraced a careful search of several rather grand antique shops where she displayed the kind of knowledge which impressed their proprietors, and a critical and often uncomplimentary perusal of almost the entire stock of an extremely expensive decorator's premises.

'For seating,' she explained, after introducing Clary to the decorator. 'Antique chairs and sofas were not built for comfort. Use them as ornaments if you like them, but sit on modern stuff.'

The afternoon was an education, but Clary was glad when they arrived back at the apartment. It was weak, but she wanted to be as close to Morgan as she could be in the time they had left.

He was not there. Clary showered and pulled on the dress she had brought, the coppery one she had worn at Chase, and went out into the large sitting-room and he was waiting, seated in a large chair reading the paper. He remembered the dress. As he rose to his feet he gave her a comprehensive look, his sardonic glance lingering on her taut face.

'Making a point?' he murmured. 'I'd begun to think my memories were too highly coloured to be accurate. It's a relief to find they're not.'

She smiled, because it was all she could do to hide how the sight of him affected her. The crisp black and white of his dinner jacket and shirt threw into prominence the sculptured strength of his features. His half-closed eyes flamed with triumph and desire.

Roughly she asked, 'Where are we going tonight?'

'To a very quiet dinner with an old admirer of Mama's.'

She relaxed. While she dressed she had worried about the dangers of too public a dinner. Gossip in Auckland tended to travel as fast as radio waves, and she was still afraid for Angus.

'Ashamed to be seen with me, Clary?'

The question was softly delivered but she read the danger and blinked, wilfully misunderstanding him. 'No, you look very elegant, very sexy. As I'm sure you know.'

'You think I'm a conceited ape.'

She shook her head and turned away from the gold-green gaze. 'I think you're an extremely intelligent person. You know that I——' her tongue seemed to thicken in her mouth, '—that you are very attractive,' she finished with plodding care.

'But you are strong enough to resist that animal magnetism.'

The exquisite sarcasm made her flinch. Her eyelids closed for a second over her burning eyes but when she turned back to face him she was gravely composed. 'I suppose you're entitled to a little satisfaction. If you like to hear me admit it, then no, I'm not strong enough to resist it. You know how I feel about you.'

'There is,' he said savagely, 'something peculiarly degrading about being seen as a stud.'

'You should be used to it.' The words came bitterly across her tongue.

White-faced, they stared at each other until a slight sound at the door broke into their attention. As his mother came in Morgan complimented her with a teasing urbanity which was as far removed from the naked aggression of a moment before as anything could have been.

Mrs Hargreaves appeared to notice nothing, although the tension could almost be seen. However, Clary was granted a few moments to compose herself, moments during which she realised that a confrontation had been postponed, not cancelled.

Sure enough, when, after a pleasant evening, Mrs Hargreaves left them together in the sitting-room Morgan said quietly, 'Would you mind staying a moment, Clary?'

He waited until the door closed behind his mother before suggesting, 'Why don't you sit down? And try not to look as though you are a Sabine woman after her Roman abductor reached home with her.'

She headed for a chair but he took her hand and guided her towards a sofa; once there he pulled her across his lap so that her head rested on his upper arm. Clary didn't try to resist. Even as her body fired into life she recognised the purposefulness in him.

'And so,' he said gently, his breath warm on her forehead, 'tell me why you have been so charming and polite and bloody aloof all evening.'

'Angus came to see me,' she said tonelessly.

He exhaled sharply. 'Ah. And told you . . .?'

'He knows everything.'

'Does he know that we are lovers?'

She hesitated, then shook her head. A lean finger lifted her chin. She knew how his business rivals must feel when transfixed by that piercing crystalline gaze. Clary said nothing, her misery plain. When he looked at her like that she saw beyond the forceful, sophisticated man of the world to a Morgan no one else suspected. There was triumph in his gaze, and a savage determination and beneath it the steady flame of desire, banked now, held under rigorous control. She could free it from the restraints set upon it by his will and he knew it, the knowledge was there in his face.

But it was not enough. However powerful, however ecstatic, no life could be built on sex alone. And he knew that too.

'So what happens now?' he asked.

She lifted her hand and held it against his chest, absorbing the heavy thudding of his heart through the palm. 'I'll stay with your mother until the doctor tells me I can go.'

Beneath her hand his heart seemed to stop, then began again with increased speed.

'What of us?' he demanded tightly.

She looked up into a face drawn with a terrible tension. 'There is no us,' she said sadly. 'You can take me to bed any time you like—you know it, I know it—but when it's time, I'll go and we'll never see each other again.'

The tawny fire of his head bent, was lowered until his face rested against her breasts. Clary smoothed the crisp hair with tender fingers, cradled the fine shape of his skull in her hands, listened to his harsh breathing and knew that she was on the brink of the obsession she feared. She had to go, while there was still time for her to escape.

When he lifted his head her hands slid over the sharply defined bones of his cheeks to lie along his jaw. Incredibly, he was smiling, although there was no amusement in the angular face.

'Have you ever heard of the Furies?' he asked, and at her surprised nod elaborated, 'They were Greek and there were three of them. Thoroughly unpleasant people. The Avenger of Blood, the Jealous one and the Implacable. They were very enthusiastic when it came to punishing people for neglecting claims of kinship. I think you must be a personification of them.'

The observation pierced the armour of her control. Wincing, her heart in her eyes, she lifted her head from his shoulder and kissed his beautiful mouth with a swift, unendurable passion.

'Angus hates you beyond reasoning. I told you that we were an obsessive family,' she said harshly as she tried to free herself from him.

'You are terrified of giving in to what you see as an obsession,' he accused. 'You may not realise it, but Angus is only an excuse. You saw your father die and you are afraid that if you admit that you love me the same thing will happen to you.'

'I've already told you that I love you.'

'It's a pathetic sort of love that puts a brother before a lover.'

His anger was palpable, an icy emanation rapidly demolished by an even stronger desire. Before she could do more than shift her balance his arms tightened and his mouth took hers in a compulsive, violent kiss. Instantly she was aroused; the inherent savagery she had incited did not slacken even though after the first few seconds she made no attempt to resist.

Completely fled now were the façades of courtesy and consideration. In that silent, consuming world of the senses they were as irrelevant as rational thought. Clary lifted her throat as a sacrifice, shuddering when his teeth bit just beyond gentleness down the fine pale length of it. Her fingers curved around his cheek, every tiny nerve end rejoicing at the rasp of his beard. The neckline of her dress proved no barrier as his hand slid beneath to cover her breast. At the fierce probe of his fingers she drew a ragged breath, dimly realising in the last part of her brain that was functioning that his other hand had released the zip at the back.

In a moment she was naked above the waist except for her bra, and that was soon jerked from her, freeing her breasts. Yet he did not look at them; his bright hostile gaze was riveted to her face even when his palm slid slowly across the smooth curves.

Clary's breath caught in her throat. A tide of uncontrollable pleasure surged through her. Weightless, boneless, under the experienced manipulation of his fingers her body arched, twisting convulsively in her effort to get closer to him. Her fingers moved swiftly and in a moment his shirt was open and she was pressing open-mouthed kisses to his smooth tanned shoulder, the first shudders of delight beginning to build deep inside her.

He was trembling too, his skin hot and damp

beneath her mouth; he muttered something and that tormenting hand slid from her breast down beneath the loosened material of her dress to come to rest between her thighs.

Gasping, incoherent, Clary lifted her hips against his hand, striving to assuage some of the tormenting ache, and he groaned, and pulled his hand free and dragged the dress up to cover her breasts before clamping his arms around her.

For long moments her cheek was pressed against his chest. Deafened by the racing beat of his heart she lay quiescent while the arousal peaked before slowly subsiding into dormancy, the kind of dormancy which needed only a touch to waken. He smelt faintly of sandalwood, more of sweat and the indefinable scent of masculinity.

'It's not enough,' he said at last in impeded tones.

Lips still turned against his skin she whispered, 'I'm sorry, Morgan.'

'Sorry? My God, so am I.'

That was all, but when he left her at the door of her bedroom with a curt good night he was no longer a man ridden by an obsession. He looked indomitable, she thought warily, and the smile he gave her before closing her door on her was a masterpiece of irony.

She slept late, so late that it was almost midday when she woke. After a horrified glance at her watch she leapt out of bed and hurtled into the bathroom before dressing in such a blur of activity that she was in the sitting-room before she had time to remember the scene last night.

She was brought up just inside the doorway by the sight of Morgan, alone.

Clary came to a precipitate halt, eyeing him warily as he lifted his gaze from the newspaper and directed a hooded glance her way. 'Where's your mother?' she asked breathlessly.

'Back at the valley.' He stood up, viewing her

dawning alarm with a grim smile. 'She no longer needs you.'

'She never really has.' Clary made a brave attempt to sound accusing but her eyes dropped away from his and the words were uttered far from forcefully.

'As it happened, no, but it was reassuring to have you around. Come and have some breakfast instead of hovering by the door like a frightened dog.'

'Breakfast?'

He grinned, but beneath his lashes his eyes were watchful. 'Brunch, then.'

A very elegant brunch. Coffee and croissants, a superb fantasy of fruits, strawberries, island papaya, the scented golden rectangles of its cousin the babaco, segments of tangelo, that sweetest of the citrus family.

'Such different fruits,' Clary said, tasting the babaco for the first time. 'Where did it come from?'

'Ecuador.' He began to speak of the boom in horticulture in New Zealand, the rapidly expanding number of sub-tropical fruits which were being brought into the country by dedicated plant hunters. Slowly Clary relaxed, listening as the deep sure voice charted the progress made in the horticultural industry while she had been away.

'You sound as though it's an interest of yours,' she said.

'I believe in our future as an exporter of food as well as technology. New Zealanders seem to have a talent for improvisation which can amount to genius, as in your brother. All we need is development and marketing expertise, and that I can supply.'

The sound of the doorbell made her jump. She looked an enquiry at him, unable to see beneath the smooth mask of his features.

'Ah,' he said calmly, 'bring your coffee into the sitting-room.'

An unthinking fatalism kept her quiet, although she realised that he was geared for some kind of confrontation. Beneath their heavy lids his eyes gleamed with the light of battle; she could feel his alert vitality reach out to encompass her. He looked like a swordsman about to fight a duel. Not as though he was going to enjoy it, but as though it was something he was forced to do.

'Wait here,' he said and kissed her, hard and fierce, bruising her soft mouth with the desperation of his. Under his breath he pleaded, 'Trust me, Clary, *please*.'

Astonished, she watched his lithe figure leave the room. She was still standing in exactly the same position when he came back in through the door accompanied by a man who looked at her with her own eyes.

'Angus!' Very carefully she put her coffee cup down on a small marble table.

Angus was filled with a fierce exultation. He looked, she thought incredulously, as though he was enjoying himself. But as he saw her stricken face his own softened. 'Go away, love,' he ordered gruffly, his eyes already swinging back to the owner of this luxurious room.

It almost made her ill. Angus couldn't wait to sample the deadly fascination of measuring his strength with Morgan. The blood seemed to recede from her heart as she turned blindly towards the door.

'Stay right where you are,' Morgan said softly from across the room.

Brother and sister froze. Morgan smiled, his narrowed eyes fixed on Angus, but it was to Clary he spoke.

'Come here,' he commanded quite gently and held out his hand.

Clary stood motionless as her brother's face turned slowly towards her. She read his sudden bleak comprehension and searched for contempt, for hatred. He closed his eyes as if what he saw was unbearable, and she took a step towards him.

'Clary,' Morgan said softly.

Her eyes flicked from Angus, so dearly loved a brother, to Morgan, loved, hated, desired. She hesitated, bitterly angry with both of them. They were demanding that she make a choice, but each man knew that whatever her decision it would make her savagely unhappy.

She said, 'This has nothing to do with me, has it? I'm just the convenient focus.'

Both men broke off the silent, murderous confrontation to stare at her. She had never felt so alone, so friendless. She swallowed and continued harshly, 'It's Susan you're fighting over.'

Angus began to speak but she interrupted his first word, her eyes black with pain. 'You blame Morgan for stealing her from you. When I saw her in London she told me that he had no idea that she was married, not until after she'd left you. So you're blaming him because Susan wanted him. How many women have wanted you? Should you be blamed because they looked at you and decided that you'd probably be good in bed?'

The harsh planes and angles of Angus's face seemed to constrict as pain bit into his expression. He said nothing; he appeared to be looking at her and seeing something too horrible to credit.

'Do you want to punish Clary for Susan's decision to leave you?' Morgan's voice was level, almost indifferent, but Clary could see a tiny muscle in his jaw jerk. 'Do you despise your sister as well as your adulterous wife?'

Angus walked heavily across to the window and stood staring out. After a long, tense silence he said, 'If she is your mistress, yes.'

'And if she were my wife?'

Clary tasted the salt taste of her own blood and only then realised that she had bitten into her lip. She felt impotent, an onlooker watching two great beasts of prey, each intent on the slash across the jugular, the killing blow. They humiliated her with their casual arrogance, yet she could not intervene. She shivered on the brink of the enormous gulf that can stretch between male and female and realised that in a strange way they were ranged together against her.

'Why should I feel better about her being your wife?'

'Perhaps because it would mean that I love her.'

Almost conversationally Angus asked, 'And what would you do if someone stole her from you?'

Clary had thought no tension could be greater than that of the last few minutes, but she was mistaken. Morgan hesitated, his assurance tilting under the brutal honesty of the question. He did not look at Clary. He did not appear to look anywhere but inwards. Angus swung around, and she saw in him a threat and a promise, the full force of his will bent on the man he hated.

Holding her breath she waited, aware that he was forcing Morgan to face an issue he had not expected to have to confront.

At last he said without inflection, 'I don't believe that anything but death could take her from me. If that happened I would follow her. I have no interest in a world where she doesn't exist.'

But Angus was merciless. 'If she wanted to go, to walk out of that door and never come back. What then?'

Morgan was white beneath his tan and for the first time in ages he looked at Clary. She cried out at what she saw in his face. 'Then I'd have to let her go,' he said painfully, for once unable to conceal how difficult it was for him to accept the conclusion. 'Love is worth nothing unless it is freely given.'

Impossible not to believe him. Clary's breath came hissing between her teeth and Angus's big body seemed to relax. 'In that case,' he said, 'I withdraw my objection. But you'd better make her happy, or you will have me to answer to.'

'She is,' Morgan told him wryly as he held out his hand, 'quite capable of calling me to answer herself.'

Angus said nothing, but he shook Morgan's hand and came across to where Clary waited. He touched her cheek and said, 'Be happy, love.'

She strained up to kiss him; it was impossible to discern his emotions, but a familial instinct warned her that he was intensely unhappy.

He left them to a silence deeper and more profound than any before. Clary could not break it, she knew that Morgan had to be the one to speak. When he looked at her it was with chin held high as he hid any signs of the vulnerability Angus had forced him to reveal.

'So now you know,' he said.

Stumbling, her mouth dry, she ran to him, her arms encircling him in an embrace which was fierce and protective.

'I don't deserve that,' she whispered. 'I will never deserve that, but oh, I love you!'

'Do you, Clary?' His lean body relaxed; he lifted shaking hands to frame her face and tilted it to meet his tender gaze.

Shocked, she realised that he had not believed it, that he needed her reassurance.

'Can't you feel?' she asked huskily, guiding his hand to where her heart threatened to burst through the confines of her flesh.

But he resisted, imprisoning her in the cage of his arms.

'Not that,' he said almost bitterly. 'Oh, it's the most exquisite torment, but sex is not the most important part of our relationship. That first time I saw you, across the pony ring, I wanted to pick you up and carry you off and make love to you until I'd imprinted myself on every cell of your body, every thought process in your brain, made you completely dependent on me for happiness. Then you picked up the child and I thought you were married. I can't tell you what it was like. I felt as furious and vengeful as if I'd been betrayed. I was horrified to discover that I was coolly deciding on ways and means of breaking up the marriage.'

Clary's eyes widened in something very like the horror he had described as they searched the strained contours of his face.

'You might well be shocked,' he said half angrily. 'I shocked myself. I'd always been so determined not to get tangled up with married women ... I began to wonder if my moral standards had slipped ... I suppose I blamed you a little. Then Leona told me who you were, and I was—excited, as I'd never been before, like a youth when he realises this is it, he's about to have sex for the first time, he's going to crack the mystery of a woman's body.'

She tried to smile, awed by the strength of his emotion but hurting for him. 'I thought that it was the first car that gave rise to such anticipation.'

'That's a face-saver.' His hands moved, slid down to the slender curve of her shoulder, the fingers finding their way to the nape of her neck while his thumbs pushed her face up. 'That night showed me that although you were frightened and resentful you felt the same way, and I was gloating, I thought that from then on it would be easy. But everything went wrong. I was no longer in control. I didn't mean to ask you to go to London with me, but you got to me so hard that I blurted it out and you cut me down to size by reminding me of Susan.'

For a second every muscle in her body tensed. He gave a hard painful sigh and closed his eyes for a second. Clary's mouth shook.

He said heavily, 'My heart's love, if ever I was punished for my attitude to sex, that was it. What we have is special, it was totally outside my experience and I didn't know how to cope. I was afraid. I realised that we both needed a breathing-space, time to come to terms with the idea of love, even though the waiting would be hell. I didn't sleep that night at Chase. I walked the floor, alternately cursing my crassness and making plans.'

'What plans?' she asked softly when the deep voice hesitated.

'I decided to break with Susan, get her out of my life, then go back to Chase to establish some sort of basis for the future. I spent those weeks in a fever of activity. I had business to deal with too. Anyway, I thought in my arrogance that everything was going along nicely. Then you saw me with Susan and the world blew up in my face.'

Clary rested her proud head on his shoulder. His mouth searched the soft curls to find her temple. Through the silken tangle she could feel the heat in his kiss and the way his lips trembled as though he was in a fever. Suddenly protective, her arms tightened about him.

'It just reinforced all I'd believed of you,' she said into his neck. 'I thought that you were a rake, that you didn't care, provided the woman was beautiful and willing. You were so vivid, so blazing with life, and I could see that every woman who saw you was conscious of you. When I saw you and Susan together I felt bereft, as though something beautiful had been smirched. And I was furious. But beneath it all, I was in despair because I knew there was no future for us. I was bitterly, viciously jealous of Susan, and I told myself that I hated you.'

'My God, that was obvious,' he muttered. 'You looked magnificent, like an angry goddess. You terrified Susan and you scared the hell out of me!'

She gave a throaty chuckle and touched the tip of her tongue to the salty skin of his throat, relishing the quick intake of his breath and the sudden clenching of his arms about her. 'It didn't show,' she said.

His amusement was self-derisory. 'I realised that if I betrayed any fear you'd have the whip hand, and that would mean finish.' In an urgent, almost pleading voice he said, 'I didn't touch her after I'd seen you. I couldn't. I took her with me that night because the arrangements had been made before my visit to Chase and I couldn't in all honour back out. For some reason she insisted on coming with me, even though she knew it was all over. By then I'd organised her enrolment at that college and put her into her flat.'

'You'd paid her off,' Clary said flatly

'Yes.' He made no excuses.

Clary faced facts. What Morgan had done before she met him was no concern of hers. She had used his affair with Susan as a red herring to defend herself against the intense physical attraction and then the growing love she had felt for him. She could not agree with his attitude towards those affairs, but she was not naïve enough to believe that he had developed those attitudes without help. A man with his looks and sexuality must always have had women eager first to teach and then to sample his skills as a lover.

All that she had to ask herself now was whether he would remain faithful and with a shock of recognition she realised that she had never doubted his fidelity. It was as if that first bold, burning look had welded them together in a partnership which they both recognised, both accepted, a commitment in which there was no room for anyone else.

'I was afraid too,' she said slowly. 'I was a coward. I thought that emotions so fierce had to lead to pain.'

He lifted her chin and looked into her troubled eyes, his own very direct and loving. 'I knew what I was fighting. Angus and Susan were only your excuses. I had to convince you that you were safe with me, that I

could not betray you the way your father and Angus
were betrayed.'

She nodded, releasing the past with no regrets. 'I
love you,' she said, her expression almost blinding in
its joy, to be answered by an identical pulse of joy in
his dark features.

'I adore you,' he muttered, punctuating the words
with tiny kisses across her face. 'I worship you, I need
you, I ache for you—I *love* you! And I'm so sorry you
had to endure a scene like that with Angus, but it was
the only way I could see to break the deadlock. He had
to know that you would be happy with me, that you
love me. I knew that once he realised how much you
loved me he'd give in.'

'How did you know?'

His smile was tenderly mocking. 'Because, my
lovely, he loves you. He realised that if he forced you
to make a choice between him and me you'd be torn in
two. I gambled on him not being able to do that, and
you see, I was right.'

'You gambled on his affection for me being more
powerful than his need for revenge?' she whispered,
horrified.

'Yes. I followed a hunch—well, not that much of a
risk. I gambled on that family loyalty you bristle with.'
He laughed softly and kissed her wide eyes closed. 'I
must say I admire him. He salved some pride by
forcing that admission from me. Until I had to say it I
hadn't really accepted how much I needed you, and
loved you, and how afraid I was that my need, my love
weren't going to be enough. He and I came out of that
bout with honours about even.'

'He's never going to like you, is he?'

He responded to her sad question with the truth.
'No, I think he'll always hate my guts. He's a strong
man and a hard one, but I'll always be thankful that he
is an honest one. He realised that he couldn't take his
revenge at the expense of your happiness. Perhaps if

he falls in love again, the sting will go from his memories. And, of course, he'll see how very, very happy we are going to be . . .'

Clary nodded, intent for the moment on achieving some kind of balance between the joyful ecstasy of her love and the awakening passion which was beating up through her in slow, dark pulses.

'I'm so glad you love me,' she said dreamily, pressing slow warm kisses into his throat. 'I've been so miserable. If I'd known sooner——'

'You knew,' he said deeply, 'right from the start. You just wouldn't admit it, or accept it, not even after you seduced me with such delicious wantonness.'

Her skin prickled, first cold, then hot, at the laughter in his handsome pirate's face. 'You never actually said that you *loved* me,' she protested.

He held her away, compelling her to meet his regard. 'You knew,' he said implacably.

'I suppose I did.'

'I had to be sure,' he said, pulling her back into his arms. She shuddered as he ran his hand with leisurely precision down the length of her spine, urging her into the cradle of his hips so that his arousal became blatantly obvious. His mouth swooped, crushing hers beneath it.

Clary responded as she would always respond, accepting the swift brutality as a symbol of a need for reassurance which he would probably never express openly. He sighed, and the erotic punishment gentled.

'I was terrified this morning,' he astounded her by admitting raggedly. 'I thought I might have to prove to Angus just how much you loved me, and that would have humiliated you.'

She shivered, her quick mind supplying some of the methods he could have used to wring that proof from her. Now she knew him well enough to accept that he would have been merciless; his love was not weak or feeble. It could hurt, it could cut her to the bone, yet it was genuine emotion, not the violent lust she had once judged it to be. She lifted her eyes, meeting his with wry mockery, and saw the gold deep within flame up to hide the green. Beneath her hand his skin was heated and dry. She remembered the drawn, hungry contours which passion created in his face, and an answering flare of emotion lit the deep blue behind her lashes.

'He had to know,' he said silkily, 'that what you feel for me is stronger than any sisterly love, stronger than death, because that's the way I feel about you. I never thought it would happen to me, I was like you, scared of love. I saw what happened to my mother when my father died. That's why I handled it so badly.'

'Oh, I know,' she said almost inaudibly, kissing the crease in his cheek between each word. 'You don't— you *can't*—look at someone and fall fathoms deep in love, just like that!'

'Exactly.' He grinned wickedly. 'Perhaps we're the only two in the world to have done it.'

'Perhaps everyone in love believes that.'

'Ah, but we know it's true just for us.' He kissed her, kissed her again and then, with an effort of will which straightened the line of his mouth, put her away from him. 'Right, now we have to organise a wedding. I might just be able to keep my hands off you for the three days it will take——'

'You don't have to.'

He gave her a fierce, lancing glare. 'Don't have to what? Damn it, Clary, I want to marry you!'

She touched his mouth with a delicate probing forefinger. 'You don't have to wait, darling.'

His tongue curled around the fingertip. As she withdrew it he asked unevenly, 'Are you seducing me again?'

Strangely shy, her cheeks glowing with colour, she nodded.

'And you do it so well,' he said on an odd inflection. 'Do you mind if we wait until we're married?'

'No, of course not,' she said in a small voice.

He smiled very tenderly down at her. 'My heart's delight, this is new territory for me, a different country. Right from the start I knew that it wouldn't take much pressure from me to get you into bed, but I—oh, call it superstition, call it what you like—I was afraid I might lose you if I was too greedy, too hasty. I wanted your loving surrender, not your resentful compliance. As I told you, I wanted everything, and I was prepared to wait for it.'

Such iron self-control, she thought dazedly while her lips shaped words she barely heard. 'Then did I spoil everything that night by the pool?'

'No,' he whispered, sliding his arms about her as he collapsed slowly back on to the sofa.

When he lifted his head she was aching and clamorous with desire, and the colour ran dark along his suddenly prominent cheekbones. The pace of Clary's heart matched his, pounding so noisily that it was impossible to tell whose was loudest. He was tense with a feverish passion, fighting hard to regain that control she had thought unassailable.

'No,' he muttered, 'that was magical. You came up out of the water like an enchantress and my heart stopped. I felt like the shepherd when the moon goddess chose him for her lover, as if I'd been honoured above all men. And when we made love you were warm and erotic and ardent, generous and wildly passionate, and I lost my head, I had to lose myself in you even though it meant my plans went to hell.'

'What plans?' She spoke drowsily, fighting to control the hunger which could only be eased in the blind ecstasy of love.

'Oh, I wanted you on edge and eager, too frustrated to be able to deny me when we faced Angus.' His mouth twisted derisively before relaxing into soft laughter. 'But you came to me and you gave me all that I had ever wanted. I felt ten feet tall because your surrender meant that I had you, mine for all time. Angus was easy to deal with after that.'

She nodded. 'I love you.'

He touched his lips to her forehead, to her dazzled eyes, then to the freckles across her nose, finally, tormentingly, to the cleft in her chin. 'And I love you,' he murmured. 'It's a very willing surrender, my dearest love.'

She turned her face into the warmth and security of him, happy as she had never been before in her life, lulled by this tenderness she had not expected in him. 'Oh, a *very* willing surrender. For all time.'

There would be times of tribulation ahead, but this complete confidence in each other's love, this was for ever. Smiling, Clary reached for him and relinquished the last fear and let it drift away.

SOLITAIRE – Lisa Gregory   £3.50

Emptiness and heartache lay behind the facade of Jennifer Taylor's glittering Hollywood career. Bitter betrayal had driven her to become a successful actress, but now at the top, where else could she go?

SWEET SUMMER HEAT – Katherine Burton   £2.99

Rebecca Whitney has a great future ahead of her until a sultry encounter with a former lover leaves her devastated...

THE LIGHT FANTASTIC – Peggy Nicholson   £2.99

In this debut novel, Peggy Nicholson focuses on her own profession... Award-winning author Tripp Wetherby's fear of flying could ruin the promotional tour for his latest blockbuster. Rennie Markell is employed to cure his phobia, whatever it takes!

These three new titles will be out in bookshops from February 1990.

WORLDWIDE

Available from Boots, Martins, John Menzies, W.H. Smith, Woolworths and other paperback stockists.

2 NEW TITLES
FOR MARCH 1990

Jo *by Tracy Hughes.*
Book two in the sensational
quartet of sisters in search of
love…

In her latest cause, Jo's fiery
nature helps her as an
idealistic campaigner
against the corrupting
influence of the rock
music industry. Until she
meets the industry's
heartbreaker, E. Z. Ellis,
whose lyrics force her to think
twice.   £2.99

Sally Bradford's debut
novel **The Arrangement** is
a poignant romance that
will appeal to readers
everywhere.

Lawyer, Juliet Cavanagh,
wanted a child, but not
the complications of a
marriage. Brady Talcott
answered her
advertisement for a
prospective father, but
he had conditions of
his own…   £2.99

W⦿RLDWIDE

A Mother's Day Treat

This beautifully packaged set of 4 brand new Romances makes an ideal choice of Mother's Day gift.

BLUEBIRDS IN THE SPRING
Jeanne Allen
THE ONLY MAN
Rosemary Hammond
MUTUAL ATTRACTION
Margaret Mayo
RUNAWAY
Kate Walker

These top authors have been selected for their blend of styles, and with romance the key ingredient to all the storylines, what better way to treat your mother... or even yourself.

Available from February 1990.
Price £5.40

HOW TO ENTER

All the words listed overleaf, below the word puzzle, are hidden in the grid. You can find them by reading the letters forward, backwards, up or down, or diagonally. When you find a word, circle it or put a line through it, the remaining letters (which you can read from left to right, from the top of the puzzle through to the bottom) will ask a romantic question.

After you have filled in all the words, don't forget to fill in your name and address in the space provided and pop this page in an envelope (you don't need a stamp) and post it today. Hurry - competition ends March 31st 1990.

Mills & Boon Competition,
FREEPOST,
P.O. Box 236,
Croydon,
Surrey. CR9 9EL

Only one entry per household

Hidden Question _____

_____

Name _____

Address _____

_____

_____

_____ Postcode _____

You may be mailed with other offers as a result of this application.

COMP 8

TASTY FOOD COMPETITION!

How would you like a years supply of Mills & Boon Romances ABSOLUTELY FREE? Well, you can win them! All you have to do is complete the word puzzle below and send it in to us by March. 31st. 1990. The first 5 correct entries picked out of the bag after that date will win **a years supply of Mills & Boon Romances** (*ten books every month - worth £162*) What could be easier?

```
H O L L A N D A I S E R
E Y E G G O W H A O H A R
R S E E C L A I R U C T
B T K K A E T S I F I A
E E T I S M A L C F U T
U R C M T L H E E L Q O
G S I U T F O N O E D U
N H L S O T O N E F M I
I S R S O M A C W A A L
R I A E E T I R J A E L
E F G L L P T O T V R E
M O U S S E E O D O C P
```

CLAM	HOLLANDAISE	OYSTERS	SPICE
COD	JAM	PRAWN	STEAK
CREAM	LEEK	QUICHE	TART
ECLAIR	LEMON	RATATOUILLE	
EGG	MELON	RICE	
FISH	MERINGUE	RISOTTO	
GARLIC	MOUSSE	SALT	
HERB	MUSSELS	SOUFFLE	

PLEASE TURN OVER FOR DETAILS ON HOW TO ENTER ▷

Mills & Boon

Just answer these simple questions for your FREE book

1 **Who is your favourite author?** _____

2 **The last romance you read** *(apart from this one)* **was?** _____

3 **How many Mills & Boon Romances have you bought in the last 6 months?** _____

4 **How did you first hear about Mills & Boon?** *(Tick one)*
☐ Friend   ☐ Television   ☐ Magazines or newspapers
☐ Saw them in the shops   ☐ Received a mailing
☐ other *(please describe)* _____

5 **Where did you get this book?**

_____

6 **Which age group are you in?**
☐ Under 24   ☐ 25-34   ☐ 35-44
☐ 45-54   ☐ 55-64   ☐ Over 65

7 **After you read your Mills & Boon novels, what do you do with them?**
☐ Keep them   ☐ Give them away
☐ Lend them to friends
☐ Other *(Please describe)*
_____
_____

8 **What do you like about Mills & Boon Romances?**

_____

9 **Are you a Mills & Boon subscriber?**   ☐ Yes   ☐ No

Fill in your name and address, put this page in an envelope and post TODAY to: **Mills & Boon Reader Survey, FREEPOST, P.O. Box 236, Croydon, Surrey. CR9 9EL**

NO STAMP NEEDED

Name (Mrs. / Miss. / Ms. / Mr.) _____

Address _____

_____

_____ Postcode _____

You may be mailed with offers as a result of this questionnaire

PWQ1